MANAGING SUICIDE RISK IN PRIMARY CARE

About the Authors

Craig J. Bryan, PsyD, is Assistant Professor in the Department of Psychiatry at the University of Texas Health Science Center. Dr. Bryan received his PsyD in clinical psychology in 2006 from Baylor University, and completed his clinical psychology residency at the Wilford Hall Medical Center, Lackland Air Force Base, TX. He was retained as faculty in the Department of Psychology at Wilford Hall Medical Center, where he was Chief of the Primary Care Psychology Service at Kelly Family Medicine Clinic, as well as the Suicide Prevention Program Manager for Lackland AFB. In addition to seeing patients in family medicine, Dr. Bryan trained and supervised clinical psychology interns, licensed clinical psychologists, and licensed clinical social workers in the BHC model of behavioral health. Dr. Bryan currently researches suicidal behaviors, suicide prevention strategies, and psychological health and resilience. He has chaired the American Association of Suicidology's Primary Care Task Force to develop training curriculum for primary care medical providers in the assessment and management of suicidal patients. He regularly provides training to clinicians and medical professionals about managing suicidal patients. For his contributions to primary care behavioral health and suicide prevention, Dr. Bryan was recognized by the Society for Military Psychology with the Arthur W. Melton Award for Early Career Achievement.

M. David Rudd, PhD, is Dean of the College of Social and Behavioral Sciences at the University of Utah and scientific director for the National Center for Veterans Studies at the university. His undergraduate degree is from Princeton University. He completed his doctoral training at the University of Texas-Austin and completed a post-doctoral fellowship in cognitive therapy at the Beck Institute in Philadelphia under the direction of Aaron T. Beck. He is a Diplomate of the American Board of Professional Psychology and a Fellow of three professional societies, including the American Psychological Association (Division 12 and Division 29), the International Association of Suicide Research, and the Academy of Cognitive Therapy (a founding Fellow). He was recently elected a Distinguished Practitioner and Scholar of the National Academies of Practice in Psychology. In addition to his clinical work, Dr. Rudd is an active researcher with over 170 publications. He is currently conducting a $1.97 million clinical trial for suicidal soldiers at Fort Carson, Colorado. He has authored several books, including *Treating Suicidal Behavior* (2001, Guilford, 2nd printing in 2004), *Suicide Science: Expanding the Boundaries* (2001, Kluwer Academic Publishers), *The Assessment and Management of Suicidality: A Pocket Guide* (Professional Resource Press, 2006), and the recently released *The Interpersonal Theory of Suicide* (with Joiner, VanOrden, & Witte) from the American Psychological Association Press. His research has been recognized with awards both national and international. He has served as a consultant to many organizations nationally and internationally, including the United States Air Force, the U.S. Army, the Department of Defense, and the Beijing Suicide Prevention and Research Center. Dr. Rudd serves on a number of editorial boards, is past Chair of the Texas State Board of Examiners of Psychologists, past President of the Texas Psychological Association, past President of Division 12 Section VII of the American Psychological Association, past President of the American Association of Suicidology, a previous member of the APA Council of Representatives, and currently serves on the board of the PDV Foundation. Dr. Rudd has testified five times before the U.S. Congress, both House and Senate, on issues related to veterans and suicide.

Managing Suicide Risk in Primary Care

CRAIG J. BRYAN, PsyD

M. DAVID RUDD, PhD

Springer Publishing Company, LLC
11 West 42nd Street
New York, NY 10036
www.springerpub.com

Acquisitions Editor: Jennifer Perillo
Senior Editor: Rose Mary Piscitelli
Cover design: Mimi Flow
Project Manager: Amor Nanas
Composition: The Manila Typesetting Company

ISBN: 978-0-8261-1071-8
E-book ISBN: 978-0-8261-1072-5

10 11 12 13/ 5 4 3 2 1

Library of Congress Cataloging-in-Publication Data

Bryan, Craig J.
Managing suicide risk in primary care / Craig J. Bryan, M. David Rudd.
p. ; cm.
Includes bibliographical references and index.
ISBN 978-0-8261-1071-8 — ISBN 978-0-8261-1072-5 (e-book) 1. Suicide—Prevention. 2. Primary care (Medicine) I. Rudd, M. David. II. Title.
[DNLM: 1. Suicide—prevention & control. 2. Primary Health Care. 3. Risk Assessment. WM 165]
RC569.B79 2010
616.85'8445—dc22

2010036599

Printed in the United States of America by Gasch Printing

Contents

Introduction

This book is a culmination of several years of work. I (C.J.B.) started working in family medicine as a behavioral health consultant (BHC) immediately after my internship training and awarding of my doctoral degree. During my internship, learning how to work as a BHC was a requirement and training took place in the very family medicine clinic I later worked in as a staff provider for several years. While I was an intern on that rotation, I was taught that routine screening for suicidality was outside the scope of a BHC and the standard of care in primary care. Suicidality, I was told, was a clinical issue for specialty mental health settings, not primary care; because we worked as consultants to primary care providers (PCPs), if a PCP did not specifically ask about suicide risk, there was no need to pursue it. At that time, if patients reported suicidality to their PCPs, it was not uncommon for them to be transported to the emergency department or referred to an affiliated outpatient mental health clinic located several miles away. Although BHCs would often address issues about suicide risk and assist PCPs in making decisions about clinical management of suicidal patients, in general, suicidal patients were not seen by BHCs. As an intern, this seemed like a waste of resources and a failure to capitalize upon the basic philosophy of the BHC model: to integrate mind and body and improve health care service delivery for patients with psychosocial health issues. So at the conclusion of my internship year, when I was placed in the family medicine clinic to work as a BHC, one of the first changes I implemented was routine screening of suicidality for all patients seen by BHCs. I also worked aggressively with the PCPs within the first few months of my staff assignment to build the expectation that suicidal patients would now be evaluated "in-house" for dispositional recommendations, as opposed to the time-consuming and costly process of transporting these patients to the hospital or outpatient clinic. I was more than happy to see any and all suicidal patients who came into the clinic, and the PCPs were more than happy to immediately push them my way.

At that time, my approach to suicidal patients was to conduct a thorough risk assessment using the exact same approach and paperwork I had learned and used in outpatient specialty mental health clinics. It was therefore not uncommon for me to extend well beyond the 30-minute appointment timeframe in order to complete these evaluations, which typically put me behind in my schedule but not so much that it caused any substantial difficulties or patient dissatisfaction. I enjoyed working with suicidal patients, so this approach initially worked very well, and the PCPs were highly satisfied with the care that was being provided to their patients. It only took a few months, however, for me to start doubting this particular approach to managing suicidal patients.

I remember one day early in my assignment at family medicine when I evaluated three at-risk patients above and beyond the daily scheduled appointments. I walked out of the clinic late that night exhausted but excited that I had been able to help so many patients in distress. The excitement—or "adrenaline rush," as so many of my interns and trainees have come to call it—is a common experience for BHCs following a very busy day. For most BHCs, this adrenaline rush is experienced as a type of "flow" that results in heightened focus, efficient decision-making, and enhanced performance. As a BHC trainer, I have come to realize that trainees who describe a "flow" experience (as opposed to an overwhelming stress experience) tend to do very well in primary care. Leaving the clinic that night in a state of "flow," I felt very good about the work I was doing and how we had improved our ability to manage suicidal patients in primary care.

Only a month or so later (within the first 6 months of working in family medicine), I remember another day when a PCP knocked on my examination room door while I was with a patient. The PCP asked me to evaluate a patient who had just reported suicidal ideation during the general examination. As he was filling me in on the case, another PCP walked down the hall in apparent distress and quickly explained that she had a patient she wanted me to see right away because the patient had attempted suicide the week before and was requesting sleep medications to reduce her agitation at night, but the PCP understandably felt uncomfortable about prescribing. I told both PCPs that I would get to their respective patients as soon as possible and instructed them to have staff maintain visual contact with each until I could squeeze them in. I finished up the routine appointment and went to inform the patient who was scheduled in the next routine appointment slot that I would be running behind due to an emergent situation. My plan was to evaluate one of the suicidal patients, then see the scheduled routine appointment, then take the next suicidal patient, then return to my regular schedule, hopefully only 30 minutes behind. As I pulled in the first suicidal patient, however, a third PCP knocked on the door to request a walk-in evaluation for a patient who stated they thought it would be better off if they were dead. It was at this point that I started to worry about my ability to manage all of these walk-in services in addition to my routine schedule; at this point, I had two regularly scheduled patients waiting to be seen, and now a third walk-in was waiting. The trend only continued; by the end of the day, I evaluated five at-risk patients in addition to my 10 regularly scheduled patients.

When I left the clinic late on that night, I was again exhausted and excited, but this time, frustration and worry were also present. Of the five walk-ins I had seen, four were at very low risk for suicide and did not need immediate evaluation. I was frustrated with my PCP colleagues for "overreacting" to these cases, but I knew they were simply practicing consistent with what I had encouraged and advised them to do: Immediately refer to me any patient who might possibly be at risk for suicide for a walk-in evaluation. So I ended up frustrated with myself for implementing such a policy and started questioning my approach to managing suicidal patients. What if I have another day like this? Is it really necessary to spend so much time conducting risk assessments with every single patient? Is there a better way to do this? I mulled over these questions for several days, reviewing the many textbooks and journal articles that I had on managing suicidal risk. I came to the conclusion that my time-intensive approach, which adopted a specialty mental health perspective, was appropriate; it did not occur to me at the time that the literature I was reviewing was based upon managing suicidal patients in traditional, outpatient mental health settings, not primary care.

Within a month, I had another day in which I was again overrun by walk-in requests for at-risk patients. Unfortunately for me, my routinely scheduled patients on this day were less understanding than the patients on the previous days, and a few complained; one even left without being seen. This disturbed me considerably, not only because high patient satisfaction is very important to me, but also because I was unable to help these patients who were suffering in some way and desired behavioral health services to improve their health and well-being. When I left the clinic that night, there was no excitement, only anxiety and doubt. As I reconsidered the day, I again started questioning my clinical approach, increasingly skeptical that it was workable in this setting. I thought back to my internship training, during which I had been encouraged to stay away from suicidality in primary care because it was outside the scope of BHC practice, and begrudgingly admitted that this perspective had some inherent value. At the same time, I was certain that taking a hands-off approach to suicidality added very little to the health care of those patients who were most distressed and in need of assistance. Because both positions contained intrinsic truths (and limitations) to them, it became clear that a more balanced approach based upon the tenants of what seemed to be opposing forces—efficiency and comprehensiveness—was needed.

I again returned to my various textbooks and professional guidelines and started dialogues with a wide range of colleagues and clinicians from both specialty mental health settings and primary care settings. It did not take long to recognize a significant problem: There was absolutely nothing written on the topic of managing suicidal risk in primary care. In all the textbooks, articles, and practice manuals written on BHC practice, I was shocked to find such little guidance on suicidality—the single most important (and arguably only) behavioral health emergency. Even the 72-page practice manual developed to guide BHC work conducted within my clinic had only a single, ambiguously worded paragraph that addressed the issue of "patients in crisis." It was easy to find recommendations and resources on any clinical issue imaginable except suicidality, almost as if the issue did not exist. Imagine if there were no guidelines for nonspecialty primary care medical providers (e.g., noncardiologists) in the care of patients at risk for acute myocardial infarction or the management of chronic heart disease; this would be considered unacceptable. Yet in the area of suicide risk in primary care, the professional literature had nothing for BHCs. When I spoke with many of my BHC colleagues about this, there was overwhelming consensus that there was almost ubiquitous confusion and widely different opinions about how to appropriately handle suicidal patients and that "something needs to be written about it."

One of the colleagues with whom I spoke was David Rudd—my coauthor on this book. He instantly put the core issue into focus: "The problem is you're thinking like a specialty mental health provider but you're in a primary care setting. You need to think like the primary care provider that you are." So began the ongoing dialogue that has culminated in this book. The four most salient issues that David and I have discussed over the past few years include:

1. *Clinical approaches must be consistent with the context of primary care.* To improve the management of suicidal risk in primary care, any approach must fundamentally embrace the philosophy and clinical reality of primary care and must not mistakenly apply specialty mental health principles and expectations to a setting where they are inappropriate and cannot be realistically sustained, as this increases vulnerability to adverse outcomes and liability.
2. *Clinical approaches must be consistent with the consultative model.* To remain within the scope of care of the BHC model, any approach must preserve the consultative relationship between the PCP and BHC, in which the PCP maintains primary responsibility for all aspects of the treatment plan. Approaches that move outside the consultative model by placing primary decision-making responsibility in the hands of the BHC raises vulnerability for malpractice liability.

3. *Clinical approaches must be informed by science and empiricism.* To balance the competing demands for efficiency and comprehensiveness and to provide the highest level of evidence-based medicine, any approach must be based upon the most current scientific knowledge base of suicidal behaviors and clinical practice.
4. *Clinical approaches must be competency-based.* To ensure adequate skill mastery and clinical competence, any approach must be definable and measurable, with identified skill sets (i.e., competencies) directly contributing to best practices and expectations of clinical care. Approaches must therefore be described with adequate detail for ease of implementation and measurement of skill mastery.

This book therefore can be organized into three general sections. In the first section, we discuss the context of primary care and the BHC model in particular. As will be made clear in Chapter 1, there is compelling evidence pointing to primary care as a critical setting to impact suicide risk at a global level through early and effective identification and treatment of behavioral health issues, as well as at a more targeted level through the refinement of suicide risk management techniques and strategies. In Chapter 2, we discuss the BHC model of integrated primary care to provide a backdrop and rationale for the particular presentation of information provided in this book. We chose to focus on the BHC model due in large part to our experience working within this model of care and its widespread use. From a more practical standpoint, we chose to focus on the BHC model because of its considerable difference from traditional, specialty mental health models of care, which require a greater deal of flexibility and adaptability than other models (e.g., the collocated clinic model) that do not markedly change practice patterns for the mental health professional. In the second section, we delve into the mechanics of clinical encounters with suicidal patients, with a particular emphasis on the appropriate adaptation of risk management procedures and strategies for the primary care setting. Chapter 3 therefore discusses those basic variables essential for effective risk management: establishing collaborative treatment relationships and working from an empirically supported model of suicidal behavior. We then detail a straightforward and efficient approach to accurate risk assessment in Chapter 4, which leads directly to a step-by-step description of basic risk management interventions in Chapter 5. Following these core risk management strategies, Chapter 6 presents a thorough discussion of several specific empirically supported interventions that fit seamlessly within the constraints of primary care. In the final section, we transition to the "bigger picture" by first detailing in Chapter 7 a series of concrete actions that clinics can take to prepare for suicidal crises, thereby increasing the likelihood for effective clinical care of suicidal patients while managing legal liability. We provide consultation tips and strategies for BHCs in Chapter 8 that are intended to maximize the BHC's ability to positively impact providers' practice and clinic standards. We include in this chapter a thorough discussion of the Food and Drug Administration's black-box warning label for antidepressants and provide recommendations for educating patients and consulting with prescribers about these medications. We then address special concerns about providing care to suicidal patients in primary care clinics, including commonly occurring issues such as treatment ambivalence and nonadherence. Finally, we conclude with a discussion of legal issues related to the clinical care of suicidal patients that are specifically tailored to primary care settings.

Other colleagues with whom we have dialogued considerably on this topic include Kent Corso, PsyD, Tracy Neal-Walden, PhD, Jeff Goodie, PhD, and Chris Hunter, PhD—all psychologists who have spent a considerable amount of their professional time working as BHCs and who have similarly struggled with the issue of suicidality in primary care. As David and I have formulated many of the ideas presented in this book, these four colleagues have served as sounding boards to further develop and hone these ideas, especially with respect to the pragmatics of daily BHC practice. They have also been invaluable in stimulating considerable discussion and debate among the BHC community (and also the mental health community in general) about the issue of managing suicidality in primary care, with an eye toward moving our profession to better-defined practices that enhance the health care of our patient populations. I must also note the contributions of Kirk Strosahl, PhD, who markedly influenced my understanding of the role of the BHC. In particular, he has challenged me to consider the "bigger picture" of behavioral health consultation, especially the considerable indirect impact a behaviorist can have on the population as a whole by gradually shaping a PCP's routine clinical practice.

What is clear is that mental health professionals are increasingly being integrated in primary care clinics and general medical settings, and the issue of suicidality in these practice settings can no longer be ignored. As integrated care continues to expand, the need for reasonable, empirically informed approaches for managing suicidal patients in nontraditional mental health settings becomes ever more salient. This book is just the first step toward the establishment of an empirically informed, competency-based approach to the issue of suicidal risk in primary care. As our science and practice continue to evolve in primary care, so, too, will our understanding of optimal clinical approaches for managing suicidality in these settings.

Craig J. Bryan, PsyD

CHAPTER 1

Why Primary Care?

Over the past few decades, a significant transition has occurred in the way health care services are delivered in the United States. At the forefront of this transition is the primary care clinic, which has seen a shift from a primarily acute health care model to a model of prevention and chronic disease management. Within population health models, the provision of basic medical services to a large percentage of the community is emphasized, with briefer medical appointments coinciding with a substantial increase in the total number of patients seen during a typical day of practice. In our current health care system, the primary care physician (PCP) is typically the first point of contact for accessing medical services, whether the need is for basic health, mental health, or substance abuse treatment. It is "the doctor" to whom a patient first goes to raise concerns about health, well-being, and life problems. Likewise, the PCP is almost always the first medical professional with whom a patient discusses mental health problems or behavioral difficulties. Even when presenting for physical complaints, research has shown that psychosocial and behavioral issues drive the overwhelming majority of these visits (Gatchel & Oordt, 2003; Kroenke & Mangelsdorf, 1989).

In addition to being the first medical provider seen by most individuals for the full spectrum of health concerns, the PCP is frequently the last medical provider seen by those who kill themselves. Perhaps this is because patients do not know that PCPs do not have the same level of specialized training or experience in managing suicide risk as mental health providers. Perhaps this is because patients are seeking assistance from the medical provider they know best. Whatever the reasons why PCPs and other general medical practitioners are so commonly the final health care contact for victims of suicide, it seems likely that patients are simply following the rule to "go to the doctor" when they are in distress and need help.

Like it or not, as the entry point to the health care system, the primary care team will inevitably encounter suicidal patients seeking medical and mental health services. Because of this, primary care teams need to be effective at managing suicidal patients for three compelling reasons (cf. Chiles & Strosahl, 2005). First, because primary care has become the de facto mental health care system in the United States, PCPs will almost assuredly be the first stop for suicidal patients seeking assistance. Second, because psychiatric conditions are reasonably prevalent in the primary care patient population and are prominent risk factors and contributors to suicidal behaviors, accurate recognition and treatment by PCPs is critical for managing suicide risk. Third, because of financial or resource limitations, many suicidal patients do not have access to mental health care and will not seek out specialty services beyond the primary care system. Each of these three factors will be discussed further to highlight the central role that primary care plays in addressing and managing suicide risk.

PRIMARY CARE: THE DE FACTO MENTAL HEALTH CARE SYSTEM

It has been estimated that approximately 70% of primary care medical appointments are for issues associated with psychosocial factors (Gatchel & Oordt, 2003). In fact, one study found that of the 10 most common physical complaints reported in primary care, a remarkable 85% resulted in no diagnosable organic etiology during a 3-year follow-up period (Kroenke & Mangelsdorf, 1989). Much more conservative estimates indicate that one third of all somatic symptoms reported in primary care visits are "medically unexplained," although the proportion of what is considered medically unexplained ranges from 20% to 74% depending on how a symptom is defined as such (Kroenke, 2006).

Within primary care, behavioral and psychosocial health issues present in a wide range of forms that include full-blown psychiatric disorders (e.g., major depressive disorder, generalized anxiety disorder, posttraumatic stress disorder) to health-compromising behaviors that contribute to and maintain disease processes (e.g., smoking, physical inactivity, diet, nutrition). Given that approximately 80% of the U.S. population visits with their PCP at least once per year (Narrow, Regier, Rae, Manderscheid, & Locke, 1993), the PCP will inevitably come into contact with the full spectrum of mental health conditions. In fact, one study of consecutively scheduled adult patients in primary care found that 19% meet criteria for major depressive disorder, 15% for generalized anxiety disorder, 8% for panic disorder, 8% for substance abuse, and between 36% and 77% met criteria for more than one disorder (Olfson et al., 2000). PCPs often find themselves responsible for treating behavior problems, chronic psychiatric conditions, substance abuse, and mood disorders in a variety of forms across the entire lifespan—from children to elderly adults. Impressively, PCPs manage to accomplish this all while simultaneously managing their patients' equally wide-ranging medical needs.

In a given year, just over one quarter of the U.S. population will meet criteria for a mental health disorder, of which only half will seek treatment (Kessler, Demler, Frank et al., 2005; Kessler et al., 2001; Regier et al., 1993). According to the Epidemiological Catchment Area study completed almost two decades ago, of those who do seek treatment for mental health issues, around half will receive care solely from their primary care provider (Regier et al., 1993). A similar service utilization pattern was found in the National Comorbidity Study (Kessler et al., 1994). Since then, general medical settings such as primary care have become the predominant source of mental health care in the United States and have seen the most rapid expansion of utilization by the general population, outpacing growth in specialty mental health settings by more than double across all levels of mental health severity (Wang et al., 2006). It is important to note that these data account primarily for psychiatric conditions and do not take into consideration the large number of patients seen in primary care with psychosocial and behavioral problems that are subsyndromal (e.g., mild depression, occasional panic attacks, nonspecific anxiety) or do not fit into any particular diagnostic category, yet nonetheless compromise health and well-being (e.g., grief, acute stress, interpersonal conflict, unhealthy lifestyle patterns). In light of these facts, it is no wonder that primary care has been termed the de facto mental health care system in the United States (Regier et al., 1993).

The unparalleled growth in primary care utilization could potentially be explained by simultaneous increases in the assignment of PCPs as the "gatekeepers" for specialty care, improved identification and detection strategies for mental health conditions in primary care, and/or development and marketing of antidepressant and other psychotropic medications with lower risk profiles (Gray, Brody, & Johnson, 2005; Wang et al., 2006). The evolving role of pharmaceutical companies, in particular, seems to have played a significant role in the shifting of psychiatric treatment from the mental health specialist to the realm of the PCP. As noted by Gray et al. (2005), with the introduction of Prozac in 1986, mental health care experienced a rapid shift away from specialist-driven treatment based around psychotherapy toward medication treatment that was much safer than earlier generations of antidepressants and much more cost effective than psychotherapy. Not surprisingly, utilization of psychotherapy decreased over the next 20 years (Olfson et al., 2002), while drug companies continued to develop and market new selective serotonin reuptake inhibitor (SSRI) medications for depression. As the biomedical model of depression and psychiatric conditions gained widespread adoption and popularity, psychotherapists from all professional disciplines separated themselves from the medical profession, effectively establishing psychotherapy as a non–health care profession (Cummings & O'Donahue, 2008). Not surprisingly, within a relatively short period, SSRIs replaced psychotherapy as the frontline intervention for mental health conditions.

Also contributing to decreased utilization of specialty mental health care is PCP dissatisfaction with the availability and quality of the mental health system. When compared with other medical subspecialties, mental health specialists receive the highest level of dissatisfaction ratings from PCPs, especially among family physicians and general internists (Williams et al., 1999). It should not come as a surprise that satisfaction predicts treatment practices: PCPs reporting higher levels of satisfaction are more likely to refer a depressed patient to mental health specialists than dissatisfied PCPs, while lower satisfaction is related to lower rates of referral. PCPs are also keenly aware of the rising cost of specialty mental health care, which further reduces their likelihood to refer patients to mental health specialists (Williams et al., 1999). With these numerous barriers to mental health care, it often takes many years—up to decades—for individuals with psychiatric conditions to initiate contact with specialty mental health treatment (Wang et al., 2005). In the intervening years, these patients continue to visit their PCPs, who might not accurately detect the psychiatric condition or recognize the role that these psychosocial issues have on the patient's health. Even when these psychosocial factors are accurately recognized, the PCP might not have the capability to provide the most effective treatments.

In general, we simply do not know for sure why people choose to visit—or not to visit—a health care provider. What we do know, however, is that the decision to seek medical care is not determined by the presence or absence of illness; disability and morbidity alone account for only one quarter of the decision to seek medical care (Berkanovic, Telesky, & Reeder, 1981). A much more important driver of medical utilization than functional disability is subjective discomfort and distress. As noted earlier, we know that the overwhelming majority of medical visits in primary care have a psychosocial basis, the most frequent being psychiatric disorders, substance abuse and dependence, poor social support, lack of coping skills, and social and occupational stressors (Strosahl, 2001). Many of these issues occur in combination among the highest utilizers of medical services (Arnow, 2004; Deykin et al., 2001; Katon et al., 1992). Psychosocial issues have consistently been linked to poor general health status, functional disability, and long-term medical morbidity and mortality. Even patients with mild levels of depression use more than double the primary care services as patients without any symptoms of depression (Simon, 1992). This increased service utilization pattern among patients with psychosocial problems is due to the higher prevalence of nonspecific, vaguely defined physical symptoms that cause considerable distress and contribute to negative self-perceptions about health, which raises their motivation to seek out medical care to identify the problem (Arnow, 2004; Deykin et al., 2001; Smith, Monson, & Ray, 1986). The first stop for these patients is almost always the primary care clinic.

Suicidal patients access primary care services at an even higher rate than patients with psychosocial health issues who are not suicidal; specifically, patients reporting suicidal ideation also report more problems with poor health in general, sleep problems, smoking habits, and higher levels of psychiatric symptoms than patients with psychosocial stressors but no suicidal ideation. Each of these problems and behaviors associated with suicidality contributes to greater subjective discomfort and more frequent visits. Chronic pain is an especially well-established medical risk factor for suicidal ideation and behaviors, with up to 13% of chronic pain patients reporting suicidal ideation and another 19% reporting nonsuicidal morbid ideation (i.e., a wish to die or be killed without suicidal intent; Smith, Perlis, & Haythornthwaite, 2004). Abdominal pain, in particular, seems to be reported with greater frequency than other chronic pain conditions among suicidal patients. Not surprisingly, in the presence of mental health symptoms and problems, the prevalence of suicidal ideation rises—up to 22% among chronic pain patients who are prescribed antidepressants or anxiolytics by their general practitioner for mood or anxiety disorders (Verger et al., 2007).

Shockingly, almost half of individuals who die by suicide make contact with a primary care provider in the month before their death (Luoma, Martin, & Pearson, 2002), and nearly 20% who kill themselves make contact within one day of their death (Pirkis & Burgess, 1998). These numbers increase dramatically among elderly patients, with an astounding 73% of elderly suicide victims visisting their PCP in the month preceding their suicide and 45% visiting within the preceding week (Juurlink et al., 2004). In comparison, only 15% of suicide victims visit with a mental health professional in the month preceding their death (Luoma et al., 2002). As mentioned previously, primary care medical providers are oftentimes the last medical professionals that a suicidal individual will see before his or her death.

Suicidal individuals report a wide range of physical health complaints including higher levels of bodily pain, lower energy, and greater physical limitations (Goldney, Fisher, Wilson, & Cheok, 2001), with the relative risk of suicidal ideation and death by suicide increasing with the total number of illnesses with which a patient has been diagnosed (Druss & Pincus, 2000; Juurlink et al., 2004). The frequency of medical visits in the month preceding a suicide also increases considerably; in one study, visit frequency spiked to an average of three visits in the month immediately preceding the suicide (Juurlink et al., 2004), in stark contrast to the typical one or two visits per year for most individuals.

This same study also found that the most frequent chief complaints during these medical visits are not always psychiatric in nature. Anxiety, unspecified gastrointestinal symptoms, depression, unspecified cardiac symptoms, and hypertension were the five most common diagnoses listed in the week before the patients' suicides. Importantly, gastrointestinal symptoms, cardiac symptoms, and hypertension are strongly influenced by psychosocial factors in general and depression in particular (Elliott, 2007), but are often seen by both the patient and the provider as "pure" physical conditions.

As symptoms escalate and contribute to greater levels of functional impairment, ignoring or missing the psychosocial needs of the patient—which can often be masked by or disguised as physical complaints—can lead to increased utilization of medical visits, especially in acute care or emergency settings such as hospitals (Arnow, 2004). As these problems mount and psychological distress expands, suicide risk becomes increasingly likely to emerge. The ability for the primary care system to respond earlier and more effectively to psychosocial stressors therefore has considerable potential for "heading off" suicide risk at its earliest stages of development. It is not surprising, then, that primary care and general medical settings have been identified as a key setting for addressing the public health issue that is suicide (Luoma et al., 2002; Pirkis & Burgess, 1998; Schulberg et al., 2004; U.S. Public Health Service, 1999), especially for older adults, who have elevated depression and suicide rates but often do not receive adequate primary care or specialty mental health treatment to address these health problems (Unutzer et al., 2002).

THE PREVALENCE OF MENTAL HEALTH CONDITIONS

Epidemiological studies over the past few decades have revealed that approximately one quarter of the U.S. population will meet criteria for a psychiatric disorder each year (Kessler, Chiu, Demler, & Walters, 2005; Regier et al., 1993), and just under half will meet criteria for a psychiatric disorder at some point during their life (Kessler, Berglund, Demler, Jin, & Walters, 2005). This annual incidence rate of psychiatric disorders has remained stable from 1990 to 2003 (Kessler, Demler, Frank et al., 2005), with no indicators of significant change during the past two decades. Considering that 80% of the U.S. population will visit their PCP at least once each year (Narrow et al., 1993), one can quickly see that the overwhelming majority of individuals with psychiatric conditions will come into contact and receive medical interventions from a PCP at some point annually.

The rapid expansion of PCP utilization for mental health services and treatment among the general population that is occurring across all levels of mental health severity, from mild to severe, is disconcerting, given that only a minority of patients (19.6%) receive minimally adequate treatment from general medical settings alone (Wang et al., 2002). Although PCPs largely provide effective and appropriate medical care for the mental health needs of their patients, mental health treatment delivered solely in primary care settings is more likely to be inadequate in terms of intensity and mode of intervention, particularly in light of converging evidence that strongly favors the superior effectiveness of psychopharmacologic treatment combined with behavioral interventions. The superiority of combined treatments is especially pronounced among individuals with more severe psychiatric conditions. Unfortunately, PCPs often find themselves in the position of attempting to manage what can be at times highly complex mental health issues in addition to a wide range of physical health problems, typically within the span of a 10- to 15-minute appointment.

Given the fast-paced context of primary care, it is not surprising that the Medical Outcomes Study (Wells et al., 1989) has demonstrated that psychiatric disorders are generally underrecognized in general health care settings, with only half of depressed patients being accurately detected. Further contributing to underrecognition of psychiatric conditions is the manner in which physicians arrive at the diagnoses that guide their treatment interventions. Williams and colleagues (1999) found, for example, that depression is often diagnosed based on the physician's overall clinical impression of the patient rather than based on the symptom criteria of the *Diagnostic and Statistical Manual of Mental Disorders, Fourth Edition* (*DSM-IV*; American Psychiatric Association, 1994). Although the PCPs in this study often did not use formal diagnostic criteria during patient encounters, they nonetheless expressed high confidence in their diagnostic skills. This confidence in diagnosis, in combination with the relative safety of the SSRIs, could potentially explain the finding in one regional health care system that less than half of the patients who were prescribed SSRIs met full criteria for depression (Strosahl, 2001)—the primary criterion for the empirically derived suitability of this therapy. Nonclinical factors such as patient variables (e.g., age, sex, employment status, marital status) and physician variables (e.g., training background) have also been found to be just as important in the decision to prescribe antidepressants, anxiolytics, and hypnotics among general practitioners as clinical features (Kisely, Linden, Bellantuono, Simon, & Jones, 2000). In light of such data, criticisms have unfortunately (and in our opinion unfairly) been leveled at PCPs for relatively poor recognition and treatment of mental health conditions—especially from mental health professionals.

Despite these criticisms, it is clear that, in our current health care system, PCPs are providing—and will continue to provide—both medical and psychiatric interventions to their patients, often in the form of psychotropic medications. Nonpsychiatric PCPs currently prescribe more than 75% of all psychotropic agents in the United States (Beardsley et al., 1998; Goodwin, Gould, Blanco, & Olfson, 2001), especially the SSRIs. Confidence in SSRIs as a therapeutic mode is very high among family physicians, even with mildly or moderately depressed patients, for whom antidepressant medication treatment has questionable efficacy above and beyond placebo. Specifically, SSRIs have been found to be no more clinically efficacious than placebo conditions among mildly to moderately depressed patients in a recent meta-analysis of all U.S. Food and Drug Administration clinical trials (Kirsch et al., 2008). Among severely depressed patients, superior efficacy of SSRIs was supported, although this difference might be related more to decreased responsiveness to placebo than to increased responsiveness to the antidepressant.

Psychiatric disorders are only the tip of the iceberg, however. Nonpsychiatric behavioral and motivational issues are central to most health complaints in primary care. The U.S. Department of Health and Human Services has noted, for example, that unhealthy lifestyles are responsible for most of the top 10 causes of mortality and morbidity in the country and are estimated to play a greater role in mortality and morbidity than genetic, biological, and environmental factors (Mokdad et al., 2004). As noted previously, one 3-year study of primary care patients found that 85% of their most common complaints could not be linked to any identifiable biologic or organic cause (Kroenke & Mangelsdorff, 1989). Health conditions such as chronic pain, headaches, sleep disturbances, and gastrointestinal problems, for example, are significantly influenced by stress and mood fluctuations (e.g., Lepine & Briley, 2004), but these complaints are traditionally viewed as "pure" physical conditions for which patients seek treatment from PCPs and other medical professionals instead of mental health specialists. Smoking, eating habits, physical activity, alcohol abuse, and medication adherence are other behavioral issues that impact health outcomes. In fact, medication adherence—an issue of motivation, choice, and behavioral action—is a primary contributor to treatment "failure" in up to 60% of patients with chronic health conditions (Dunbar-Jacob & Mortimer-Stephens, 2001). Not surprisingly, a considerable amount of the time a PCP spends with a given patient is actually focused on educating and advising about behavioral change, whether related to changing diet, exercise, or adherence with treatment recommendations (Robinson, 2004; Robinson & Reiter, 2007).

Similarly, comorbid psychiatric-physical disorders are significantly more impairing than either "pure" psychiatric or "pure" physical disorders alone (Kessler, Ormel, Demler, & Stang, 2003). Among the four most commonly occurring chronic physical disorders in a large epidemiological study—hypertension, arthritis, asthma, and ulcers—functional impairment (i.e., missed days at work) was largely confined to those cases with comorbid mental health conditions (Kessler et al., 2003). The Medical Outcomes Study, conducted over a decade earlier, likewise revealed that depressive symptoms are more debilitating than diabetes, arthritis, gastrointestinal disorders, back problems, and hypertension (Wells et al., 1989). Functional disabilities are not only difficult and expensive to manage within the health care system but also a significant concern for employers due to the associated absenteeism and reductions in productivity. Psychological distress, whether it meets the threshold for a diagnosable psychiatric condition or not, can complicate medical treatment considerably. The risk for morbidity, mortality, and recurrence of chronic illness is much higher for patients with psychological distress or poor coping skills (Frasure-Smith, 1991; Fawzy et al., 1993). Psychosocial stress, especially a sense of hopelessness, accounts for approximately 30% of the attributable risk of acute myocardial infarction (Das et al., 2006), and a history of depression doubles the risk of coronary heart disease and raises the risk of hypertension or stroke by 50% (Elliott, 2007). Although the reason for this link remains unclear, one potential mediating factor that has been proposed is that psychological distress such as depression or substance abuse reduces adherence to medical recommendations (Robinson, Wischman, & Del Vento, 1996).

In addition to their adverse effect on physical health and well-being, psychological distress, poor coping skills, and psychiatric disorders serve as significant risk factors for suicide (American Psychiatric Association, 2003). Of those who die by suicide, an estimated 90% experience a psychiatric condition at the time of their death (Maris, Berman, & Silverman, 2000). Suicide consistently ranks among the top 10 causes for death each year within the United States by age group, claiming approximately 31,000 lives annually (Hoyert, Heron, Murphy, & Kung, 2006). From the ages of 10 to 34 years (i.e., nearly one third of the average lifespan of a typical U.S. citizen), suicide ranks among the top three causes for death.

Even more pernicious than psychological distress or psychiatric disorder alone are suicidal ideation and intentional self-injurious behaviors, both of which are estimated to occur among 4.6% of the U.S. population in a given year. Of those who report intentional self-injurious behaviors, a little more than half report the intent to die at the time of the act (i.e., a suicide attempt; Nock & Kessler, 2006). Trends in the prevalence of suicidal ideation, plans, and attempts have remained fairly stable over the past few decades (Kessler, Berglund, Borges, Nock, & Wang, 2005), suggesting that suicide prevention efforts and gains in treatment have not yet had a marked effect on national suicide rates. A more recent longitudinal study found that among a sample of males who were followed annually from the ages of 9 to 29 years, 1-week point prevalence rates of suicidal ideation ranged from 2.6% to 16.3%, with most new cases emerging during adolescence (Kerr et al., 2008). By the age of 29 years, however, more than half (57.3%) of the entire sample self-reported suicidal ideation at least once during the 20-year span of the study—a much higher prevalence rate than typically found in epidemiological studies. Kerr and colleagues posited that this high rate differed so dramatically from most lifetime prevalence estimates of suicidal ideation because of their continual and repeated assessment of suicidal ideation during shorter periods, as opposed to the single-point retrospective reporting typically used in epidemiological studies. In short, accuracy of self-report can be increased when asking respondents to report brief, transient episodes of suicidal ideation within the past few months as opposed to the past few years or decades, the latter of which is prone to memory decay.

The implications of this most recent study are sobering: Suicidal ideation is likely much more common than typically assumed, so much so that one could argue that suicidal thinking is not abnormal at all, but rather an inherent part of the human condition (cf. Chiles & Stroshal, 2005). This adds considerably to the challenge of determining which suicidal individuals will experience resolution in suicide risk, whether naturally or via treatment intervention, and which will escalate to the point of making an attempt.

A substantial proportion of suicide victims, possibly as high as one half, are in active treatment at the time of their death (Fawcett, 1999). Randomized controlled trials for the treatment of suicide attempts or intentional self-harm behaviors have found re-attempt rates among patients as high as 47% during treatment (highest in the treatment as usual or control arm of the study), with those making suicide attempts in treatment routinely making more than one attempt (see Rudd, Joiner, & Rajab, 2004, for a review). Data are also available about both suicide and attempt rates for targeted disorders. For example, with bipolar disorder, 25% to 50% will make a suicide attempt during the course of the illness, with 10% to 20% dying (Goodwin & Jamison, 1990). For those with schizophrenia, between 20% and 40% will make a suicide attempt (Meltzer, 1995) and 5% will die (Caldwell & Gottesman, 1990; Palmer, Pankratz, & Bostwick, 2005). For major depression, 2% receiving outpatient treatment will die by suicide and 9% of patients receiving inpatient treatment will die (Bostwick & Pankrantz, 2000). Without a doubt, psychiatric disorders are a significant risk factor for suicide.

There are also converging and convincing data about the high-risk nature of multiple suicide attempters (i.e., those making more than one lifetime suicide attempt). In relationship to single attempters, multiple suicide attempters evidence more significant suicidal thinking, depression, and hopelessness; higher rates of alcohol and substance abuse; the poorest histories of interpersonal coping; greater perceived stress; and the least available and accessible social support networks. Multiple attempters also evidence greater diagnostic complexity, with more axes I and II comorbidity, and are more likely to make a subsequent suicide attempt (Brown, TenHave, Henriques, Xie, Hollander, & Beck, 2005; Forman, Berk, Henriques, Brown, & Beck, 2004; Reynolds & Eaton, 1986; Rudd, Joiner, & Hasan, 1996; Stein, Apter, Ratzoni, Har-Even, & Avidan, 1998). Available findings on multiple attempters are very consistent, with effects remaining significant even after controlling for the diagnosis of borderline personality disorder (Forman et al., 2004; Rudd, Joiner & Hasan, 1996).

Among primary care populations, studies have found a general prevalence rate for suicidal ideation and suicidal behaviors to be under 5%, depending on the nature of the setting and population being investigated. In the Epidemiological Catchment Area study, a 2.2% annual prevalence rate for suicidal ideation was found among patients accessing general medical settings (Cooper-Patrick, Crum, & Ford, 1994). Olfson and colleagues (1996) similarly found that 2.4% of adult patients reported suicidal ideation within the month preceding their primary care visit, more than half of whom were not receiving mental health treatment. Among urban medical outpatients, the rate of suicidal ideation is 3.3% (Zimmerman, Lish, Lush, Farber, Plescia, & Kuzma, 1995). A more recent Australian study of general medical settings found that approximately 5% of older adults (older than 60 years) endorsed suicidal ideation (Pfaff & Almeida, 2005). All of these findings are close to the estimated prevalence of suicidal ideation among the U.S. population at large (3.3%; Kessler, Berglund, Borges et al., 2005), although in light of Kerr and colleagues' (2008) longitudinal study noted earlier, it is possible that this is a considerable underestimation of the frequency of suicidal ideation over time. When specifically considering patients with mental health symptoms and problems, however, the prevalence of suicidal ideation rises. Among those referred to a primary care behavioral health provider for a range of psychosocial issues, for example, 12.4% report suicidal ideation (Bryan, Corso, Rudd, & Cordero, 2008) and up to 22% of patients who are prescribed psychotropic medications for mood or anxiety disorders report suicidal ideation (Verger et al., 2007).

What is increasingly clear in the emerging clinical and epidemiological data is that mental health conditions can be fatal, but the mortality rate of mental health conditions can be reduced with adequate treatment, particularly cognitive-behavioral treatments that focus on suicidal behaviors (Tarrier, Taylor, & Gooding, 2008). Despite the emergence of newer and more effective treatments for suicidal behaviors and the observed increase in mental health treatment in general over the past decades, the prevalence rate of suicidal behaviors has nonetheless remained remarkably stable (Kessler, Berglund, Borges et al., 2005). This discouraging finding could be due, in part, to delays in accessing mental health services. With the shift in our society's mental health care system from that of specialty care to primary care, it is also possible that suicidal individuals are not receiving an adequate level of treatment. Without a doubt, the shift in mental health care delivery system, in combination with the fact that suicidal individuals utilize general medical services approximately three times more frequently than nonsuicidal individuals, will only result in PCPs coming into increased contact with suicidal patients (Goldney et al., 2001). Considerable barriers exist, however, for accessing the mental health care system in the United States, which limits the likelihood that PCPs will be able to efficiently transition suicidal patients to specialty care settings.

BARRIERS TO ACCESSING MENTAL HEALTH CARE

In addition to an increased emphasis on pharmacologic treatment as a sole treatment for mental health issues, considerable barriers remain for patients who would benefit from accessing specialty mental health care. The primary reason individuals with mental health conditions remain untreated is because more than half simply do not believe they require any such treatment (Kessler et al., 2001). Of those untreated individuals who do recognize a need for treatment, the overwhelming majority (72.1%) prefer to solve the problem on their own (Kessler et al., 2001). Primary care patients with higher levels of depression also report a greater number of barriers to mental health care than primary care patients with minimal depressive symptoms, including greater mental health stigma, less motivation to seek out care, concerns about experiencing negative or undesirable feelings while in treatment, and a greater belief that treatment will be unhelpful or harmful (Mohr, Ho, Duffecy, Baron, Lehman, Jin, & Reifler, 2010). Patients who would most benefit from additional mental health services are therefore less likely to seek care.

Other common barriers include factors such as uncertainty about how to access services, time constraints, and inability to afford services. This problem has been compounded by the growing number of uninsured in the United States, which increased by 19% from 1990 to 2001 (DeLeon, Giesting, & Kenkel, 2003). Uninsured people commonly do not have access to any form of medical care, let alone specialty mental health. Even for those who do have health insurance coverage within a managed care system, patients can become easily confused about their benefits and the processes for accessing specialty mental health services. Specialty mental health care has become increasingly difficult to access, as patients' requests for needed mental health services are denied or restricted by managed care organizations, which often view mental health services as separate from medical care and therefore reimburse mental health professionals separately. As access to mental health care is restricted, patients are forced to "compete" for a smaller pool of available professionals, which increases the wait time for new appointments (in some areas up to 6 weeks). This is assuming, of course, that the patient can find a specialist at all who is accepting new patients. In rural areas with fewer mental health specialists, access to care is considerably more limited. Even in urban settings, wait-lists for mental health specialists, especially psychiatrists, can extend for up to 6 weeks. In the end, around one third up to one half of patients who are referred by their PCP to a specialty mental health provider will not show up for an initial appointment (Unutzer, Schoenbaum, Druss, & Katon, 2006), although some estimates have found a much lower (i.e., 25%) follow-up rate (Strosahl, 2001). The simple fact of the matter is that PCPs should expect that very few of their patients will actually follow through with a referral to a mental health specialist.

The supply-and-demand problem is compounded by the disproportionately large amount of mental health services that are consumed by individuals without any apparent psychiatric disorders or problems (Wang, Lane, Olfson, Pincus, Wells, & Kessler, 2005). Of those who access mental health services, only half are estimated to meet criteria for a psychiatric condition (Kessler, Demler, Frank et al., 2005). Although individuals with no psychiatric disorders are less likely to receive treatment overall and once they are in treatment generally utilize fewer visits than those with psychiatric disorders, they nonetheless account for almost one third of all mental health visits because they make up such a large majority of the population. The odds of receiving mental health services are particularly low for individuals from lower socioeconomic backgrounds, even those with more severe psychopathology who would benefit most from specialty mental health treatment (Katz, Kessler, Frank, Leaf, & Lin, 1997; Wang et al., 2005). Surprisingly, for low-income groups, having health insurance does not increase the likelihood of receiving mental health treatment or adequacy of care, suggesting that financial barriers are particularly formidable and cannot be overcome through insurance alone (Wang et al., 2005). For example, limited means of transportation, instability in employment, frequent changes in living conditions, and geographic location are many factors associated with lower socioeconomic status that directly interfere with treatment access and adherence (Brown, 2006). These findings point to the need for an enhanced reallocation of medical resources that better matches the health care needs of the population—such that mild or subsyndromal psychiatric conditions receive lower levels of care, thereby opening access to higher levels of care for more severe psychiatric conditions.

IMPROVING THE HEALTH CARE SYSTEM

The cost of our current health care system's design to both patients and medical providers is considerable. As discussed by Robinson and Reiter (2007), primary care clinics experience considerable strain due to the large volume of psychosocial issues presented by patients in the absence of adequate access to mental health specialists. PCPs often do not feel appropriately trained to manage or treat these psychosocial problems and are frustrated with the limited referral options for patients who would benefit from behavioral interventions. Frustration for the primary care team is compounded by patients who return to the primary care clinic with increasing frequency and in greater distress when they are unable to access mental health services. These "high utilizers" take a considerable toll on clinic resources and limit access to other patients. In the absence of mental health services, patients suffer since the treatment they receive is often limited to medications. Given the mounting data finding insufficiency of pharmacotherapy alone and the demonstrated superiority of combined medication with behavioral treatments, it is arguable that patients are not receiving optimal psychiatric treatments in primary care. Simply put, in our present health care system, people with behavioral or psychosocial problems are not getting the care they need or deserve. This problem is particularly magnified and poignant for those individuals who suffer so much that they consider ending their own lives. Primary care teams are overwhelmed and inadequately prepared or trained to manage the wide range of psychiatric and behavioral issues that present in the substantial majority of patients they see. Despite growing exposure to the mental health needs of their patients, many barriers exist that reduce the PCP's ability to meet those needs.

As already noted, underrecognition of behavioral problems by both PCPs and patients is a significant barrier to effective treatment. Not only do most patients believe they do not need to access mental health services (Kessler et al., 2001), but mental health conditions and behavioral problems are often missed and/or undertreated (e.g., Wells et al., 1992). Underrecognition is not surprising, however, when one considers that a typical PCP appointment is less than 15 minutes in length, and the typical patient presents with an average of three health complaints per appointment (Kaplan, Gandek, Greenfield, Rogers, & Ware, 1995).

The brief duration of a routine medical appointment in primary care settings is a significant barrier to accurate identification of suicidal patients, as PCPs are reluctant to probe for psychosocial issues when under the combined pressures of limited time and lack of confidence in their ability to adequately respond to and intervene with such issues. For example, among a sample of pediatricians and family physicians, nearly half reported they had at least one adolescent patient who had attempted suicide during the previous year (Frankenfield et al., 2000). Despite this high number, only 23% of the physicians with suicidal adolescent patients routinely screened for suicide risk factors. Physicians who perceived they had adequate time during the routine medical appointment to address suicide risk and who felt well trained to detect suicide risk factors were much more likely to screen for suicide risk routinely. Unfortunately, extending appointment length is not a change in medical practice that is likely to occur any time in the near future despite evidence that PCPs with longer medical appointment times are more likely to identify patients with suicidal ideation (Verger et al., 2007).

The problem of underrecognition is not solely a function of PCPs, however. Patients also contribute to underrecognition by minimizing or downplaying psychiatric symptoms and behavioral problems and prioritizing physical symptoms even if these symptoms are caused by or secondary to psychosocial stressors (Bray et al., 2004; Kroenke, 2006; Patterson et al., 2002). For example, in a study of older adults presenting to a primary care clinic, approximately one quarter reported significantly elevated levels of depression when assessed with the Center for Epidemiological Studies Depression Survey, but only 5% of the patients actually disclosed symptoms of depression to their PCP during the medical appointment; the remainder of the depressed patients presented with somatic medical complaints (Pfaff & Almeida, 2005). This pattern is not much better for patients considering suicide, of whom only around one in six will disclose such thoughts to their PCP during a routine medical appointment (Bryan et al., 2008). Importantly, training and education in mental health issues and suicide can have a positive impact on the detection of mental health issues, whether or not a patient readily discloses such problems. PCPs who received continuing medical education (CME) training in depression, for instance, identified suicidal patients over three and a half times more frequently than PCPs without training in depression (Verger et al., 2007).

Enhanced training of PCPs is an important component to improving the detection and management of suicidal patients within primary care. However, given the substantial time and resource limitations for PCPs, training alone might be insufficient. Although PCP training programs (which usually focus on depression) increase PCPs' ability to detect suicidal ideation by more than double and contribute to increased prescription rates for antidepressants, they do not increase the likelihood of referral to specialty mental health care settings (Nutting et al., 2005). Given the numerous barriers to referral and follow-through noted earlier, this finding is not surprising, although nonetheless unfortunate in light of growing evidence that cognitive-behavioral interventions delivered on an individual basis are quite effective for reducing suicidal behaviors (Tarrier, Taylor, & Gooding, 2008). In a system marked by deficiencies in connecting patients to the best treatments, the need for a new model of empirically based behavioral treatments is clear.

Fortunately, health care professionals have begun to recognize the limitations of our current system and have initiated the development of new models of service delivery to address these problems. Within many of these new health care models (to be discussed in detail in Chapter 2), a central feature is the movement of mental health services into the primary care setting in order to circumvent the many barriers to adequate care and to alleviate the strain felt by PCPs. This shifting of mental health professionals from the traditionally separate mental health system into the primary care system seeks to accomplish a number of important health care goals.

First, mental health professionals within primary care can improve the identification of those psychosocial health issues that underlie the majority of presenting problems within this setting. Improved identification contributes to enhanced treatment and management via an integrated and holistic approach to health care, as opposed to the primarily biological approach, which is predominantly medication-driven (at the expense of psychosocial factors) in primary care settings, and the primarily psychosocial approach, which is predominantly therapy-driven (at the expense of biological factors) in specialty mental health settings. For example, a patient who presents to a primary care clinic complaining of recent onset of sleep disturbances might, during the course of an evaluation, by a mental health professional, report a recent life stressor that triggered the sleep problem. In this case, the mental health professional can teach the patient simple stress management skills and sleep guidelines to address the problem as opposed to the PCP prescribing sleep medications.

Second, mental health professionals can serve as an internal resource for PCPs with questions about psychosocial or behavioral health issues without the need for referral to an external specialty clinic or setting. This immediate access to the mental health professional who can provide rapid feedback and consultation to both the patient and the PCP enhances care and optimizes matching of patient needs with the most appropriate level of care. For the aforementioned patient with sleep disturbances, a brief intervention for stress management within primary care saves a referral to a specialty clinic for the same issue, which keeps a slot open for another patient with more severe psychiatric psychopathology.

Third, moving mental health specialists to primary care has the potential to prevent the development of more severe psychopathology through early recognition and intervention. Returning again to our patient with sleep disturbances, early skills training could potentially prevent further symptom exacerbation and intensification that might develop into a depressive disorder.

These three goals are directly applicable to the suicidal patient. Moving mental health professionals into the primary care setting can improve the detection of suicidal patients and enhance subsequent intervention since "in-house" mental health professionals can quickly address PCPs' concerns and questions about at-risk patients and provide immediate feedback and recommendations regarding strategies to manage suicidal patients. As the specialty mental health system's access is opened due to enhanced matching of care, suicidal patients can be more easily connected with higher levels of mental health treatment when needed, especially during crises. Finally, early detection of at-risk patients and early interventions targeting variables that contribute to suicide risk can potentially reduce or prevent the escalation of suicide risk before it becomes too severe.

The primary care clinic can be a difficult setting in which to adequately and properly address suicide risk, however. The context of primary care clinics—characterized by brief appointments, high patient volume, rapid decision-making, and incomplete clinical information—runs counter to the general clinical approach for working with suicidal patients within traditional mental health settings. In specialty mental health settings, characterized by lengthier appointment times (up to 50 minutes) and narrower clinical focus, clinicians obtain a much larger amount of clinical data to formulate risk assessments and drive their interventions, stemming from an orientation toward detailed and slower-paced discussions emphasizing change in multiple areas of the patient's life. When considering the typical 50-minute appointment duration in mental health settings, which at times can even seem inadequate for highly complex cases such as chronically suicidal patients, PCPs and mental health professionals understandably doubt the capacity for any provider to effectively address suicide risk in a primary care setting. Many PCPs and mental health professionals therefore believe that it is difficult, if not outright impossible, to complete anything close to a reasonable risk assessment and provide effective interventions for suicidal patients within primary care. Anxiety about managing suicidal patients within primary care lends itself to a "hands-off" approach, in which the suicidal patient is "discharged" from the general health care system and "admitted" into the specialty mental health system—another manifestation of the artificial separation of mind and body.

Interestingly enough, in our experience training behavioral health providers[1] to work within primary care clinics and general medical settings, we have found this mentality and perspective to be driven more by behavioral health and mental health providers than PCPs. Because most behavioral health providers receive professional training first within the traditional model of specialty mental health care, they are trained to assess and treat patients within the extended timeframe of the "50-minute hour." As behavioral health providers undergo training to work in primary care, they commonly struggle to modify their practice to fit the fast pace of this new clinical setting, which at the outset seems antithetical to "good" mental health care in general and management of suicide risk in particular.

A common assumption among behavioral health providers and mental health providers is that suicide risk assessment must inherently be lengthy and time-consuming in order to be accomplished in a competent and effective manner. This assumption is generally borne out of fears of litigation from within the specialty mental health care system, in which lawyers attempt to identify those areas of care that were overlooked or inadequately completed in order to establish negligence. Unfortunately, this has driven many behavioral health providers to adopt the aforementioned "hands-off" perspective that suicide risk is outside the scope of primary care and therefore should not be routinely screened for or assessed. This perspective leads to the faulty and troubling assumption that nothing reasonable can be done to intervene with suicidal patients in primary care.

Indeed, it can be very difficult for behavioral health providers to shake off their early professional training as specialty mental health providers, especially as it relates to psychiatric emergencies and crises. What behavioral health providers and specialty mental health providers often fail to consider, however, is that a significant time gap commonly occurs between the patient's "exit" from the general medical system and "entry" into the specialty mental health system, assuming the transfer ever occurs.

Consider the common practice within primary care to provide a patient with a list of names and phone numbers of mental health providers

[1] From this point forward in this book, we will use the term *behavioral health provider* to refer to those mental health professionals who have received specialized training to work within primary care, which captures the broader perspective of behavioral health care, including acute and chronic disease management (i.e., behavioral medicine) and lifestyle change (i.e., health psychology), in addition to traditional psychiatric care. We will use the term *mental health provider* to refer to those mental health professionals working in traditional specialty mental health settings.

along with the instruction to call for an appointment. The patient might not ever call a single provider for any number of reasons. If they do call, it is possible they will not quickly find a provider who is accepting new patients (especially patients in crisis) and therefore give up the search. For those who do manage to set up an appointment, there remains the possibility that the patient will not immediately establish an effective therapeutic relationship with the mental health provider, whether because the patient does not like the provider or does not feel comfortable with him or her, and drops out of treatment prematurely. Premature termination for such reasons might contribute to misconceptions about mental health (e.g., "All mental health is the same; none of them can help me") that serves as a barrier for accessing services in the future. The frustrations that can exist for a patient transitioning from primary care to specialty care are especially disconcerting considering that the very type of patient who must deal with such difficulties is the one who is least able to do so successfully; psychosocial and psychiatric problems are often associated with lowered distress tolerance. Frustration is compounded for suicidal patients, who, by their very nature, have poor distress tolerance as well as general impairment in effective problem-solving. These patients can end up stuck between two systems, unable to receive adequate care. In such situations, PCPs can find themselves similarly stuck in the position of potential liability for negligence in the event of an adverse outcome (e.g., death by suicide).

It is imperative to note that due to the nature of services in primary care, even when suicidal patients have been successfully connected with specialty mental health providers, their cases are not "closed," since they will continue to return to the primary care clinic for other health care needs. As a result, PCPs are faced with three critical issues: first, what to do "in the meantime" while they await the transfer of suicidal patients to specialty care; second, what to do when suicidal patients return to the clinic for routine health care needs (which will almost always involve one or more significant psychosocial factors); third, what to do when suicidal patients return due to treatment "failure" within the specialty setting. Primary care clinics are additionally faced with managing those suicidal patients who outright refuse to seek out or follow up with specialty mental health care at all.

The convergence of these various factors highlights the need to clarify and improve clinical strategies for managing suicidal patients within primary care. Unfortunately, suicide risk is an area that is often overlooked or omitted in most primary care behavioral health practice manuals and texts. As a result, primary care behavioral health providers often find themselves confronted in these settings with a host of questions related to suicidal patients that have not yet been adequately addressed:

- What level of suicide risk can be effectively and safely managed in primary care?
- What sort of interventions are appropriate for the primary care setting?
- What about antidepressants?
- When and how do I refer to specialty mental health?
- How much follow-up do I need to provide?
- What are the legal expectations for primary care practice?
- What do I need to document in the medical record?

Each of these questions reflects the ambiguous issue of suicide risk management within primary care behavioral health, which leads to inconsistencies in clinical care. In our experience as trainers of and consultants to primary care behavioral health providers, we have found that some behavioral health providers conduct risk assessments and utilize risk management strategies in primary care that do not differ substantially from assessments characteristic of specialty mental health clinics. These behavioral health providers are reluctant to abandon their specialty mental health training in the area of suicide risk, almost always due to concerns about legal liability. As such, they adopt a "better-safe-than-sorry" approach by adopting the practices of specialty mental health even when these standards are clearly inappropriate for the primary care setting. This approach is understandable and, in our opinion, is a direct by-product of the general lack of attention given to this important issue.

On the other end of the spectrum are those behavioral health providers who do not screen for or assess suicide risk at all and immediately refer patients reporting any hint of suicidality to a specialty mental health setting. This group typically argues that there is an inherent incompatibility between the time-intensive process needed to conduct a risk assessment and the contextual setting of the primary care clinic. Primary care behavioral health providers should therefore adopt a practice standard that does not differ from that of PCPs (i.e., not to screen routinely for suicide and refer to specialty care). These behavioral health providers tend to maintain this perspective despite awareness of the many barriers to accessing specialty mental health care in our current health care system and consequently adopt a "head-in-the-sand" approach that falsely partitions off suicide risk from general health. What is most interesting about this particular perspective is that it completely contradicts the basic philosophy and tenants of primary care behavioral health care, which takes a holistic, biopsychosocial perspective of health. An unfortunate consequence of this approach is that it directly counters the behavioral health provider's goal to raise the level of care within primary care medical settings.

A more balanced approach to managing risk in primary care is clearly needed. The current state of ambiguity and inconsistency in professional expectations contributes to a wide range of clinical practices that are vulnerable to undue influence by the clinician's emotional states (notably anxiety and fear), instead of practice informed by science and empiricism. In this book, our goal is to present and discuss strategies for competent, empirically based suicide risk management strategies that provide a high level of clinical care and are practical within the pace and context of the primary care clinic. It is our opinion that the primary care behavioral health model is an effective and well-supported method for improving the health care of the general population and holds particular promise for addressing the public health problem of suicide. As noted earlier, we have additionally found that it is behavioral health and mental health providers, not PCPs, who are most reluctant to modify clinical practice when working with suicidal patients within primary care. As such, this book is written through the lens of the primary care behavioral health model and is geared toward the behavioral health provider working within a primary care setting. Recognizing that our health care system as a whole is still far from realizing a shift toward this integrated model of health care, however, it is our intention to present these strategies and competencies in a manner that can also be implemented by medical professionals in primary care settings without integrated behavioral health providers.

CORE COMPETENCIES FOR BEHAVIORAL HEALTH CONSULTANTS

1. Be familiar with the prevalence of psychosocial and behavioral health issues within primary care and the impact of psychosocial factors on patient health and functioning.
2. Be familiar with suicide-related statistics in primary care.
3. Recognize barriers to specialty mental health care and limitations to behavioral health treatment within primary care settings.

CHAPTER 2

The Behavioral Health Consultant Model

Managed care has had a considerable impact on the health care system in general and mental health care system in particular within the United States and will continue to do so in the future. As discussed by Strosahl (2001), in the first phase of health care reform, managed care placed an excessive emphasis on supply-side cost containment strategies. As managed care moves into a second phase of health care reform, the focus is shifting toward improved efficiency and effectiveness of health care delivery. Since cost containment strategies seem to have reached a limit, a basic redesign of services and processes will therefore be necessary to further reduce health care costs. Not only will this require the identification of a balance between cost and quality, but also the consolidation of redundant and overlapping systems that provide both health and mental health services. In terms of system consolidation, a movement is already underway to combine multiple services within fewer delivery systems, which helps to reduce costs while providing consumers with their preferred service delivery model. This consolidation of services has been particularly true for the primary health and mental health care systems, the separation of which has artificially split mind and body and contributed to rising health costs (Strosahl & Sobel, 1996).

REFORMING PRIMARY CARE

As mental health care moves to integrate itself within the primary care system, the natural tendency is to simply transfer traditional mental health services and procedures to the primary care setting without any modification or alteration. This approach has a lower likelihood for success, however, due to the considerable differences that inherently exist between the primary care and specialty mental health systems. Attempts to integrate the two systems under this approach have been shown to be generally ineffective for reforming the health care system or improving service delivery to the population because this model generally continues to focus only on the provision of mental health treatment to a comparatively small segment of the population with identified psychiatric conditions (Garcia-Shelton, 2006). By retaining the 50-minute hour, time-unlimited psychotherapy model within the primary care setting, mental health providers were simply unable to match the pace and philosophy of primary care and could not adequately respond to the full range and prevalence of the population's behavioral health needs. Available mental health appointments quickly filled up, such that access to care was just as limited in these newer integrated settings as they were in traditional mental health clinics. Referrals from primary care providers (PCPs) soon dropped off as the mental health providers became overwhelmed with business. These change models (termed type I models by Strosahl, 2001) tend to maintain the perspective that physical health and mental health are separate problems and do not fully integrate the two systems into a consolidated health care approach. Mental health providers are therefore not seen as core members of the primary care team, and very little improvement in the system occurs.

Much greater success in integration occurred when mental health services were significantly reengineered and redesigned to fit within the service delivery model and population-based philosophy of primary care (i.e., type II models; Strosahl, 2001). The population-based care model is grounded in public health concepts that are designed not only to address the needs of "sick" patients, but also to identify those patients who are at risk for becoming "sick" and intervening with them before the onset of illness. Greater success has also been associated with models that implement a broader definition of "behavioral" health as opposed to simply "mental" health, the latter of which tends to focus narrowly on psychiatric disorders. Broader behavioral health approaches include the management of psychosocial aspects of chronic and acute diseases (i.e., behavioral medicine) and using behavioral perspectives to modify lifestyle and health risk issues (i.e., health psychology). This macroscopic view of behavioral health includes early identification and treatment, with an emphasis on long-term prevention and wellness, and is therefore more consistent with the philosophy of primary care.

Two distinct but complementary approaches make up population-based care: In the horizontal approach, the goal is to provide low-intensity interventions for as many members of the population as possible to prevent the onset of illness and preserve health, whereas in the vertical approach, the goal is to identify specific subpopulations with specialized needs and deliver more focused and coordinated services to these individuals. Through the adoption of a population-based care philosophy, behavioral health services have realized considerable success integrating into primary care settings and transforming the health care system.

Arguably the most dramatic and important redesign of behavioral health services occurred through the development of horizontal integration programs within primary care. Horizontal integration programs are designed to impact the largest percentage of the population as possible through the application of brief psychosocial interventions, such that the behavioral health of the entire population can be positively affected (Strosahl, 2001). This is the fundamental approach and philosophy of the primary care system, in sharp contrast to the traditional mental health system, which emphasizes high-intensity services for a much smaller segment of the population. Considering that 80% of the population will have at least one medical visit per year in primary care, horizontal integration is a critical characteristic of health care service delivery if one hopes to have any notable impact on health. Behavioral health providers accomplish this in primary care through low-frequency, brief appointments utilizing focused interventions and by referring patients with severe conditions to specialty service providers (i.e., the traditional mental health system). Another important contribution of the horizontally integrated system is the indirect impact of the behavioral health provider on the population through consultation with PCPs and other primary care staff members. Through comanagement of cases and ongoing consultation with PCPs, the behavioral health provider is positioned to raise the skill level of the PCP in recognizing and intervening with psychosocial health issues within the span of the typical primary care visit. Specifically, PCPs who learn to implement behavioral strategies themselves over the course of hundreds of patients can markedly improve the health of a much larger segment of the population than the behavioral health provider can alone.

Vertical integration is the second dimension for integrating behavioral health services into primary care and involves providing targeted, specialized health care services for identified subpopulations. Typically, these subpopulations include high-frequency or high-cost patient populations (e.g., depression, chronic pain, substance abuse) for whom a more systematic and delineated approach to health care is ideal. Behavioral health providers can have a tremendously positive impact on the health of higher-utilizing patients since such patients often have higher levels of psychosocial distress and functional impairment.

A well-designed integrated behavioral health system would integrate both horizontally and vertically in order to address the sheer volume of patients accessing services while simultaneously providing focused services to those subgroups with more complex and/or severe health conditions. While most patients will require only brief, low-intensity "routine" interventions to keep them on the path to health and daily functioning, a smaller subset will require more sophisticated services. The combined attention to horizontal and vertical integration more fully addresses the population's spectrum of needs. As noted by Strosahl (2001), a highly integrated behavioral health system will therefore require both a combination of horizontal integration programs for maximal population impact and vertical integration programs for high-impact or high-frequency subgroups.

MODELS OF PRIMARY CARE BEHAVIORAL HEALTH

Several approaches to integrate mental health care into primary care have been developed and implemented over the years and have been discussed extensively by Gatchel and Oordt (2003). One way to categorize and compare these various models is by the extent to which they fit into three dimensions of care: collocation, collaboration, and integration (Strosahl, 1998). As noted by Gatchel and Oordt (2003), the specific model that is ultimately selected and implemented within a given clinic depends on such factors as organizational structure, physical space limitations, finances, and preferences of medical providers. Naturally, each model varies in terms of strengths and limitations. Table 2.1 summarizes the distinctions between each model.

Collocated Clinics Model

In the collocated clinics model, a traditional primary care clinic and a traditional mental health clinic are placed within the same physical structure. The two clinics might share appointment and administrative support services, and even a common waiting room, but overall, the two clinics remain separate and distinct operations with little integration of services. Collocation of services can provide considerable advantages, including ease of referrals from primary care to mental health care, especially if a shared appointment scheduling system is implemented. The potential for reduced stigma can also be accomplished since the patient is visiting a general medical clinic instead of a separate mental health clinic. Collocation can also increase the frequency of contact between mental health and primary care medical providers, which could in turn positively impact comfort with each other's work. The collocated clinics model does not capitalize upon collaboration or integration, however. Because primary care and mental health care remain separate services, once a patient is referred to mental health, the PCP relinquishes control for treatment decision-making and responsibility for care. Treatment planning is completed independently by the mental health provider, who must therefore obtain

TABLE 2.1

Models of Primary Care Behavioral Health

Model	*Collocation*	*Collaboration*	*Integration*	*Standard of Care*
Collocated clinics	**Low to moderate** Located in same building, possible shared administrative and support services, often located in different wings	**Low** Mental health treatment decisions made independently by behavioral health provider	**Low** Behavioral health seen as separate from primary care	Specialty mental health
Primary care provider	**High** Located in same building as member of primary care team	**Low to moderate** Mental health treatment decisions made independently by behavioral health provider	**Moderate** Behavioral health seen as part of primary care, but remains a separate subspecialty service	Specialty mental health
Staff adviser	**Low** Behavioral health provider typically off-site, available via phone or pager	**Low to moderate** Mental health treatment decisions made by PCP with limited input from behavioral health provider on infrequent basis	**Low** Behavioral health seen as separate from primary care, no direct interaction with patients	Primary care
Behavioral health consultant	**High** Located in same building as primary care team, shares office space and supportive services	**High** Mental health treatment decisions made collaboratively by PCP and BHC, with responsibility retained by the PCP	**High** Behavioral health viewed as central component to primary care	Primary care

separate informed consent as a specialty service. Access to mental health services can quickly become limited, as the mental health provider's available appointment slots are filled with the traditionally high-intensity, longer-term vertical approach to treatment. Consequently, only a relatively small percentage of the primary care population can receive mental health services at any given time. Although the collocated clinics model improves convenience for both patients and providers, it does not fundamentally change the nature of mental health service delivery.

Primary Care Provider Model

A second model is the PCP model, which is similar to the collocated clinics model but expands the opportunities for greater collaboration and integration. In this model, the behavioral health provider is a full member of the primary care team. As such, they are located within the primary care clinic in the same area as other medical providers. PCPs refer patients to the behavioral health provider, who then conducts an in-depth assessment and develops a treatment plan in a manner that generally does not differ from specialty mental health settings (e.g., 50-minute appointments, emphasis on psychiatric diagnosis), although length of treatment is often much briefer than in typical outpatient psychotherapy settings (e.g., limited to 6 sessions vs. 12 or more sessions).

As a member of the primary care team, the behavioral health provider is positioned to increase the amount of contact and dialogue with primary care medical providers (i.e., collaboration) than in specialty mental health settings or the collocated clinics model, but services still do not reach full integration with the larger primary care service. In essence, the behavioral health provider practices traditional specialty mental health services as a member of the primary care team. Similar to the collocated clinics model, the PCP model has the advantage of convenience for both patients and primary care medical providers. It also has the potential to destigmatize mental health care because of its placement within the primary care clinic. The proximity of primary care medical and behavioral health providers also lends itself to improved collaboration and consultation between the two systems, although the model retains a predominant vertical integration approach that limits the impact of the behavioral health provider to a relatively small segment of the population. Although an improvement over the traditional primary care and mental health care systems, the PCP model does not redesign the mental health service delivery model enough to have a substantial impact on the population as a whole.

Staff Adviser Model

In the staff adviser model, a behavioral health provider serves as a subject matter expert to the primary care medical team but generally does not provide direct interventions or care to patients. Collocation of the behavioral health provider is not a priority in this model; the behavioral health provider might be located off-site and be available via telephone or pager. PCPs contact the behavioral health provider to obtain advice and guidance for specific questions related to the health care of a patient and retain full responsibility for any treatment decisions that are made. Behavioral health providers can play a significant role in educating PCPs about mental health and psychosocial aspects of health care and can have an important influence on the delivery of treatments but are quite limited by the comparatively low contact—if any contact occurs at all—with the actual patients. As such, integration of services is quite low in this model. Behavioral health providers have very limited responsibility for patient care or treatment decisions within this model; such responsibility is completely retained by the PCP.

Behavioral Health Consultant Model

A final model of primary care behavioral health that has received considerable attention and widespread implementation is the behavioral health consultant (BHC) model. In this model, the behavioral health provider functions as a BHC embedded within the primary care team. Because the BHC becomes a full member of the primary care team, this model demands collocation of services, typically placed within the same clinical area as the PCPs and other medical staff members. PCPs refer patients to the BHC for assistance in identifying and targeting behavioral and psychosocial aspects of health care. The BHC's goal, then, is to help the PCP develop a holistic, biopsychosocial treatment plan that can be carried out by all members of the primary care team under the direction of the PCP. BHC appointments are very brief in comparison to specialty mental health settings (i.e., 15–30 minutes), with the course of care typically extending no longer than one to four appointments. The brevity of clinical contact is a direct reflection of the model's emphasis on horizontal integration: low-intensity interventions for the maximal percentage of the population. Similarly, the BHC adopts a population-based care approach that views all patients within the clinic's empanelment as being within the purview of the BHC's care.

Within this model, any given patient is just as likely to meet with the BHC when visiting the clinic as any other member of the primary care team.

Decisions regarding treatment planning are made collaboratively between the BHC and PCP but are centralized under the direction and guidance of the PCP. This centralization of care maximizes integration of services by putting all members of the team on the same page and working toward the same goals, no matter the specific role of the individual primary care team member. The PCP therefore has final say in all treatment decision-making and ultimately retains responsibility for the treatment plan. An obvious advantage to a well-designed and well-integrated BHC service is that it has the potential to raise the clinic's level of care well above the practice standards of traditional primary care.

THE BEHAVIORAL HEALTH CONSULTATION MODEL IN PRACTICE

We favor the BHC model of primary care behavioral health because of its demonstrated clinical effectiveness and efficiency, which has been key to its increasingly prevalent implementation within the community health care system, the Department of Defense, the Veterans Administration, and an ever-expanding number of academic medical centers. This book has been written with the BHC model as a guiding framework not only for its utility and widespread use, but also because its design and implementation most closely matches the primary care medical system.

As has been briefly mentioned already, the BHC model places a premium on horizontal integration under the guiding principles of population-based care. The BHC's primary goal is to positively impact the health care of as many patients within the population as possible. To accomplish this objective, the nature of mental health service delivery must be dramatically redesigned, such that interventions are of lower intensity in order to increase penetration within the population. The BHC model therefore differs from specialty mental health care in a number of ways.

The Consultative Relationship

In sharp contrast to specialty mental health settings and other models of primary care behavioral health, the BHC does not assume responsibility for, or control over, the patient's health care plan. The BHC's role is to support and increase the effectiveness of the PCP's treatment plan by providing brief evaluations and interventions in conjunction with and in many cases on behalf of the PCP and to provide recommendations to the PCP regarding the development of treatment plans. The BHC does not supplant the PCP's treatment plan with separate or distinct behavioral goals. This is not to say that BHCs do not teach patients specific self-management skills or directly deliver behavioral interventions; this is a very common practice and is a central role of the BHC. As a consultant to the PCP, it is important that the BHC recognize that their clinical work with a patient is accomplished with an eye toward supporting or furthering the treatment goals identified and established by the PCP. It follows that within this model, the BHC's customers are not only the patients, but also the PCPs, since the BHC's work is in direct support of the PCPs' goals. This is in sharp contrast to the specialty mental health setting, in which the primary customer is the patient alone.

It is imperative to understand that the consultative relationship is defined by the nature of the relationship the BHC maintains with both the patient and the PCP, not by any specific interventions or techniques utilized by the BHC. PCPs and BHCs must therefore clearly articulate the nature of the BHC service to patients and ensure the patient understands that the PCP retains full control of their care. Likewise, the consultative relationship demands regular feedback to and collaboration with the PCP regarding the BHC's evaluations and recommendations. When a BHC develops treatment goals and plans without coordinating with the PCP, the BHC undermines the ability for the PCP to oversee care delivery. Such autonomy in decision-making moves the BHC into the realm of specialty mental health care, which has very different standards and expectations for clinical practice. With the PCP in full control of the treatment plan, however, the team practices within the standards of the primary care system. One can quickly see how the addition of a behavioral health provider serving in the role of a consultant can have a clear advantage for the primary care team in meeting and exceeding the standard of care.

Appointment Structure

A typical BHC appointment lasts less than 30 minutes, consistent with the model of primary care. The patient's initial appointment is often the only appointment they will have with the BHC, and rarely will the patient meet with the BHC more than a handful of times. Recent studies of BHC services found that at least 90% of patients referred to a BHC service keep fewer than three appointments, with up to two thirds being seen only once (Bryan, Morrow, & Appolonio, 2009; Cigrang, Dobmeyer, Becknell, Roa-Navarrete, & Yerian, 2006). On average, a BHC can see anywhere between 10 and 15 patients per day and upward to 20 patients per day. This brief, accelerated pace enables the BHC to come into direct contact with many more patients than would be possible within specialty care mental health. In fact, a BHC is likely to encounter more new patients in any single day in primary care than a specialty mental health provider would encounter in an entire week. Initial evaluations and access standards for a BHC are largely determined by PCP preference (e.g., same day, within 72 hours), with follow-up BHC appointments commonly scheduled around the PCP's follow-up plan to minimize time demands on patients and maintain the integrative nature of services.

Clinical Services Provided

The speed of the primary care clinic does not allow for in-depth assessment or clinical interviewing. As such, the BHC does not focus exclusively on differential diagnosis with an eye toward resolution of a clinical disorder per se but rather adopts a problem-focused approach to assessment with the goal of returning the patient to optimal daily functioning. Consequently, BHCs are more concerned with identifying how the patient's presenting complaints are interfering with life and developing strategies to enhance the patient's ability to function effectively and are less concerned with which diagnostic label or code to apply in a given case. At their core, BHCs must be generalists and pragmatists and must be knowledgeable enough about a wide range of health issues to make rapid, accurate decisions with a limited amount of data.

For example, of the nine criteria for a major depressive episode, the two symptom criteria that carry the most variance for a diagnosis are depressed mood and anhedonia. BHCs therefore strategically assess these two variables well and spend less time assessing symptoms such as concentration impairment, energy change, or appetite changes when attempting to arrive at a reasonably accurate diagnostic impression to guide treatment recommendations for a patient presenting with possible depression. Effective BHCs likewise are aware of considerable research demonstrating that increased engagement in meaningful and enjoyable activities is one of the most powerful interventions for depressive disorders and is a robust preventative strategy for remission over time (Dimidjian et al., 2006; Elliott, 2007). When working with depressed patients, then, effective BHCs are much less likely to be concerned with obtaining a highly refined differential diagnosis (e.g., major depressive disorder, single episode vs. major depressive disorder, recurrent vs. dysthymic disorder) but are more likely to focus on developing recommendations that emphasize behavioral activation and the reduction of barriers to increased activity level, since such changes will contribute to clinical improvements in mood and functioning regardless of depressive severity (Dimidjian et al., 2006).

Because the BHC's primary role is to support the PCP's treatment plan, the BHC's clinical interventions will generally focus on whatever problem has been identified by the PCP with the goal to resolve or manage this problem. For example, a patient who is referred to the BHC for sleep problems might additionally present with low energy, decreased appetite, and decreased enjoyment in daily activities, indicating the likelihood of a depressive disorder. Based on the clinical evaluation, the BHC might determine that the sleep problems are actually a symptom of depression and develop interventions that directly target depressed mood. Although depression was not the PCP's identified problem per se, the development of interventions and recommendations targeting depression would be appropriate in this case since they are directly contributing to the referral issue—sleep disturbances.

In contrast, if the patient also reports chronic lower back pain but the BHC's functional assessment does not find a prominent link between the pain and sleep disturbance, the BHC would probably not prioritize interventions and recommendations targeting chronic pain. Because the PCP is one of the BHC's customers, the pain would probably not be prioritized in this case, although the BHC would likely follow up with the PCP to recommend targeting pain for BHC intervention at some point in the future when the PCP incorporates this health issue in his or her treatment plan.

Ongoing Care

Although BHC consultation is generally quite brief in duration, it is not uncommon for BHCs to remain involved in the ongoing comanagement of patient care for extended periods, especially for patients with chronic illness or disease such as chronic pain or diabetes. Such appointments are generally focused on lifestyle or health risk factors (e.g., smoking cessation, weight loss, regular monitoring of blood glucose levels) that might be related to progressive illnesses such as fibromyalgia or cardiac disease. Interventions might also target treatment adherence issues including tolerance of drug side effects and negative beliefs regarding medication use.

BHCs also play a critical role in helping to maintain improved functioning in those patients who have responded to acute phases of treatment, such as assisting PCPs with the long-term management of patients with recurrent psychiatric illnesses. For example, patients who experience three or more major depressive episodes have a 70% to 80% likelihood for relapse within 3 years, whereas those with no previous depression history relapse at a rate of 20% to 30% (Judd, 1997). These data suggest that those patients recovering from their first depressive episode are therefore at a critical juncture in the long-term course of their disorder; aggressive and efficacious treatments delivered during this recovery phase could affect future risk for relapse. For example, antidepressant medication that extends beyond symptom remission has been found to reduce relapse rates by 25% to 50% (American Psychiatric Association, 2000). In combination with brief behavioral treatments, relapse rates are further reduced (Jarrett et al., 2001). Furthermore, cognitive-behavioral interventions sequenced after full or partial response to pharmacotherapy and focused on relapse prevention have been found to be protective against depressive relapse or recurrence (e.g., Segal et al., 2003), even when spaced out at monthly intervals (Reynolds et al., 1999)—a pace that is not unrealistic for a primary care setting. Clearly, BHCs can play a critical role in the ongoing care and management of chronic illness that augments basic medical treatment.

MODIFYING TECHNIQUES TO FIT THE PRIMARY CARE SETTING

The fast-paced and population-based care approach of the primary care clinic requires the behavioral health provider to modify traditional mental health interventions to fit within this context. As already discussed, conducting assessments and delivering interventions using a traditional mental health approach is impractical within the primary care setting that focuses on brief strategies such as patient education and self-management. To put this in perspective, consider that the typical PCP will see anywhere from 20 to 30 patients per day in 10- to 15-minute appointments, whereas the typical specialty mental health provider will see an average of 8 to 10 patients per day in 50-minute appointment blocks. If behavioral health providers are going to bring the most efficacious interventions to primary care, they must identify ways to modify traditional mental health protocols and interventions so they match the philosophy and service delivery model of primary care. As a general rule of thumb, behavioral health interventions that cannot be delivered or taught in less than 5 to 10 minutes are probably not practical within this setting.

A second critical characteristic of any behavioral health intervention delivered in primary care is that it be empirically supported. Evidence-based medicine is a core philosophy of primary care that involves the judicious application of current best evidence in treatment decision-making. Evidence-based medicine combines clinical expertise, applicable data accumulated through systematic research, and recognition of patient preference. Evidence-based medicine is therefore more than simply reviewing clinical trials and implementing procedures based on the results of these studies. As noted by Robinson (2004), evidence-based medicine also takes into consideration cost-effectiveness, balance of risks and benefits to the patient, strength of the empirical evidence, and patient preferences regarding specific interventions.

Evidence-based principles have become a routine part of clinical practice within primary care; as such, behavioral health providers who cannot demonstrate or provide evidence supporting their consultation and interventions will generally be viewed with skepticism by PCPs and will struggle to fully integrate within primary care practice.

THE ROLE OF BEHAVIORAL HEALTH CONSULTATION IN MANAGING SUICIDE RISK

The movement toward integration of medical and mental health care services will require a fundamental shift in how mental health services are delivered in order to maximize success and efficiency. This will likewise require a shift in the manner with which behavioral health providers and primary care medical staff approach suicidal patients within primary care settings. Holding on to the specialty mental health care approach to managing suicide risk in primary care is not feasible or appropriate within the primary care system since specialty mental health models are not founded upon the principles of population-based care. The BHC who adopts a population health perspective with respect to suicidality, in contrast to a specialty mental health perspective, is uniquely positioned to have a significant impact on the suicide risk level of the entire population both directly and indirectly. Guided by this perspective, the BHC recognizes that all patients within the population fall somewhere on the suicide risk continuum—from very low to extremely high (i.e., imminent) risk—and that each individual has a unique level of risk that fluctuates over time.

Fluid Vulnerability Theory From a Population-Based Perspective

The population approach to suicide risk is consistent with the fundamental assumptions of the fluid vulnerability theory of suicide (Rudd, 2006a). Fluid vulnerability theory proposes two dimensions of suicide risk: baseline risk and acute risk. Baseline (or chronic) risk is an individual's level of risk when he or she is not acutely distressed or dysphoric and is at his or her relative best. According to fluid vulnerability theory, baseline risk varies from individual to individual based upon the individual's unique constellation of static risk factors that increase vulnerability for suicidal crises. For example, problem-solving deficits, a history of abuse, and biological or genetic predispositions for psychiatric conditions or impulsivity raise the individual's set point for suicide risk. Baseline risk is higher for those individuals with a history of two or more suicide attempts (i.e., multiple attempters) when compared with individuals who have never attempted suicide or have attempted suicide only once. Importantly, as baseline level of risk rises, acute suicidal episodes become more easily triggered and last for longer periods of time because individuals with high baseline risk levels are inherently more vulnerable to suicidal crises, which are more easily triggered.

In contrast to baseline risk, acute risk is the short-term dimension of risk that occurs when the suicidal individual is symptomatic and in crisis. Acute risk is elevated by aggravating risk factors such as psychiatric symptoms, substance abuse, and life stressors (e.g., relationship problems, financial stress) and is inherently time-limited in nature. Acute suicidal episodes eventually return to baseline risk levels but do not necessarily ameliorate completely. Because risk level can return to baseline only, multiple attempters always remain at elevated risk for suicide and are more easily "triggered" into acute crises. For many multiple attempters, it is common for a new suicidal crisis to activate before a previous one has fully resolved; such individuals are chronically suicidal and often live in a constant state of emotional turmoil.

Fluid vulnerability theory also incorporates the notion of protective factors, which serve as "buffers" against suicide, in contrast to the aggravating risk factors that elevate risk. Individuals with limited protective factors such as effective coping skills and problem solving strategies and inadequate social support networks are therefore more vulnerable to suicidal crises. This is particularly true for multiple attempters, who generally lack protective factors as compared with single attempters and those who have never attempted. Multiple attempters are therefore at greater risk for suicide due to a combination of decreased resources that typically serve to mitigate the effects of aggravating risk factors.

Fluid vulnerability theory provides a succinct and straightforward model for understanding the process of suicide risk over time at both the individual and the population levels. Through the lens of fluid vulnerability theory, each individual within the population is viewed as being potentially at risk for suicide, with some being at much greater risk. Through early contact with large numbers of individual patients in an integrated primary care system, the BHC has the potential to directly affect the risk level of many more patients than in a specialty mental health setting by reducing aggravating risk factors and strengthening protective factors. At the same time, through ongoing consultation designed to affect and improve the practice of many PCPs within the clinic, BHCs additionally have the potential to indirectly impact the risk level for a very large portion of the population. Fluid vulnerability theory therefore provides a framework within which to understand the role that an integrated primary care clinic can play in the management of suicide risk.

Horizontal Integration Programs for Suicide Risk

Most patients who present to primary care at any given time will be at low risk for suicide. As mentioned in the previous chapter, fewer than 5% of the primary care population will endorse suicidal symptoms such as ideation or planning at any given time, with increased frequency of suicidality being observed among those patients with psychosocial and/or mental health symptoms. By taking a high-volume, "all-comers" approach to behavioral health problems, utilizing low-intensity interventions, emphasizing self-management skills designed to reduce those psychiatric and behavioral symptoms that elevate suicide risk, the BHC can potentially prevent the escalation of risk in a much larger percentage of the population than could be feasible in a specialty mental health setting. The suicidal condition is, at its core, an inability to cope with psychological distress and effectively solve problems in life. These two fundamental skills—distress tolerance (i.e., coping) and problem-solving—are the bread-and-butter of BHC intervention. BHCs who have horizontally integrated their services within the primary care clinic teach the basics of distress tolerance and problem-solving skills to a very large number of patients during brief medical appointments. For example, a BHC might teach a patient to use brief relaxation strategies to reduce the intensity of physiological agitation contributing to anxiety and sleep disturbances.

The BHC can have an even greater, indirect impact on the risk level of the population by consulting with PCPs and primary care staff about identifying and responding to suicidal patients. As PCPs become more confident in their ability to respond to "routine" behavioral health problems and even behavioral "emergencies" such as suicide risk, they become less likely to overreact to these situations or otherwise inadvertently reinforce suicidal behaviors. Furthermore, as the PCP takes on greater responsibility for managing suicidal patients, especially lower-risk patients, the BHC can direct an increased amount of attention toward the development of more specialized vertical integration programs to better target suicide risk among patients accessing the primary care clinic. The primary goal for horizontal integration programs can therefore best be understood as preventing acute suicidal episodes through the reduction of aggravating factors and enhancement of protective factors.

Like any other health condition in primary care, more specialized services are needed for high-utilizing or more complicated patients. Suicidal patients, especially those with higher levels of risk such as multiple attempters, often report many more health symptoms than nonsuicidal patients such as higher levels of bodily pain, lower energy, and greater physical limitations (Goldney et al., 2001), with suicide risk generally increasing as the number of diagnosed illnesses rises (Juurlink et al., 2004). It should therefore come as no surprise that suicidal patients utilize primary care medical services with greater frequency than nonsuicidal patients (Juurlink et al., 2004; Stenager & Jensen, 1994) particularly because their distress level increases. Higher-risk suicidal patients therefore require more focused and greater coordination of services than the general population and lower-risk patients.

Vertical Integration Programs for Suicide Risk

As already noted, most patients (around 95%) who present to the primary care clinic at any given time for medical care do not report or demonstrate significant suicidality. Even among those patients with elevated levels of depression, only around 10% are at moderate or higher risk for suicide (Schulberg et al., 2005), meaning that, in addition to thinking about suicide, they also articulated at a minimum a specific suicide plan. Without a doubt, higher levels of suicide risk indicate referral to specialty mental health care. However, it is important to recall that these suicidal patients will nonetheless continue to utilize primary care medical services for their health care needs with greater frequency than nonsuicidal patients. Vertical integration programs designed for suicidal patients can therefore be a highly effective and useful service for the primary care clinic.

Within primary care, the primary goal of vertical integration programs is to facilitate the patient's return to baseline as quickly and efficiently as possible. This could entail a wide range of clinical interventions including both medical and psychosocial interventions such as antidepressant medication for depressive symptoms, education in stimulus control and sleep hygiene for sleep disturbances, training in brief relaxation to reduce physiological agitation, or mindfulness skills to enhance distress tolerance. Vertical integration programs also include the establishment of procedures for transferring patients to higher levels of mental health care when needed and instituting risk management procedures within the clinic such as high-risk logs, chart alert systems, and "warm hand-off" policies, each of which will be discussed in greater detail in Chapter 7.

The Consultative Relationship

A considerable challenge for the BHC when working with suicidal patients is remaining in the role of a consultant to the PCP, who more often than not would prefer to turn over primary responsibility for managing high-risk patients to the BHC. A PCP's reluctance to remain in charge of the suicidal patient's care usually stems from the perspective that the BHC is an "expert" in such matters and excessive PCP involvement would simply interfere with effective care. Such a stance is almost always due more to the PCP's fear of suicide than their actual level of competence, however. Such a "hands-off" approach by the PCP could actually place the primary care team at increased risk for litigation, however, since the BHC who assumes primary responsibility for treatment decisions moves outside the scope of the consultative relationship and into the role of an autonomous behavioral health provider. When this transition in responsibility occurs, the BHC moves outside the standard of care for primary care and into the standard of care for specialty mental health—a position that is not sustainable due to the contextual limits of primary care. It is therefore critical that BHCs and PCPs recognize that although BHCs play an important role in providing interventions and teaching self-management skills to suicidal patients, this is done with the goal to support the PCP's treatment plan as a consultant. Even in cases of behavioral emergencies, PCPs always remain in charge of each patient's care.

In contrast to the PCP who prefers to push primary responsibility for high-risk cases to the BHC are those PCPs who tend to overrespond to suicidal patients despite a BHC's recommendation for outpatient care. These PCPs tend to be driven by anxieties about litigation and usually overvalue inpatient hospitalization as the gold standard for managing suicide risk, even when outpatient safety can be maintained and is indicated. In these cases, BHCs might find their recommendations regarding outpatient management and treatment "overruled" by PCPs who prefer to take a "better-safe-than-sorry" approach. Although it is certain that the PCP has the final say regarding patient care decisions, BHCs can play a valuable role in helping PCPs to make judicious decisions about when it is appropriate (or not indicated) to seek out inpatient care. Tips and strategies for consulting with PCPs regarding suicidal patients will be discussed further in Chapter 8.

Appointment Structure for Suicidal Patients in Primary Care

In many ways, primary care settings offer an advantage over specialty mental health settings for the management of suicide risk since patients can more easily and flexibly access services in the action-oriented, high-volume primary care setting. With effectively designed horizontal and vertical integration programs for suicidal patients, the BHC's appointment structure and format will not considerably change, even for higher-risk patients. Behavioral health and mental health providers often assume that a thorough risk assessment must be time-intensive and therefore cannot be completed within the span of a typical primary care appointment. This is not an accurate view of risk assessment, however. Accurate and effective risk assessment is actually determined by the nature of the clinical information elicited during the clinical encounter, not the speed or duration of the encounter itself. Accurate risk assessments can be conducted competently (or incompetently) during a brief clinical encounter just as assuredly as a risk assessment can be conducted competently (or incompetently) during a very long encounter. When considering risk assessment and management in primary care, it is critical to keep in mind the context of the setting, which is geared toward rapid decision-making and brief, direct interventions emphasizing self-management. Most patients have an expectation and readiness for this efficiency when presenting to the primary care clinic and therefore expect clear, crisp instruction.

This is not to suggest that there will never be times when particularly complex, high-risk cases will require more than the general 30-minute consultation appointment in order to provide adequate clinical services. A highly suicidal patient is a behavioral health emergency and should always be handled as such, which might require the BHC and primary care team to spend more time than they would with a typical primary care patient. An analogous medical situation is the middle-aged Caucasian male who presents to a primary care clinic with chest pains, shortness of breath, and lightheadedness. Regardless of the patient's presenting complaint, a PCP will respond to such a symptom report with a specific series of procedures to assess for the likelihood of myocardial infarction, respond appropriately to stabilize the patient, and, if necessary, facilitate the transition to specialty care. All members of the primary care team work together to ensure this medical emergency is effectively managed regardless of resource and time utilization. Behavioral health emergencies should be approached using a similar team approach and should not be managed solely by the BHC or any other single provider. Emergencies that are collaboratively managed by the entire primary care team improve the ability to contain crises in a more effective and time-efficient manner. Clinic crisis management procedures and approaches will therefore be thoroughly detailed in Chapter 7.

Clinical Services Provided

As with any other presenting health concern in primary care, clinical services for suicidal patients are problem-focused in nature using an evidence-based model for care. For example, by selectively choosing which suicide-related factors and variables to assess based on available and relevant empirical evidence, the BHC can prioritize those variables that carry the greatest amount of variance in predicting suicidal behaviors. This leads to an optimal maximization of both accuracy and efficiency in risk assessments. Within primary care, the BHC's principal goal for a risk assessment is therefore generally not to classify the appropriate psychiatric diagnosis for a suicidal patient, but rather to understand the function of their suicidal crisis within the context of their life and their psychosocial problems. In other words, it is less important to figure out if the suicidal patient has depression versus anxiety than it is to understand how their symptomatic experience and functional impairment contributes to and maintains the suicidal crisis. This functional approach to suicide risk and clinical presentation, discussed further in Chapter 3, enables the primary care team to be less distracted by clinical labels and more focused on the problem at hand (i.e., managing the suicidal crisis).

Clinical interventions in primary care are likewise based on a philosophy of evidence-based medicine and are designed to directly target suicidal symptoms while remaining practical for the primary care setting. Interventions for suicidal patients should target those factors that perpetuate and aggravate the suicidal crisis and will therefore almost always involve cognitive and behavioral interventions but can also include pharmacologic therapies. BHC interventions for suicide risk, as with all other clinical problems in primary care, are brief and problem-focused and capitalize upon patient self-management. An evidence-based approach to suicide risk assessment will be discussed in Chapter 5, and brief clinical interventions for suicidal patients will be detailed in Chapter 6.

Ongoing Care for Suicidal Patients

In primary care, there is no such thing as a "closed case," in contrast to specialty mental health. There are no termination sessions or formal ending to therapeutic relationships in primary care; patients remain a part of the primary care empanelment and reemerge periodically as their health status fluctuates. This means the primary care team will almost assuredly come into repeated contact with suicidal patients, even those whom have been referred to specialty mental health settings and initiated treatment. Primary care medical providers must therefore be prepared for ongoing risk management for any patient presenting with suicidality and must guard against the tendency to assume that "the job is done" once a suicidal patient has been connected with specialty care.

This is especially true for multiple attempters, who remain at chronically elevated levels of risk for suicide. For multiple attempters, suicidal ideation and behaviors have become a highly reinforced and habitual behavioral response pattern to emotional distress and life problems, such that complete resolution or elimination of suicide risk is oftentimes not a realistic treatment goal. Instead, a chronic disease management approach analogous to the long-term management of medical conditions such as diabetes or hypertension is therefore recommended for multiple attempters.

With diabetes or hypertension, for example, a primary treatment goal is to teach the patient self-management of the condition (e.g., exercise, diet, frequent glucose or blood pressure monitoring) with ongoing monitoring to ensure adherence to treatment recommendations. Similarly, in cases of chronically suicidal patients, the clinical focus should become monitoring the patient's adherence to treatment recommendations (e.g., behavioral planning, crisis response skills, medication adherence) over the long term, with an eye toward early containment of acute "flare-ups" and rapid return to baseline functioning. In many ways, the primary care team can have an extremely influential and significant impact on the long-term health and well-being of chronically suicidal patients due to the relative ease with which the patient can reenter the system, in contrast to the specialty mental health system, which is marked by less permeable and accessible paths for reentry. Issues related to long-term management and tracking of suicidal patients will therefore be discussed in Chapter 7, and common risk management concerns such as treatment nonadherence and refusal of specialty mental health services will be discussed in Chapter 9.

CORE COMPETENCIES FOR THE BEHAVIORAL HEALTH CONSULTANT

1. Be familiar with early attempts to integrate the primary care and mental health care system and the various models for integrating the two systems in terms of collocation, collaboration, and integration.
2. Understand the philosophy of population-based care on two dimensions: horizontal and vertical integration.
3. Be familiar with the BHC model of primary care behavioral health.
4. Describe the two dimensions of suicide risk proposed by fluid vulnerability theory.
5. Describe the various roles of the BHC in the short- and long-term management of suicidal patients in primary care.

CHAPTER 3

Foundations for Effective Clinical Care

Suicide remains a taboo topic within our society as a whole. The lack of understanding of suicide applies not only to the general population but also to medical and mental health professionals. Indeed, most medical and mental health providers have not spent much time seeking to understand suicide. This is due in part to a surprising dearth of training about suicide at the professional level. More than three decades ago, Burstein, Adams, and Giffen (1973) identified deficiencies in mental health professional training in suicide risk assessment. These authors found dramatic differences between psychologist and psychiatrist trainees in the ability to assess suicide risk as compared with supervisor ratings and noted that one of the only identifiable differences between the better performance of the psychology interns was their use of semistructured interviews in comparison to the nondirective and unstructured interview approach of the psychiatry residents, leading the authors to conclude that "more planful teaching approaches might yield good results" (p. 793).

More recently and somewhat shockingly, Bongar and Harmatz (1991) reported that only 40% of graduate training programs in clinical psychology offered formal training (i.e., courses or specific training sessions) in the assessment and management of suicide risk. The picture is worse for social workers, of whom only 21% have received formal training during their professional education and training (Feldman & Freedenthal, 2006). Feldman and Freedenthal (2006) additionally noted that of those social workers who pursue additional professional training in suicide risk assessment and intervention, only half receive more than two hours of training; among psychologists, the average amount of formal training totals only one hour on average (Guy, Brown, & Poelstra, 1990).

Particularly troubling about these statistics is that despite the lack of formal training, the overwhelming majority of psychologists and social workers will almost uniformly encounter suicidal patients in clinical settings (Pope & Tabachnick, 1993; Rudd, 2006b) and will conduct suicide risk assessments routinely.

The relative lack of formal training in suicide assessment and intervention among mental health professionals lends itself to considerable misunderstandings and misconceptions about suicide and a general inability to explain suicidal behaviors to either patients or medical providers. From a clinical perspective, this is of grave concern because suicidal patients are often confused and distressed about their suicidal experience and look to the BHC to understand what is happening to them. Likewise, BHCs who cannot succinctly explain suicidal behaviors to PCPs are unlikely to positively influence the general health care of suicidal patients.

A core competency in suicide assessment and intervention is the ability to articulate an understandable biopsychosocial model of suicidal behaviors (Rudd, Cukrowicz, & Bryan, 2008; Suicide Prevention Resource Center [SPRC], 2006). The model should be one that can be related in simple terms to patients and can lend itself to clear and straightforward treatment targets, including suicidal thoughts and behaviors, as well as associated symptoms such as depression, anxiety, hopelessness, and substance abuse. Just as critical as the BHC's ability to relate a biopsychosocial model of suicidal behaviors to patients is the BHC's ability to clearly articulate it to primary care staff members who will invariably turn to the BHC for guidance and assistance as the "expert" on this topic. Inherent in any biopsychosocial model is a recognition of the relative contributions of biological and genetic (e.g., family history, inheritability of psychiatric disorders), psychological (e.g., mood states, impaired problem-solving, hopelessness), and social (e.g., supportive relationships, access to resources) factors in suicide. An effective BHC must therefore have a clear and straightforward model of suicidal behavior.

A BIOPSYCHOSOCIAL MODEL OF SUICIDE: THE SUICIDAL MODE

A biopsychosocial model of suicide consistent with the fluid vulnerability theory of suicide risk discussed in the previous chapter is the suicidal mode (Rudd, 2006a), graphically displayed in Figure 3.1. The suicidal mode is a network of cognitive, behavioral, physical, and emotional features that are simultaneously activated in the presence of a triggering event or stressor and are maintained by their mutual interaction. Consistent with the tenets of fluid

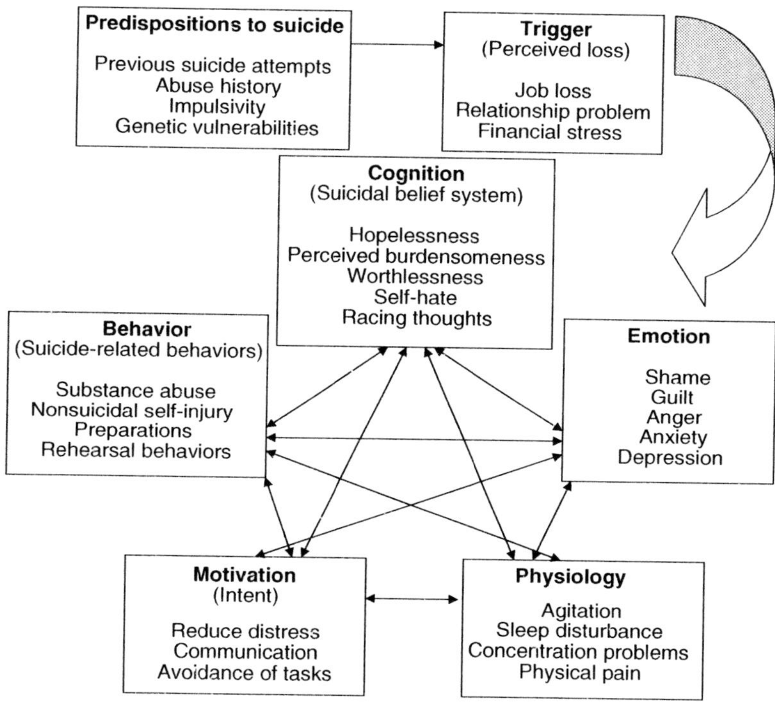

FIGURE 3.1
The suicidal mode.

vulnerability theory, each individual has a baseline level of risk for suicide that is affected by their unique combination of predisposing factors to include both genetic/biological factors and environmental influences. In the presence of triggering events, usually life stressors or perceived losses of some kind, the network of systems that make up the suicidal mode is activated and the patient experiences an acute suicidal crisis. Suicidal crises resolve subsequent to the deactivation of the various systems of the suicidal mode, at which point the patient returns to their baseline risk level.

Predispositions to Suicide

In terms of genetic links to suicide, twin studies have found that 13% to 19% of monozygotic twin pairs were concordant for death by suicide as compared with less than 1% of the dyzygotic twin pairs (Roy, 1992). In another interesting study of the Old Order Amish over a span of 100 years, a total of 26 deaths by suicide occurred, the majority of which came from only four families (Egeland & Sussex, 1985). Although these same families had very high rates of depression as well, other families with similarly high rates of depression did not demonstrate any suicides, suggesting there was something unique about those four families that cannot be accounted for by depression alone. Because the suicides seemed to be confined to specific families above and beyond depression, this study also speaks to the importance of recognizing suicidal behaviors as related to, but distinct from, psychiatric disorders in general. A growing amount of evidence has also pointed to the s/s polymorphism on chromosome 17, which contributes to serotonin system dysregulation. This particular genotype has been correlated with death by suicide, although additional research is needed to further understand this potential genetic link (Joiner, Johnson, & Soderstrom, 2002).

Neurobiologically, the serotonin system has been implicated in numerous studies that have consistently found lowered 5-hydroxyindoleacetic acid (5-HIAA)—the primary metabolite of serotonin—among suicide attempters and suicide victims, with no evidence for changes in levels of any other neurotransmitter metabolite (Asberg, 1997; Lester, 1995), suggesting that serotonin is linked to suicidal behaviors much more strongly than any other neurotransmitter system. Serotonin activity in general seems to be lowered among suicidal individuals even when compared with nonsuicidal depressed individuals (Duval et al., 2001), especially in the prefrontal cortex (Oquendo et al., 2003), the region of the brain most directly involved in impulse control.

Hyperactivity of the hypothalamic-pituitary-adrenal (HPA) axis, the body's primary "stress reaction" system (aka the "fight-or-flight" system), has also been linked to suicidal behaviors (Mann & Currier, 2007). The HPA axis is responsible for the release of cortisol in response to stress. During prolonged periods of chronic stress, cortisol continues to build in the system and circulate throughout the body, which renders the HPA axis unresponsive and dysfunctional. This hyperactivity of the HPA system has been linked to major depression, especially more severe or agitated depression (Mann & Currier, 2007), as well as to a significantly elevated risk for death by suicide (Coryell & Schlesser, 2001). Coryell and Schlesser (2001) reported, for instance, that in the dexamethasone suppression test (DST, a biological test used to measure HPA axis activity), nonsuppressors are 14 times more likely to kill themselves than suppressors over a 15-year follow-up period and noted that previous suicide attempt was only associated with a threefold increase in risk. DST nonsuppression might be associated with suicide because it also predicts failure to respond to antidepressant treatment and early depressive relapse (Mann & Currier, 2007), suggesting more persistent and severe forms of depression. HPA axis hyperactivity has even been linked to self-injuring behaviors in rhesus monkeys (Tiefenbacher et al., 2004). These HPA axis findings might shed some light in understanding the heightened risk associated with multiple suicide attempters, whose lives tend to be highly chaotic over extended periods, contributing to chronic experiences of distress and turmoil.

Of course, genetic and biological factors alone do not fully explain why some people seem to be at greater risk for suicide than others. Life experiences such as early abuse or trauma (Brown, Cohen, Johnson, & Smailes, 1999) or emotionally invalidating childhood environments (Linehan, 1993) also confer vulnerabilities to suicide. More recent research has found that engagement in painful or provocative experiences in life such as high-risk activities and impulsive behaviors is associated with greater risk for suicide (Van Orden, Witte, Gordon, Bender, & Joiner, 2008). Likewise, a history of self-injurious and suicidal behaviors, especially multiple suicide attempts, substantially raises an individual's baseline risk for suicide above and beyond any other risk factor for suicide (Joiner et al., 2005). Even exposure to unwanted painful experiences that are not initiated by the individual can contribute to increased baseline risk. Childhood physical abuse or rape, for example, exhibits a stronger relationship to later suicide attempts than verbal abuse or molestation (Joiner et al., 2007). All of these experiences—exposure to abuse, high-risk activities, and provocative experiences—are intimately connected to an individual's physiological functioning, since such experiences and stressors activate the HPA axis. Adults who have been abused as children, for example, appear to have dysregulated HPA systems (Newport et al., 2004) and are much more likely to be multiple attempters. Similarly, individuals diagnosed with borderline personality disorder, a psychiatric condition associated with repeated suicidal behaviors, have demonstrated increased HPA axis activity as compared with individuals without the diagnosis (Lieb et al., 2004).

Interaction effects between genes and childhood trauma also seem particularly predictive of suicide. Specific variants of the HPA axis-regulating *FKBP5* gene, for instance, have been found to interact with childhood trauma in predictive models of suicide attempts (Roy, Gorodetsky, Yuan, Goldman, & Enoch, 2010). In fact, chronic childhood abuse appears to be related more to HPA axis hyperactivity than psychiatric diagnoses including borderline personality disorder, major depressive disorder, or posttraumatic stress disorder (Rinne et al., 2002). Because the interactions between biological and environmental predisposing factors appear to be relatively fixed or static in nature, they ultimately raise the individual's baseline risk for suicide.

Triggering Events

In the presence of an interpersonal or environmental stressor, the suicidal mode is activated and manifested as the suicidal crisis. These triggering events include such factors as job loss, financial stress, or relationship problems; they are almost always perceived as a loss of some kind to the individual (Bastia & Kar, 2009). Psychological autopsy studies comparing suicide victims to controls have found, for instance, that suicide victims were more likely to have experienced recent adverse life events, especially interpersonal problems, in the week immediately preceding death (Appleby, Cooper, Amos, & Faragher, 1999). Individuals who kill themselves also have greater rates of relationship difficulties with significant others, friends, and family members (Appleby, Shaw, et al., 1999; Bastia & Kar, 1999; Wyder, Ward, & De Leo, 2009). Other social stressors such as legal problems including arrest and/or incarceration (Appleby, Shaw, et al., 1999) and unemployment (Brown, Beck, Steer, & Grisham, 2000) also occur more frequently among suicide victims. Critically, suicides among children and young adolescents seem to have fewer precipitants than older adolescents and adults (Dervic, Brent, & Oquendo, 2008), the most common precipitants being disciplinary events and family arguments. In addition, as compared with older adolescents, romantic relationship failures are exceedingly rare in children younger than 14 years. These triggering events serve to activate the various systems of the suicidal mode that manifest in the form of psychiatric symptoms, distorted thought processes, negative emotional states, and behavioral disturbance. The suicidal mode should therefore be seen as a diathesis-stress model for understanding suicidal behavior.

The Suicidal Mode

The suicidal mode itself consists of five interrelated and interdependent systems that activate as a network and sustain the suicidal episode over time: the cognitive, behavioral, emotional, physical, and motivational systems. These various systems are activated in synchrony in response to external events and life circumstances, are mutually reinforcing and interdependent, and provide a mechanism for accomplishing internal goals (commonly, relief from psychological pain).

The cognitive system involves all aspects of information processing including attention, meaning-making, memory, and recall. These elements form the core of the person's assumptions, rules, and beliefs about self, others, and the future (e.g., "The only option is death"; "I'd be better off dead"; "I'm such a burden on others"; "Things will never get any better") that comprise what Rudd (2006a) has referred to as the suicidal belief system. The cognitive system also includes impaired problem solving, absence of cognitive flexibility, and extreme cognitive distortions, all of which characterize the suicidal thought process. One particularly pernicious cognitive symptom associated with increased suicidality is the experience of racing and crowded thoughts that are perceived to be uncontrollable (Benazzi, 2005). The experience of these uncontrollable thoughts can cause considerable emotional distress and is often associated with autonomic arousal experienced as physiological restlessness or agitation, as well as a cascade of activation across all systems of the suicidal mode.

The emotional system produces affective experiences that serve to shape adaptive and maladaptive thoughts and behaviors through the basic principles of learning (cf. Beck, Emery, & Greenberg, 1985); specifically, negative emotions decrease the frequency of certain behaviors (i.e., punishment), whereas positive emotions increase behaviors (i.e., reinforcement). During suicidal crises, aversive emotions are activated and become very intense. Shame, guilt, anger, anxiety, and depression are particularly powerful and frequently occurring emotions associated with suicidal mode activation. Suicidal thinking and suicidal behaviors can actually serve to decrease aversive emotions (Brown, 1998), which function as a negative reinforcement contingency that sustains the perception that suicidality is the only way to reduce or end suffering. The relief experienced secondary to suicidal thinking and behaviors increases the likelihood of future suicidal mode activation. Furthermore, the experience of negative emotions in certain situations or events sensitizes the suicidal mode for future activation under similar circumstances. Over time, this state-dependent activation pattern lowers the threshold for repeated suicidal crises. Generalization of these state-dependent cues to new situations can lead to activation in a wider range of contexts—a characteristic particularly true for multiple attempters.

The motivational system of the suicidal mode refers primarily to intent—in other words, the purpose or the function underlying the suicidal ideation or suicidal behavior. Intent is the central feature that differentiates suicidal behaviors from other intentional, nonsuicidal self-injurious behaviors (e.g., cutting to reduce emotional distress or using the appearance of suicide for interpersonal or other secondary gain). Intent is a key variable for understanding suicide risk (Bryan & Rudd, 2006) and is directly reflected in the suicidal individual's behaviors and actions. For example, behaviors such as preparing for death or practicing the suicide attempt elevate the individual's resolve to engage in the act and reduce barriers to the act. Indeed, suicidal intent and behaviors are so intimately linked with one another that behavioral indicators of suicidal intent have demonstrated much better utility in predicting suicidal behaviors than subjective indicators of intent such as self-reported desire for death and/or life (Joiner, Rudd, & Rajab, 1997; Minnix, Romero, Joiner, & Weinberg, 2007).

The behavioral system includes those actions that are automatically activated in response to cognitive and affective processes and are closely associated with suicidal intent. This system includes a wide spectrum of behaviors including substance abuse (which inhibits problem-solving and reduces behavioral control), nonsuicidal self-injury (e.g., cutting or burning one's arm to reduce emotional distress), preparatory behaviors or rehearsal (e.g., buying a gun, counting pills, tying a noose), and suicidal acts (i.e., suicide attempts). Each of these behavioral patterns elevates a patient's tolerance for physical and emotional pain while simultaneously lowering their fear of death, a construct that has been termed the *acquired capability for suicide* (Joiner, 2005; Van Orden, Witte, Cukrowicz, Braithwaite, Selby, & Joiner, 2010). The behavioral system also includes those vulnerability factors that contribute to suicide risk—interpersonal skills deficiencies, absence of self-soothing skills, social withdrawal, and poor emotion regulation strategies.

Finally, the physical system comprises those physiological reactions and symptoms that are automatically activated in conjunction with cognitive, affective, and behavioral processes. For example, HPA activation during periods of negative emotional states can contribute to unpleasant physical symptoms such as agitation, insomnia, and concentration impairment. Extended HPA activation can also contribute to increased somatic complaints and immune suppression, which can lead to increases in medical utilization that are often observed during acute suicidal crises. These uncomfortable physical experiences fuel emotional distress and can impair cognitive processes such as problem solving. Physiological restlessness and psychomotor agitation, in particular, are associated with increased suicidality (Benazzi, 2005).

Once the suicidal mode is activated in response to an acute stressor, it reinforces and even elevates the individual's baseline vulnerability to suicide such that they are more likely to become suicidal again in the future in response to similar stressors (i.e., the process of sensitization) and in response to additional stressors that differ slightly from the original stressor (i.e., the process of generalization). Suicidal behaviors do not generally emerge spontaneously as a coping strategy, but rather are acquired through a dual process of habituation to the negative aspects of suicide and the development of fearlessness through repeated exposure to painful and provocative experiences (Joiner, 2005). This habituation process mirrors that of substance addiction, in that suicidal ideation and behaviors must become more extreme over time in order to generate the same level of reinforcing effect. Thus, as suicidal behaviors become normative for the individual, they serve to facilitate future (and more severe) suicidal behaviors.

This is most easily demonstrated by the chronically suicidal multiple attempter, who has acquired over the course of his or her life a distress tolerance response style characterized predominantly by suicidal behaviors as a coping strategy. A history of multiple suicide attempts is the single most robust predictor of future suicidal behavior, easily washing out any other risk factor for suicide. Furthermore, rehearsal and preparation for suicide—for example, developing a specific suicide plan, acquiring the means for suicide, counting pills, holding a gun to one's head, and other such "practice" activities—is another significant predictor of suicidal behaviors that further reflects its learned nature. As the suicidal individuals mentally or behaviorally practice the steps leading up to a suicide attempt, they engage in a process of habituation that shapes their behavior into closer and closer approximations of the final act.

In summary, the suicidal mode is a useful model for understanding the complex interaction of the multiple components of suicide risk. Couched within fluid vulnerability theory, suicidal episodes can be understood as the propensity to activation of suicidal crises. Suicidal mode activation is manifested as a combination of psychological, behavioral, and physiological systems and coincides with the concept of acute suicide risk. Individuals with higher levels of baseline risk (e.g., multiple attempters) experience more frequent and longer-lasting suicidal episodes because they have greater vulnerability for suicidal mode activation (sort of like having a "hair trigger" for suicidal crises). Resolution of the suicidal crisis therefore requires the deactivation of these various systems of the suicidal mode in order to return the patient to his or her baseline level of risk.

A FUNCTIONAL APPROACH TO SUICIDAL BEHAVIOR

Syndromal classification, whether categorical or dimensional, is the traditional medical and psychiatric approach to organizing behavioral disorders according to clusters of signs and symptoms that are assumed to underlie and give rise to the behavioral disorder. The dominance of syndromal classification schemes within the mental health field is encapsulated within the *Diagnostic and Statistical Manual of Mental Disorders, Fourth Edition* (*DSM-IV*; American Psychiatric Association, 1994), which categorizes psychiatric disorders according to the same syndromal classification scheme of the *International Classification of Diseases* (*ICD*) system, the classification scheme utilized by the full spectrum of medical professions. As noted by Hayes, Wilson, Gifford, Follete, and Strosahl (1996), a primary goal of syndromal classification is the identification of disorders with a known etiology, course, and treatment response. Within physical medicine, signs (i.e., what is observed) and symptoms (i.e., what is reported by the patient) are eventually linked to their underlying processes, at which time the syndrome is reclassified as a disease. Unfortunately, links between psychiatric syndromes (i.e., signs and symptoms) and their underlying disease processes (i.e., function) have been notably deficient, with virtually no behavioral or psychiatric disease processes being identified.

In the syndromal approach, suicidal ideation and behaviors are viewed as symptoms (i.e., the patient discloses them, but they are not actually observed or seen by the clinician) of some underlying psychiatric disorder. From this perspective, clinical treatment focuses not on suicide risk itself, but rather the psychiatric illness under the premise that targeting the illness will reduce the symptoms of suicidal ideation and behaviors. Within medical settings including primary care, suicidality is almost always associated with depression, as can readily be seen in many medical practice guidelines (see Table 3.1 for examples). The fact that the *DSM-IV* lists suicidal ideation and behaviors as symptom criteria for only two psychiatric disorders—major depressive disorder and borderline personality disorder—further reinforces this depression/suicidality association. The limitations of the syndromal approach to suicidality become clear, however, in light of the overwhelming body of literature demonstrating that suicidal ideation and behaviors are not limited to depression alone, but rather cut across a wide range of psychiatric disorders including eating disorders, anxiety disorders, bipolar disorders, and antisocial personality disorder, to name just a few (Harris & Barraclough, 1997). A different model for understanding suicide risk is therefore needed.

In contrast to syndromal classification approaches, functional classification approaches do not organize themselves around the surface characteristics (i.e., signs and symptoms) of a given behavioral pattern, but rather organize around the underlying processes that precipitate and maintain the behavioral pattern (Hayes et al., 1996). Functional classification approaches emphasize the situational cues that affect the likelihood of a given behavior's occurrence and the subsequent consequences of a behavior that can increase or decrease the likelihood of the behavior occurring again. In other words, the context of the behavior must be understood in order to understand why or how it operates and which methods could potentially alter or modify the behavior.

For example, one patient might experience suicidal episodes within the context of marital distress secondary to a recently discovered affair, whereas another patient might experience suicidal episodes within the context of a chronic and recurrent psychiatric condition such as bipolar disorder. The contextual differences between these two suicidal states lend themselves to different strategies for reducing and managing the crisis. Although similar techniques and procedures might be used for both patients (e.g., crisis

TABLE 3.1
Sample Medical Practice Guidelines for the Assessment of Suicide Risk

Source	*Language*
U.S. Preventative Service Task Force (2004)	"A more feasible means of decreasing suicide may be to focus on the high-risk groups, such as depressed primary care patients for whom routine screening is already recommended, and to focus efforts to decrease risk on improving the adequate management of depression. Improving depression management may both improve depressive outcomes and decrease suicide risk." (pp. 822–823)
McNamee and Offord (1990)	"[P]hysicians should routinely evaluate suicidal risk among patients at high risk, particularly if there is evidence of current psychiatric disorder, especially psychosis, depression or substance abuse." (p. 1228)
American Medical Association (2003)	"All adolescents should be asked annually about behaviors or emotions that indicate recurrent or severe depression or risk of suicide. Screening for depression or suicidal risk should be performed on adolescents who exhibit cumulative risk as determined by declining school grades, chronic melancholy, family dysfunction, homosexual orientation, physical or sexual abuse, alcohol or other drug use, previous suicide attempt, and suicidal plans." (p. 6)
American Academy of Pediatrics (2000)	"All adolescents with symptoms of depression should be asked about suicidal ideation, and an estimation of the degree of suicidal intent should be made." (p. 872) "Pediatricians should ask questions about depression, suicidal thoughts, and other risk factors associated with suicide in routine history-taking throughout adolescence." (p. 873)
American Academy of Child and Adolescent Psychiatry (2001)	"Clinicians should ascertain the suicidality of depressed adolescents (i.e., whether and how often they think about suicide and whether they have ever attempted suicide). If suicidal ideation or recent suicidal behavior is present in a depressed teen, they should continue to be monitored." (p. 265)

response plans, cognitive restructuring), the BHC who delivers these interventions and procedures without accurately recognizing the contextual variables of the crisis limits his or her ability to effectively and efficiently improve the patient's condition.

Likewise, failure to understand the consequences of suicidal ideation and behaviors directly blocks the BHC's ability to remove suicide as a viable option for the patient. In particular, the BHC must recognize that suicidal ideation and behaviors are by their very nature reinforcing to the patient. If it were

TABLE 3.2
A Functional Model of Suicidal Behaviors

Source of Reinforcement	*Type of Reinforcement*	
	Positive	*Negative*
Internal	Generate desirable internal states (e.g., relaxation, relief, calmness) "To feel something"	Reduce aversive internal states (e.g., anger, anxiety, agitation, shame) "To get rid of bad feelings"
Social	Obtain positive interpersonal experiences (e.g., communication, attention) "To get something from others"	Avoid undesirable interpersonal tasks (e.g., work duties, relationship problems) "To get out of doing something"

not inherently reinforcing, suicidality would quickly fade away and never take hold because behaviors that are not reinforced do not persist over time. Behavioral reinforcement can occur by two processes: the addition of something pleasurable or desirable (i.e., positive reinforcement) or the removal of something aversive or undesirable (i.e., negative reinforcement). A second dimension of reinforcement is its source: either as an intrapsychic event that arises from within the individual (i.e., internal) or from a social source occurring outside of the individual (i.e., external). These four reinforcement patterns are displayed in Table 3.2 and serve as a model for the various functions of suicidal ideation and behaviors.

Suicidal behaviors can serve one or more of four functions. Suicidal behaviors operating on an internal positive reinforcement schedule serve to generate some sort of positive internal state such as calmness or emotional relief. This function can also include a sense of justice associated with the individual's subjective sense of "deserved" punishment for perceived wrongs. Internal negative reinforcement, in contrast, involves the reduction of aversive or uncomfortable internal states that are almost always negative emotional experiences. Shame, anger, agitation, and depression are common emotional states experienced by suicidal individuals, who typically view suicide as an option for eliminating or avoiding these aversive emotional states. Suicide can also be seen as a method for managing or controlling harsh or overly critical self-statements associated with the suicidal belief system (e.g., "I'm no good," "I screw everything up," "I'm a burden on others").

It is critical for BHCs to recognize that suicidal behaviors can also be reinforced by the social environment so they do not inadvertently increase the likelihood or frequency of suicidal behaviors during clinical encounters. External positive reinforcement occurs when the social environment adds a positive or desirable interpersonal experience for the suicidal individual, such as increased attention or concern. This is particularly relevant when considering family and social support networks, who might respond to suicide risk by excessively taking care of the suicidal individual, increasing the time spent with the individual, and prioritizing the needs of the individual above other aspects of life. Providers are similarly vulnerable to inadvertently reinforcing suicidal behaviors through this same process by extending session length, increasing session frequency, responding to crisis calls at all hours of the day, and so forth. Although responding with concern and compassion is a desired clinical behavior and increasing the frequency or intensity of one's contact with a patient during a suicidal crisis is an appropriate clinical response, BHCs must be cautious not to inadvertently increase the likelihood of suicidal behaviors among patients who might mistakenly believe that "people only care when I'm in crisis."

Suicidal behaviors can also operate as a function of external negative reinforcement when these behaviors contribute to avoidance or reduction of interpersonal demands. For example, a suicidal individual might have stressful responsibilities taken away or expectations reduced during crises. Hospitalization can potentially function as an external negative reinforcement for some suicidal individuals because inpatient care can temporarily remove the overwhelming demands of daily life. Similarly, PCPs who recommend that suicidal patients not work or engage in other daily activities (e.g., providing a "doctor's note") might in some cases reinforce the suicidal crisis or increase the likelihood of future suicidal crises inadvertently during periods of increased interpersonal demands.

It is important to clarify that this is not to suggest that a BHC or PCP should never extend appointment length or increase the frequency of clinical contact with suicidal patients. Increased clinical contact is an important strategy for managing acute suicide risk. Our intent in discussing these issues is to highlight the importance of understanding the various functions of suicidal behaviors and the importance of identifying the unique functions that operate for any given suicidal patient so that when providers do increase clinical contact with high-risk patients, they do so in a manner that does not heighten or sustain suicidal crises. BHCs and medical providers who recognize the various functions of suicidal behavior will be much better equipped to respond to suicidal patients in a clinically effective manner.

Of the four behavioral functions, suicidal behaviors are driven most prominently by internal negative reinforcement: Individuals think about suicide and engage in suicidal behaviors because these things are effective at reducing or eliminating aversive psychological states in the short term (Chiles & Strosahl, 2005; Jobes, 2006; Joiner, 2005; Loo, 1986; Rudd, Joiner, & Rajab, 2001; Smith & Bloom, 1985). A similar internal negative reinforcement function has been found to underlie nonsuicidal self-injurious behaviors (Nock & Prinstein, 2004), which can explain in part why nonsuicidal self-injury increases risk for suicide and among certain subgroups of patients overlaps with suicidality. As noted by Chiles and Strosahl (2005, p. 58), "suicidal patients are always experiencing significant emotional pain, regardless of the source of such pain," with suicidal behaviors serving the purpose to gain control over these unwanted experiences. In many cases, suicidal behaviors involve some combination of the four functions, requiring the BHC to understand the relative contributions of each in order to optimize clinical care. Interventions that do not adequately target the suicidal behavior's central functions will generally be ineffective for containing suicide risk.

The relationship between suicidal behaviors and psychiatric disorders is cast in a new light when seen from a functional perspective. From a functional perspective, suicide risk is not viewed as a symptom of any particular psychiatric condition but rather as a response strategy used by an individual to manage or cope with a unique clustering of psychiatric symptoms. Suicidal ideation and behaviors therefore exist across the full range of psychiatric conditions because they serve as a mechanism to reduce the personal suffering and solve those problems associated with psychiatric conditions, regardless of syndromal classification. The clinical implications of such a perspective are subtle but profound: Intervention from a functional approach shifts away from treatment of the psychiatric diagnosis toward the replacement of suicidal behaviors as a problem-solving strategy. In short, patients think about suicide and engage in suicide-related behaviors because these strategies are remarkably effective for reducing internal states of discomfort. Suicidal ideation and behaviors persist over time because they work; if they did not, the individual would eliminate them as methods for problem-solving and distress tolerance. The BHC must therefore understand why the suicidality has emerged and what purpose it serves in order to replace it with alternative strategies and behaviors.

A COLLABORATIVE APPROACH TO WORKING WITH SUICIDAL PATIENTS

A great deal has been written about the importance of therapeutic alliance—alternatively referred to as rapport or therapeutic relationship within the mental health professions or bedside manner within the medical professions—on treatment adherence and outcomes. One of the most consistent research findings in mental health treatment research is that a strong therapeutic alliance is associated with treatment outcome even when symptomatic differences are accounted for, and alliance is typically found to account for an equivalent or greater amount of outcome variability than other treatment factors (Martin et al., 2000). Many mental health professionals commonly misinterpret these findings as suggesting that therapeutic alliance is the only variable that matters in treatment outcomes and that intervention and technique are less important. Unfortunately, this drives many providers to spend an excessive amount of time and attention focused on relational variables at the expense of active application of empirically supported interventions. The assumption is that it takes a great deal of time (e.g., up to several 50-minute sessions) to establish effective therapeutic alliance, and only after this is established can active interventions be administered. If this assumption were true, however, we would expect to see clinical improvement occurring only after several appointments or sessions, not immediately. But outcomes research from both specialty mental health settings and primary care behavioral health settings indicate that the greatest amount of clinical improvement occurs within the first few contacts.

In a well-known study frequently cited to support the long-term dose effects of outpatient psychotherapy, Howard and colleagues (1984) modeled clinical response patterns across a number of psychotherapy studies and concluded that most clinical gains occur very early in therapy, with progressively diminishing returns with more visits. Specifically, approximately 50% of patients reached recovery within the first 8 sessions, 75% recovered within 52 sessions, and 85% within 100 sessions. Similar patterns in depression remission were reported by DeRubeis and Feeley (1990), who noted that 90% of overall improvements in depression associated with cognitive therapy occurred within the first 6 sessions of a 12-session treatment protocol. Outcomes research in primary care behavioral health settings has similarly found that the typical patient demonstrates clinical recovery in only two to three brief appointments (Bryan et al., 2009). In fact, most studies have failed to find significant differences in outcomes when comparing long-term therapy to brief therapy approaches, with a similar absence of evidence supporting the incremental efficacy of lengthier treatments (Steenbarger, 1994).

These findings seem to directly contradict widely held assumptions about the nature of therapeutic alliance: If establishment of an effective therapeutic alliance is a necessary contributor to treatment outcomes and patients improve immediately following the initiation of treatment, then logically, therapeutic alliance must be formed very early in the treatment process—much quicker than traditionally assumed. Indeed, this is exactly what some data have demonstrated: Very early patient-therapist interactions (Strupp, 1980) and patients' initial impressions of the provider predict clinical outcomes (Beckham, 1992). This should not be too surprising considering the overwhelming amount of evidence demonstrating the powerful effect that initial impressions and judgments play on our perceptions of and subsequent interactions with others (Ambady, Bernieri, & Richeson, 2000).

Recent research has found that provider variability in patient-rated alliance seems to account for a greater portion of the variance in treatment outcomes than patient variability (Baldwin, Wampold, & Imel, 2007). Providers who form stronger alliances with patients on average demonstrate significantly better patient outcomes than providers with weaker alliance ratings. Within the same provider, however, alliance ratings of multiple patients are not found to differentially relate to outcomes. To illustrate this, consider two providers, each of whom has 10 patients who rate the strength of their alliance with their respective provider. Provider A receives an average alliance rating that is stronger than provider B's average alliance rating; as such, provider A's patients will, as a whole, improve more than provider B's patients. When one looks at provider A's 10 patients, however, the patient who rates him highest in terms of alliance will not necessarily improve more than the patient who rates him the lowest. The same will be true of provider B: The patient with the highest rated alliance will not necessarily improve more than the patient with the lowest rating.

In other words, there seem to be certain characteristics or actions of providers that are much more important for successful treatment outcomes than characteristics or actions of patients. This is remarkably consistent with research investigating malpractice claims. Among a sample of PCPs, one interesting study found that the content of communication with patients (e.g., amount or quality of information, details about treatment options or the patient's condition) was found to have no bearing on malpractice claims, but the manner in which the PCP communicated did (Levinson, Roter, Mullooly, Dull, & Frankel, 1997). Specifically, PCPs who made orienting comments that provided structure for the appointment (e.g., "First I'll conduct my examination, then we'll discuss your concerns"), facilitated interaction and participation during the appointment (e.g., "Tell me more about that"), and demonstrated a sense of humor were significantly less likely to have been sued by a patient. Even tone of voice alone can predict malpractice claims: Surgeons speaking with more dominance and lower concern and anxiety in their voice tone are almost three times more likely to be sued than surgeons without these voice tone qualities (Ambady et al., 2002). These studies suggest that providers who take the time to hone their ability to develop an effective alliance with patients from the very start of the treatment interaction are better positioned to influence clinical care and reduce liability.

One provider variable that is particularly relevant to improved outcomes and therapeutic alliance is technique. Specific concrete actions such as setting an agenda, asking for specific examples of problems, educating patients about problems or diagnoses, teaching and practicing skills in-session, assigning homework, and monitoring adherence to assignments and interventions are associated with clinical improvement during the first few appointments of treatment more so than alliance (DeRubeis & Feeley, 1990; Feeley, DeRubeis, & Gelfand, 1999), suggesting that rapid improvement is heavily dependent upon technique even when considering therapeutic alliance. Indeed some have argued persuasively that therapeutic alliance might actually be better conceptualized as an outcome of these concrete actions (DeRubeis, Brotman, & Gibbons, 2005); in other words, using the specific concrete actions listed earlier in the very early stages of treatment contribute not only to improved clinical outcomes but also to a better alliance. Indeed, the orienting comments described earlier that were associated with decreased rates of malpractice claims against PCPs in Levinson et al.'s study (1997) are consistent with the concrete actions of setting an agenda and asking for specific examples of problems.

Taken together, these various sources of data suggest that considerable clinical impact can be made by a BHC in a very short time. Likewise, the BHC must recognize that their interactions with the patient—from the very first moments of contact—will be a powerful contributor to clinical outcome because therapeutic alliance and the interventions delivered are closely related to each other. Without effective early intervention, an inadequate therapeutic alliance is unlikely to develop. Without a solid alliance, further interventions are unlikely to be received and implemented successfully by the patient because the patient is likely to drop out of treatment prematurely. Because suicidal patients are at higher risk during transitions from higher to lower level of care (Appleby, Shaw, et al., 1999), the ability to keep suicidal patients engaged in treatment should therefore be seen as a primary treatment goal.

Given the remarkable dearth of training in suicide risk management, it is no wonder that few mental health professionals have taken the time to consider their personal understanding of suicide. This is unfortunate given that awareness of one's attitudes and beliefs about suicide has been identified as a core competency in suicide risk assessment and management (Rudd, Cukrowicz, & Bryan, 2008; SPRC, 2006). The ability to recognize one's attitudes and beliefs about suicide has been identified as a core competency because these can possibly influence a provider's emotions (e.g., anxiety, anger, frustration) during the suicide risk assessment and management process (Shea, 2002). All BHCs, providers, and members of the primary care team should therefore take some time to carefully consider the following questions, as they will help uncover one's stance and view of suicide, which will ultimately determine the approach taken with suicidal patients:

- Why do people die by suicide?
- What are my moral and spiritual beliefs about suicide?

- What have I learned about suicide during my life?
- What type of person kills themselves?
- Who do I know who has died by suicide and what do I think about them?
- Can suicide be prevented?
- What is my obligation to suicidal patients as a clinician?
- How does all of this change—if at all—within the primary care setting?

A core competency for suicide risk assessment and management involves the ability to maintain a consistent and stable therapeutic alliance with the patient. As discussed in the previous section, research has consistently found that a therapeutic alliance marked by trust and empathy is associated with patient improvement. Through therapeutic alliance, the BHC is able to deliver interventions and teach the skills with which the suicidal patient can enact change in his or her life. As a strategy for managing distress and solving problems, suicidal behaviors must be replaced with alternative coping and problem-solving skills. BHCs must be careful not to mistakenly equate therapeutic alliance with interventions, however. Therapeutic alliance in and of itself is not a coping strategy that reduces suicide risk, but rather serves as the framework within which the BHC delivers the interventions that ultimately serve to reduce suicide risk. Without a solid therapeutic alliance, successive interventions are unlikely to be successfully received by the suicidal patient.

One relationship dynamic central to clinical work with suicidal patients is the potential for a particular conflict that is inherent and unique to suicide risk assessment: The patient's goal to reduce psychological suffering through suicide directly conflicts with the BHC's goal to prevent death by suicide. This conflict must be resolved in order for the BHC and the patient to establish the working relationship necessary for clinical improvement. Resolution of this conflict can be accomplished with a straightforward and simple definition of the common goal, that is, to reduce the patient's suffering and emotional pain. Consistent with a functional model of suicide, as pain and suffering resolve, so will the risk for suicide. Defining a common goal of pain remediation therefore lays the groundwork for the development of a nonadversarial, collaborative therapeutic stance that facilitates establishing and maintaining a good working alliance with the patient. Within a collaborative stance, the patient and BHC work together as a team to target the problem of suicide.

The collaborative approach stands in stark contrast to the traditional clinical approach of understanding a patient's suicidal state, the latter of which is characterized by the provider taking a reductionistic perspective that views suicidal ideation and behavior as merely symptoms of an underlying psychiatric condition (Jobes, 2006). This reductionistic perspective is consistent with the syndromal classification approach to suicide described previously. Within the traditionally reductionistic approach, the provider acts as the expert who sits in a "one-up" position while the patient acts as the passive recipient of the provider's questions and procedures. The primary goal for the provider is to identify and diagnose the psychiatric illness believed to underlie the suicide risk and then actively target the psychiatric illness for intervention, which the patient again passively receives. The issue of suicidality within a reductionistic therapeutic relationship often takes the form of a power struggle, in which the patient struggles to retain their autonomy and freedom to choose suicide as a viable option for reducing suffering while the provider struggles to remove or limit this very autonomy in order to prevent the patient's death.

A significant limitation to the reductionistic approach is that it inherently assumes the provider can control the patient's choices and behaviors at all times. Responsibility for the patient's suicide risk is additionally placed in the expert provider's hands, whose job is to eliminate the risk through clinical intervention. The patient, as the passive recipient of treatment, is given only limited responsibility for suicidal behavior. Under such conditions, it is not surprising that many providers respond to suicidal patients with a range of emotions, including fear, anxiety, and anger. These emotional responses can cloud providers' judgment and contribute to suboptimal clinical decision-making. Fear of suicide—usually a consequence of inadequate understanding and familiarity with suicidal behaviors—can lead the provider to deny the severity of risk as he or she finds reasons to support the perspective that the patient is not really at risk for suicide. Fear and denial lead to underreaction that reduces the likelihood of delivering appropriate protective measures and ineffective interventions. Providers experiencing elevated fear can also develop a sense of hopelessness about the patient's chances for recovery, which further reinforces the provider's delivery of lower levels of clinical intervention than what might be required or indicated.

In contrast to the underreactivity resulting from fear, provider anxiety often leads to a "better-safe-than-sorry" approach that can be overprotective and limit the patient's autonomy. Overreliance on hospitalization is a common manifestation of provider anxiety. This is without a doubt the most frequent provider emotional response to a suicidal patient and is almost always driven by the provider's worries about litigation following the patient's death. Unfortunately, clinical decision-making that targets the reduction of the provider's distress as opposed to targeting the patient's symptomatology and treatment needs is never therapeutic. Furthermore, the imposition of unnecessary controls has the potential to damage therapeutic alliance in the long term.

It is not uncommon for providers to additionally respond to suicidal patients with anger, especially when the patient is not improving as expected or, even more so, when the patient is deteriorating or worsening. Chronically suicidal patients, with their recurrent crises and ongoing problems, are uniquely capable of eliciting the disdain of medical professionals, who are vulnerable to viewing such behaviors as manipulative. Maltsberger and Buie (1974) have discussed the "hatred" that providers can feel toward their suicidal patients, and how this directly undermines their ability to treat suicidal patients effectively. Rejection of the suicidal patient is the unfortunate consequence of unchecked anger.

Managing these initial emotional reactions is a critical competency for BHCs because they directly interfere with the therapeutic alliance critical for effective risk assessment and intervention. BHCs can improve the management of their emotional reactions to suicidal patients by first recognizing the potential influence of these emotional reactions and then accepting them as a part of clinical work. Denial of these personal emotional reactions unfortunately only serves to intensify their influence on clinical decision-making. BHCs should also explore their personal beliefs and assumptions about suicide by considering the questions presented at the beginning of this chapter. Adopting a collaborative approach in which the BHC and patient work together as a team, in contrast to a traditional reductionist approach when working with suicidal patients, can further minimize the impact of emotional reactions on effective risk management.

Jobes (2006) has extensively discussed and argued persuasively for a collaborative clinical approach that places suicidality as the central clinical problem and focus that is separate from psychiatric diagnosis. Within this collaborative approach, the patient is seen as the expert of his or her own personal suffering and suicidal experience and is engaged as an active collaborator in their treatment. A central philosophy of the collaborative approach is that the answers to the patient's struggles lie within and that better alternatives than suicide for coping with problems and life distress can be identified together with the provider. The advantages of a collaborative approach to working with suicidal patients, when compared with routine clinical care, include a more rapid resolution of suicidal ideation and a significant reduction in medical utilization, including fewer emergency department visits (Jobes, Wong, Conrad, Drozd, & Neal-Walden, 2005).

Four relatively simple strategies can facilitate the development of a collaborative relationship with suicidal patients: acknowledging the patient's ambivalence about living, contextualizing (i.e., normalizing) feelings of hopelessness within psychiatric illness or diagnosis and/or the patient's current life circumstances, providing an understandable and simple model of suicide, and identifying a common goal for treatment.

Acknowledging the Patient's Ambivalence About Living

When it comes to clinical care, the BHC should always consider why the suicidal patient has chosen to disclose to a health care professional that he or she is considering suicide, as opposed to simply killing himself or herself. The answer is always that the patient has not yet come to a decision about suicide and that he or she simultaneously desires death and wishes to continue living. Suicidal individuals who have made up their minds about suicide generally do not come in to meet with medical professionals. They tend to kill themselves instead without accessing care. Not surprisingly, ambivalence is associated with lower levels of suicidal intent as compared with a predominant orientation toward death (Kovacs & Beck, 1977), and if asked, most suicidal patients are able to simultaneously list both reasons for dying and reasons for living (Jobes & Mann, 1999). Although suicidal patients seen in a clinical setting are almost always ambivalent, BHCs are cautioned not to underestimate patients' attraction to suicide or minimize their desire for death as an option for eliminating suffering.

Borrowing from the basic strategies of motivational interviewing (Miller & Rollnick, 2002), BHCs can communicate a recognition of the suicidal patient's ambivalence by using simple "and" statements instead of "but" statements, the latter of which serves to discount the preceding statement (e.g., "So, on the one hand, you want to kill yourself in order to end your pain, and on the other hand, you want to live because you care about your family and friends"). In the example provided, a BHC who uses the word "but" instead of the word "and" could potentially communicate to the patient that the BHC is minimizing the patient's desire for death, which could inadvertently prompt the patient to argue the case for suicide in order to convince the BHC of the legitimacy of this perspective. Without a doubt, this is a countertherapeutic goal; BHCs should therefore accept both the desire for life and the desire for death that suicidal patients commonly experience.

Contextualizing the Patient's Experience

Many suicidal patients are confused and distressed about their suicidal state and often times experience considerable shame and isolation from others because they perceive that others cannot understand what is happening to them. The ability of the BHC to effectively communicate recognition of the suicidal state as an understandable reaction to life stress can be a powerful clinical intervention and is fundamental to the establishment of a working alliance with the patient. For example, a hierarchical approach to questioning in which the

BHC gradually progresses through an interview in intensity and sensitivity can potentially reduce anxiety or agitation in the patient while improving rapport (Bryan & Rudd, 2006; Rudd, Joiner, & Rajab, 2001). In this hierarchical approach, the patient's symptoms and suicidal thinking are normalized within the context of the life stressor and are therefore understandable as opposed to mysterious or confusing. The reduction of anxiety resulting from this contextualization of the suicidal experience enhances the honesty of the patient's report and provides for more detailed responses, leading to a more accurate risk assessment. The act of contextualizing the patient's suicidal experience at its core communicates the message: "I understand what is happening, it makes sense to me, and I can help."

Providing an Understandable Model of Suicidal Behaviors

Explaining suicidal thinking and behaviors using a model that is simple and easy to understand can considerably reduce the patient's subjective distress and improve their confidence in the BHC as a competent health care provider with the ability to help them. Consistent with the functional model of suicidal behaviors, the BHC should emphasize that suicidal behaviors serve the primary purpose of reducing or alleviating psychological pain triggered by life stressors. Likewise, the BHC should explain how the patient's thoughts, emotions, and physical functioning interact as a part of the suicidal episode. Oftentimes, the PCP and BHC are the first people with whom the patient has disclosed their suicidal thoughts or desires. Being able to clearly articulate a simple model of suicidal behaviors (e.g., the suicidal mode) to the patient demonstrates the BHC's competence and ability to help the patient.

Identifying a Common Goal for Treatment

Although the clinician's primary goal with suicidal patients is to avoid or prevent death by suicide, the patient's primary goal is almost always the reduction of psychological distress and suffering through suicide. BHCs must therefore be able to successfully reconcile this difference in goals and work with the patient to establish a common objective. Since suicidal behaviors exist primarily as a method for reducing psychological suffering, the development and successful implementation of alternative strategies for reducing suffering can effectively render suicide an "obsolete" option. The BHC should therefore work to establish with the suicidal patient the shared goal of reducing pain. At its most fundamental level, this requires the BHC to never argue with patients about whether or not they can kill themselves. Taking a stance that respects the patient's capacity to end their life, does not eliminate the patient's sense of power and control over pain that suicide provides for them, and acknowledges the simple truth that the patient absolutely can, at some point, make this choice despite the BHC's best intentions and efforts.

Understandably, this might seem like a provocative clinical position to take, but this subtle shift in position can have a powerful impact on the BHC's ability to connect with and influence the patient because it embraces the patient's experience and minimizes therapeutic tension. All BHC and PCP interventions and recommendations should therefore be presented and introduced from the framework of collaborative pain reduction regardless of whether a given intervention is a self-management skill, psychotropic medication, use of a crisis response plan, increased social support and activity level, or referral to a mental health specialty setting.

CLINICAL TERMINOLOGY AND THERAPEUTIC ALLIANCE

Consider the following clinical scenarios that PCPs and BHCs commonly encounter in primary care settings:

- Kristin is a 16-year-old girl who broke up with her boyfriend 2 weeks ago. According to her parents, Kristin sits in her room alone and has stopped going out with friends since the breakup. Earlier this week, one of Kristin's friends informed a teacher at school earlier that Kristin has been posting "suicidal" comments and statements on her social networking site. The teachers contacted the parents, who asked Kristin about this. Kristin ran into the bathroom and grabbed a handful of aspirin, declaring that she would be "better off dead" and "can't go on without him [her boyfriend]."
- George is a 75-year-old man who has lived alone since his wife died 3 years ago. He visits his PCP monthly for routine monitoring of several health conditions that are treated with a variety of medications. In the past few months, George's medical conditions, which are normally stable and well-managed, have taken a turn for the worse. Concerned about this change, George's PCP probes for possible depression, and during this evaluation, George admits to thinking about suicide "all the time." When the PCP asks George if he has "ever attempted suicide," he reports that in the past 2 weeks he has

held his loaded weapon to his head but "can't go through with it until I get things better squared away for my family."

- Beth is a 43-year-old woman with fibromyalgia and a history of anxiety, panic attacks, and several hospitalizations for overdoses and "suicide gestures" typically characterized by taking large amounts of sleep and pain medications mixed with alcohol. She frequently schedules acute appointments with her PCP for complaints of breathing difficulties, heart palpitations, and acute pain exacerbation but rarely attends routine follow-ups. Beth has scheduled another acute appointment with her PCP to obtain refills on the pain and sleep medications that have run out early due to taking more than prescribed following an argument while intoxicated with her on-again, off-again boyfriend earlier in the week. Beth indicates she has no desire to pursue outpatient mental health treatment because "I've been to plenty of shrinks in my life and they've never helped before," insisting the most recent overdose was "no big deal" and "just me being drunk and stupid like usual."

Each of these scenarios illustrates clinical problems that are very real for primary care providers. How a provider describes these actions, and the perceived level of risk associated with these actions, depends on a number of factors that can vary considerably from one provider to another. An alarming level of inconsistency in what is considered to be suicidal exists among clinicians. This variability is reflected in the language and extensive number of terms clinicians use when talking about suicide risk. Perhaps not surprisingly, these terms suffer from remarkable inconsistencies in clinician definitions (Bryan & Tomchesson, 2006), which can interfere with effective communication not only between multiple clinicians, but also between clinicians and suicidal patients.

We therefore recommend that clinicians implement the following terms to describe the different dimensions and full range of suicide risk (cf. Silverman et al., 2007):

- *Nonsuicidal morbid ideation or death ideation:* Thoughts in which death is a desired outcome, but there is no evidence of self-infliction or suicidal intent. Oftentimes, this is expressed as a wish to die without self-infliction.
- *Suicide ideation:* Thoughts in which self-inflicted death is a desired outcome and which may or may not include a plan but does not involve an explicit attempt. This is often experienced as a "weighing of options" regarding suicide.

- *Suicide threat:* Any interpersonal action, verbal or nonverbal, without a direct self-injurious component, that a reasonable person would interpret as communicating or suggesting that suicidal behavior might occur in the near future.
- *Suicide plan:* A proposed method of carrying out a design that will lead to a potentially self-injurious outcome.
- *Self-harm or nonsuicidal self-injury:* A self-inflicted, potentially injurious behavior for which there is evidence that the person did not intend to kill himself/herself (i.e., had no intent to die). Self-harm may result in no injuries, nonfatal injuries, or death.
- *Suicide attempt:* A self-inflicted, potentially injurious behavior with a nonfatal outcome for which there is evidence of intent to die. Suicide attempts may result in no injuries or nonfatal injuries. Suicide attempts that result in death are classified as suicide.
- *Suicide:* A self-inflicted death for which there is evidence (either explicit or implicit) of intent to die.

From a clinical perspective, the language one uses can have a significant impact on therapeutic alliance, as it is often the primary mechanism by which we convey empathy and understanding of the patient's situation. For example, consider a patient who cuts themselves without suicidal intent (i.e., self-harm). The BHC who refers to such behaviors as "suicide attempts" can potentially convey a general misunderstanding of the behavior pattern and could lead the self-harming patient to become defensive as they attempt to explain how they are not actually suicidal. This dynamic works against the development of a collaborative relationship. Another possible unintended outcome is the adoption of the BHC's language by the self-harming patient, which could inadvertently reinforce the patient's self-perception as a suicidal person (e.g., "I really am suicidal"), thereby escalating his or her self-harm behaviors to suicide attempts. A similar problem can occur when the BHC inappropriately uses the language of self-harm when talking with a patient who is suicidal. In such cases, the suicidal patient might perceive the BHC as minimizing his or her risk or distress. This is especially problematic when working with patients for whom suicidality functions with a strong social reinforcement component, as these patients are more likely to escalate their behaviors to demonstrate to the BHC how serious or sincere they really are.

Clinical language can conversely serve to decrease a patient's distress when used appropriately. Many patients do not understand the full spectrum of suicide-related thoughts and behaviors and will generically lump them under the umbrella of "suicide." Consequently, a self-harming patient who views himself or herself as suicidal can experience emotional relief when a BHC educates them on the differences between self-harm and suicidal behaviors or the differences between nonsuicidal morbid ideation and suicidal ideation (e.g., "I'm not as bad off as I thought"). Such education can also serve to reduce the patient's self-perception as a suicidal individual, which is a critical factor for effective deactivation of the suicidal mode (e.g., "If I'm not suicidal, then maybe I'm not as crazy as I thought"). From a practice management perspective, accurate clinical terminology can additionally improve consistency of care delivery as well as documentation of that care.

We additionally recommend that BHCs initially "match" their patients' language when conducting risk assessments and discussing suicidal and self-harm behaviors. When matching a patient's language, a BHC intentionally uses whatever terms and words the patient uses to describe the behavior (e.g., "slicing," "cutting," "carving"). Matching the patient's language is a simple strategy for building rapport and communicating understanding of their perspective and attenuating any anxiety that the patient might be experiencing. Several terms we strongly recommend against using, however, despite their widespread use across the full spectrum of clinical settings are *suicide gesture* and *parasuicide*. Providers demonstrate a remarkably high level of variability when asked to define the terms *suicide gesture* and *parasuicide* (Bryan & Tomchesson, 2007), suggesting that these two terms are poorly understood and inconsistently used, which considerably restricts professional communication. These terms have also been identified as being potentially pejorative (e.g., Linehan, 1993; Walsh, 2006).

As an illustration, in our experience working with many health care professionals across medical and mental health settings, we have often found that providers typically precede these terms with the qualifier "just" (i.e., "it's *just* a suicide gesture" or "it was *just* parasuicide"), which connotes a minimization of the self-injurious behavior. This most frequently seems to occur when providers are discussing the recurrent nonlethal self-injurious behaviors and communications of especially difficult or frustrating patients such as chronically suicidal patients diagnosed with borderline personality disorder. When used in clinical settings, these terms can potentially communicate to the suicidal patient a sense of disdain and a lack of understanding of their experience, which directly undermines therapeutic alliance, and are therefore discouraged for use.

CORE COMPETENCIES FOR THE BEHAVIORAL HEALTH CONSULTANT

1. Describe a biopsychosocial model of suicide.
2. Describe the various functions of suicidal behaviors and how clinical interactions can inadvertently reinforce suicidal behaviors.

3. Recognize the impact that one's personal beliefs and attitudes about suicide have on one's clinical approach and interactions with patients.
4. Maintain a collaborative, nonadversarial stance with suicidal patients.
5. Manage one's emotional reactions to suicidal patients.
6. Define and use standardized suicide-related terminology.

CHAPTER 4

Accurate and Brief Risk Assessment

As has been discussed in previous chapters, several factors have converged to raise awareness of the need for competent suicide risk assessment in primary care settings. First, increasing numbers of psychologists and other mental health care providers have been positioned in primary care clinics in an effort to improve both the ease of access to mental health care and the efficiency of service provision (Blount et al., 2007). Second, almost half of those who die by suicide present to a primary care clinic during the month before their death (Luoma et al., 2002), and almost 20% contact their primary care provider (PCP) within a day of their suicide (Pirkis & Burgess, 1998). Finally, recognizing that primary care is the predominant source (and in most cases, the only source) of mental health care in the United States, public health campaigns targeting suicide have identified primary care as a critical setting for frontline intervention (Blount et al., 2007). The result is a mounting need for straightforward, clinically applicable, and flexible approaches to assessing and managing suicide risk in primary care clinics. Critical to this is a need for approaches that acknowledge the unique clinical constraints of the primary care setting that differ markedly from the specialty mental health settings in which the general science and practice standards of suicide risk assessment and management have been developed.

Few would argue with the assertion that the assessment, management, and treatment of suicide risk are among the most challenging and stressful tasks for clinicians regardless of setting (cf. Jobes, Eyman, & Yufit, 1995). The unique constraints of the primary care setting (e.g., brief appointments, high patient volume, comorbid medical conditions, limited follow-up schedules, restricted management options) serve to further complicate an already complex task. Perhaps the most prominent and frequently occurring question from behavioral health providers practicing in primary care settings is "how do I complete an appropriate and accurate risk assessment within the contextual constraints of the primary care clinic?"

Before answering this question, it is useful to consider the typical diagnostic and evaluative approach to other medical or health complaints presented by a typical patient when meeting with his or her PCP. First, a patient comes in and reports symptoms and problems to the PCP, who asks evaluative questions designed to rule in potential causes for the symptoms and rule out other causes suspected to be unrelated to the problem. To aid in this process, the PCP conducts an examination and oftentimes orders tests to further refine their initial clinical impressions. The results of these tests generally serve to confirm or disconfirm suspected causes underlying the patient's complaints and are used to guide appropriate treatment. In some cases, the patient is referred to a specialist for more refined testing and/or treatment. In the meantime, the PCP initiates some form of treatment plan to manage the problem and provide symptom relief while the patient awaits this higher level of care. If a health issue requiring specialty care is identified, the specialist provides appropriate treatment and management, and when the issue has been adequately resolved, care for the patient is typically transferred back to the PCP for ongoing monitoring and preventative care.

This typical approach to primary care therefore consists of several steps. First, an initial screening that tends to be highly generalized and nonspecific occurs (e.g., patient self-report of symptoms, respiration, checking inner ears), followed by increasingly specific assessment strategies (e.g., laboratory work, throat swab, x-rays, physical manipulation of body parts) until a reasonable level of confidence regarding the cause for the problem is identified (i.e., diagnosis). Finally, an intervention is initiated by the PCP and, where indicated, a referral to a specialist is made for more advanced assessment and treatment (e.g., cardiology, endocrinology, oncology).

This same approach is recommended for the assessment and management of suicide risk in primary care: (1) screen for suicide risk, (2) for positive screens conduct a more specific suicide risk assessment, (3) arrive at a reasonable assessment of risk level, (4) initiate interventions and management strategies, and (5) refer to specialty mental health care where indicated. In this chapter, the first three steps of this approach (i.e., screening, assessment, and determination of risk) will be described in detail; intervention and referral will be discussed in subsequent chapters. A brief case vignette will be interspersed throughout the discussion during the next few chapters to serve as a reference point for illustrating concepts and steps involved in a clinical encounter for a suicidal patient. Case information will be revealed sequentially as we go through each step to mirror the chronology and process of a typical behavioral health consultant (BHC) appointment.

Mary is a 54-year-old married woman with two adult children. She is currently unemployed, with no previous employment outside the home. She lives with her husband, who is a retired military veteran. Mary is obese with several comorbid medical issues, including hypertension and obstructive sleep apnea. She attended a routine follow-up appointment with her PCP today to go over the results of recent laboratory results, which point to a diagnosis of diabetes mellitus type 2. The PCP notified the BHC of Mary's upcoming appointment and requested a consult in advance to address motivational and behavioral issues related to diet and exercise, as Mary has not always been adherent to treatments in the past. During the PCP appointment, Mary agreed to meet with the BHC for recommendations regarding diabetes management, and she was checked in for a consult. As part of routine practice, she was given a symptom checklist to complete before the BHC appointment while the PCP conferred with the BHC. The PCP stated that when he informed Mary of the diagnosis of diabetes, she "took the news hard" but overall seemed to be doing okay. The PCP stated that Mary was willing to engage with the BHC and felt she would be a good candidate for a collaborative treatment plan combining medication with behavioral treatment. The BHC agreed to evaluate Mary and follow up with the PCP afterward with specific treatment recommendations.

ROUTINELY SCREEN ALL REFERRED PATIENTS FOR SUICIDE RISK

Because suicide is such a low base-rate phenomenon, it is not possible to predict its occurrence with any reasonable level of reliability or consistency. BHC screening of every referred patient for suicide risk during initial contact is therefore recommended for increasing the likelihood of identifying individuals who might be at elevated risk. Screening is a brief and straightforward strategy conducted to identify individuals at risk for suicide, in contrast to assessment, in which a more thorough understanding of the nature and intensity of suicide risk is obtained following positive screenings (cf. Robinson & Reiter, 2007).

Another way to conceptualize the differences between screening and assessment is to consider them with respect to their ability to detect or diagnose the target construct. Screening approaches tend to maximize sensitivity at the expense of specificity because they are intended to positively identify as many suicidal individuals as possible. This expectedly results in a high false-positive rate (i.e., nonsuicidal patients being identified as suicidal). Suicide risk assessment, in contrast, emphasizes a more refined designation of risk level that maximizes specificity at the expense of potentially missing true cases (i.e., suicidal patients being incorrectly classified as nonsuicidal). In other words, suicide screening serves to "rule in" the possibility of suicide risk, while risk assessment serves to "rule out" false-positives and better refine the clinician's understanding of the true positive.

The two-stage approach of screening followed by more thorough risk assessment is therefore an effective strategy for balancing these two competing dimensions of identifying suicide risk. Screening can be accomplished in a variety of ways according to the needs and demands of each clinic, whether through clinician questioning during the appointment or through the use of brief, standardized measures that include screening items for suicidal ideation and/or behaviors.

Clinical Questioning Approaches

If using clinical questioning as the method for routine screening, BHCs should ensure that screening questions become a routine part of all patient evaluations, not just a subset of patients (e.g., the widespread practice of screening only those patients reporting depressed mood). Screening only subsets of patients, especially when designated by particular diagnoses, overlooks the well-established fact that suicide risk is not diagnosis-specific (Harris & Barraclough, 1997) and could result in missing many suicidal patients. Routine screening of all patients further ensures that BHCs do not succumb to using subjective indicators of risk or "gut feelings" to drive screening and assessment, a notoriously unreliable method for decision-making (Grove & Meehl, 1996). Routine screening of all patients therefore requires BHCs to screen for suicide even among patients who present with issues that seem to be completely unrelated to suicide risk (e.g., tobacco cessation). This position may initially seem to be unnecessarily extreme, but given the low base rate of suicidality and the data indicating that patients are unlikely to voluntarily report suicidality during medical appointments (e.g., Bryan, Corso, et al., 2009), it becomes clear that screening of all patients is the optimal method for increasing the likelihood of detection.

There are a number of ways to incorporate screening questions into one's routine evaluation, the most widely recommended being a hierarchical approach in which the BHC transitions from the patient's current symptom picture to hopelessness, and then to suicide-specific questioning (Bryan & Rudd, 2006; Rudd, Cordero, & Bryan, 2009). This hierarchical approach sequences increasingly specific questions that are more specific to the issue of suicide. For example, a straightforward screening approach might entail the following two questions:

1. It is not unusual for someone who is feeling depressed/agitated/lonely to feel hopeless. Do you ever feel hopeless about life or feel that things are never going to get any better?

2. Many times when people feel hopeless they also think about death or have thoughts about suicide. Do you ever wish you were dead or think about killing yourself?

The initial screening question probing for hopelessness is highly sensitive and will therefore "catch" a very large number of suicidal patients because hopelessness is so common among suicidal patients. However, screening for hopelessness is not very specific and will result in a lot of false-positives because the overwhelming majority of patients who are hopeless are not suicidal. The second question is therefore designed to further narrow the field while still remaining broad enough to catch as many suicidal patients as possible. By starting with a question about hopelessness, the BHC provides a bridge from the current topic of conversation to the ultimate goal of screening for suicide risk. By "easing in" to the suicide screening in this way, the BHC provides a contextual basis by which it "makes sense" to ask about suicidality, thereby reducing the patient's anxiety about discussing the issue and increasing their willingness to honestly self-disclose any such thoughts.

Another important point to emphasize is that effective screening requires the BHC to specifically probe for the target construct—in this case, suicide risk. Using hopelessness as the sole screening for suicide risk is inadequate because it is too nonspecific. Effective suicide screening requires direct, unambiguous inquiry about suicide risk in the same way that effective depression screening requires direct inquiry about mood. Asking patients if they are having "thoughts about hurting themselves" is not the same as asking patients if they are having "thoughts about suicide" or "thinking about killing yourself." As demonstrated in the second question, suicide screening should specifically ask about suicide during each clinical encounter. In the same way that PCPs check vital signs at every appointment regardless of complaint or reason for visit, so should BHCs routinely check this vital sign for psychological health.

Checklist and Questionnaire Approaches

Use of screening measures such as symptom checklists or self-report questionnaires is a simple and straightforward alternative screening method. There are a number of symptom checklists that can be used for the purposes of suicide screening such as the 9-item depression subscale of the Patient Health Questionnaire (PHQ-9; Kroenke, Spitzer, & Williams, 2001) or the 20-item Behavioral Health Measure (BHM-20; Kopta & Lowry, 2002). If BHCs choose to use checklist or survey screeners, they should ensure that the screening item directly asks about suicide in clear, easy-to-understand language. The PHQ-9, for example, asks patients to rate how often they have been bothered by "thoughts that you would be better off dead or of hurting yourself in some way" during the previous 2 weeks. The BHM-20 similarly asks patients to rate how much they have been distressed by "thoughts of ending your life" in the past 2 weeks as well as rating their subjective level of suicide risk from "extremely high risk" to "no risk."

Both of these measures have demonstrated the ability to improve detection rates of suicide ideation. For example, Bryan et al. (2009) found in a primary care clinic that 12.4% of all patients referred for a BHC evaluation screened positive on the BHM-20's suicide ideation item (i.e., "thoughts of ending your life" during the previous 2 weeks). In comparison, only one in six of these positive screens (2.1% of the entire sample) disclosed suicide ideation to their PCP during the previous medical visit occurring anywhere from 48 hours to just minutes before the screening, indicating a sixfold increase in detection of suicidal patients as compared with usual care. Unfortunately, this study was not designed to determine what proportion of patients had been explicitly asked by their PCPs about suicide risk but denied it and what proportion was not asked about suicide risk by their PCPs at all, which would further clarify the survey's ability to improve detection. In another study investigating suicide screening in primary care, inclusion of the suicide item from the PHQ-9 significantly improved detection of patients with thoughts about death or suicide (Corson, Gerrity, & Dobscha, 2004). Follow-up risk assessments of positive screens revealed that one third had confirmed suicide ideation, demonstrating the value of the two-stage process of screening (maximal sensitivity) followed by risk assessment (maximal specificity). For positive screenings, the BHC should therefore conduct a more thorough risk assessment to better understand the nature and content of the endorsed items.

Upon completion of the symptom checklist, the BHC walked Mary to his examination room. During this walk down the hallway, the BHC quickly scanned the symptom checklist, making sure he checked the suicide screening item. Mary's responses indicated a moderate level of distress and a positive endorsement of the suicide ideation item. Once in the examination room, the BHC introduced himself and explained his services and informed Mary that her PCP had requested consultation regarding diabetes management. The BHC spent a few minutes assessing Mary's perceptions about diabetes, during which Mary described a sense of failure, shame, and self-disgust:

MARY [M]: It's all my fault because I'm so fat. I did it to myself. Look at me; I'm a whale.

BHC [B]: Those are pretty negative things to think about yourself. I'm wondering if that has anything to do with the depressed mood, anxiety, stress, and low energy you reported on this checklist.

M: They are. I get so depressed when I think about my weight. I just hate myself and how I look.

B: You know, sometimes people who don't think highly of themselves and have all these other problems going on in life like feeling stressed, hopeless, and low in energy also think about things like death or even killing themselves. I see on this form that you say you've been having some thoughts about ending your life.

In this segment of the clinical encounter, the BHC opened the appointment in the standard format, which in this case was related to diabetes management. He did not immediately open with a question about the suicide screening because he did not yet have any sense of the context within which Mary would endorse suicidality. Instead, the BHC obtained basic information related the presenting complaint (diabetes) and very quickly started uncovering clues about Mary's suicide risk. The BHC was able to guide the conversation toward the eventual issue of suicidality in such a way that the issue of Mary's positive screening became a natural part of the overall evaluation and conversation.

FOR POSITIVE SCREENINGS, CONDUCT A BRIEF BUT THOROUGH RISK ASSESSMENT

Based on our experience as BHC trainers, we have found that a frequently asked question surrounds how to accurately assess suicide risk and appropriately manage that risk within the brief window of the typical BHC appointment. As with any other aspect of BHC clinical work, the BHC should approach risk assessment in a manner that accounts for the greatest amount of suicide risk with the least amount of variables. In other words, BHCs should emphasize gathering information about those factors that have the strongest empirical association with suicidal behaviors. It is therefore recommended that BHCs sequence their risk assessment questions in a particular order to minimize patient anxiety and obtain more accurate self-report leading to optimal clinical decision-making (Shea, 2002). Appropriate sequencing further maximizes the information gained from patients in the most practical, efficient, and clinically useful manner. A suggested format for sequencing of questions within primary care, along with sample queries, is presented in Figure 4.1 and will be discussed in detail next. With practice and experience, it is quite feasible to complete an accurate and high-quality risk assessment within the typical 25- to 30-minute window allotted for BHC appointments.

1. **Suicide screening**
   - Many times when people feel [describe symptoms or complaints] they also think about death or have thoughts about suicide. Do you ever wish you were dead or think about killing yourself?
   - Do things ever get so bad you think about ending your life or suicide?

2. **Differentiate suicidal ideation from nonsuicidal morbid ideation**
   - Tell me a little bit about what, specifically, you have been thinking.
   - What is it exactly that goes through your mind?
   - When you think about dying, is it because you have caused it to happen?

3. **Assess for past suicidal behaviors**
   - Have you ever had thoughts like this before?
   - Have you ever intentionally injured yourself in any way before?
   - Have you ever tried to kill yourself before?
   - So you've never cut yourself, burned yourself, held a gun to your head, taken more pills than you should, or tried to kill yourself in any other way?

4. **If positive history of suicidal behaviors, assess multiple attempt status**
   - How many times have you tried to kill yourself?
   - Let's talk about the first time . . .
     a. When did this occur?
     b. What did you do?
     c. Where were you when you did this?
     d. Did you hope you would die, or did you hope something else would happen?
     e. Afterward, were you glad to be alive or disappointed you weren't dead?
   - Let's talk a little bit about the worst time you attempted suicide; the time you were most suicidal and tried to kill yourself . . .

   [Repeat a through e above]

5. **Assess current suicidal episode**
   - Let's talk about what's going on right now. You said you've been thinking about [content].
   - Have you thought about how you might kill yourself?
   - When you think about suicide, do the thoughts come and go, or are they so intense you can't think about anything else?
   - Have you practiced [method] in any way, or have you done anything to prepare for your death?
   - Do you have access to [method]?

6. **Screen for protective factors**
   - With all that's been going on, what is keeping you alive right now?
   - What prevents you from killing yourself?

FIGURE 4.1

Recommended sequencing of risk assessment questions for BHCs.

Differentiate Nonsuicidal Morbid Ideation From Suicide Ideation

Because most suicide screening items assess for the presence of suicide ideation, the BHC should clarify if the patient is experiencing suicide ideation or nonsuicidal morbid ideation. Nonsuicidal morbid ideation includes thoughts about death or wishing one were dead without suicidal content (e.g., "If I didn't wake up tomorrow, that would be okay" or "I just wish it would all be over"). This differentiation is key since suicide ideation has a much stronger association with suicidal behaviors than nonsuicidal morbid ideation (Joiner, Rudd, & Rajab, 1997), thereby implicating different clinical responses.

The notion of a spectrum of suicide-related thoughts has a firm foundation in both the clinical and empirical literature. Joiner's (2005) interpersonal-psychological theory of suicide posits that not only is the desire for death and suicide a necessary condition for suicidal behaviors, but also that an individual must develop the capability to first overcome the fear of death and subsequently the fear of suicide, the latter of which can take either the form of decreased levels of fear about death (i.e., "fearlessness") and/or increased tolerance for the fear for death (i.e., "courage"). One study has specifically tested the possibility of a spectrum of suicidality from life weariness at the least severe end, up through death wishes, suicide ideation, suicidal planning, and suicide attempts at the most severe end (Renberg, 2001). This study found general support for a hierarchical organization of these constructs, with more severe forms of thinking generally including less severe forms of thinking, but not vice versa. Suicidal planning, for example, typically was associated with suicide ideation, desire for death, and life weariness; desire for death was associated with life weariness but not necessarily associated with suicide ideation or planning.

From a clinical perspective, research among populations across the entire lifespan has supported differences between individuals with nonsuicidal morbid ideation and individuals with suicide ideation. Among older persons, higher levels of suicide ideation are related to greater psychological symptomatology when compared with individuals with nonsuicidal morbid ideation (Scocco & De Leo, 2002). Among adult patients with major depressive disorder, severity of depressive symptomatology has likewise been found to be higher in patients with suicide ideation than patients with nonsuicidal morbid ideation, with the lowest levels of depressive symptoms being among patients denying either thought process (Fountoulakis et al., 2004). Among adult chronic pain patients, the highest levels of depression, trait anxiety, pain severity, pain-related functional impairment, and catastrophizing thought processes are found among suicide ideators, followed by nonsuicidal morbid ideators and then controls (Edwards et al., 2006). Similar patterns have been found in pediatric populations. Children and adolescents who report nonsuicidal morbid ideation have fewer depressive symptoms (i.e., irritability, depressed mood, psychomotor agitation, sadness, feelings of worthlessness, and guilt) and are less likely to have comorbid anxiety and conduct disorders as compared with those reporting suicide ideation (Liu et al., 2006). In general, this pattern of data indicates that much higher levels of psychological distress are associated with suicide ideation when compared with nonsuicidal morbid ideation, implicating different levels of clinical response and management strategies.

BHCs can differentiate suicide ideation from nonsuicidal morbid ideation by asking one or more probes or questions such as: "Tell me exactly what you've been thinking. What is it specifically that goes through your mind when thinking about this? Tell me the words that you use or say when thinking about this or describe the images that you see in your mind." In some cases, patients will still answer with unclear or ambiguous responses that do not clearly differentiate suicide from nonsuicidal morbid ideation. A patient might say, for instance, "I just wish I were in a fatal car accident" or "I just see myself dying, and I'm okay with that." BHCs can further refine this distinction by directly asking about a desire or intent toward self-infliction. For example, "When you wish you were in a fatal car accident, do you see yourself causing that accident? When you see yourself dying, is it because you killed yourself?"

As can be seen, the primary aim of initial screening is not to confirm the presence of nonsuicidal morbid ideation, but rather to rule in or rule out suicide ideation, as this ultimately drives the remainder of the risk assessment. Patients who report suicide ideation should be further assessed for suicide risk. Patients who endorse nonsuicidal morbid ideation but deny any suicide ideation generally do not require a detailed suicide risk assessment unless they report a previous history of suicidal behaviors. This difference in clinical response is due to the fact that nonsuicidal morbid ideation alone does not include an active motivation or desire to kill oneself and is a common feature of many psychiatric conditions (especially depression).

Because Mary positively endorsed the suicide screening item, the BHC begins a suicide risk assessment by attempting to clarify the nature of her suicidal thoughts. The following exchange occurs between the BHC and Mary:

B: You know, sometimes people who don't think highly of themselves and have all these other problems going on in life such as feeling stressed, hopeless, and low in energy also think about things like death or even killing themselves. I see on this form that you say you've been having some thoughts about ending your life.

M: Yeah, sometimes.

B: Can you tell me what, exactly, you've been thinking about?

M: Sometimes I think about just ending it all.

B: So you've been thinking about killing yourself?

M: Yeah.

In this segment, the BHC asks about suicide ideation and receives a somewhat ambiguous response. As a result, he follows up with a highly specific question designed to either rule in or rule out the likelihood of suicide ideation. In this case, his clarifying question results in a positive endorsement of suicide ideation.

Assess Past Suicidal Behavior

Suicide ideation is generally the most common method of screening for suicide risk. Using suicide ideation as the primary screener for suicide risk is ideal in many ways, since thinking about suicide generally precedes the emergence of suicidal behaviors. Furthermore, during the typical BHC appointment, the self-report of suicide risk is almost always disclosed by patients in terms of current or recent suicidal thoughts or urges (as opposed to distant past suicidal episodes). It is imperative, however, for BHCs to quickly transition into obtaining a brief history of the patient's suicidal behaviors. Of the many risk factors that have been empirically associated with increased risk for suicide, the single most significant and robust predictor of future suicide attempts and death by suicide across the entire life span is previous suicide attempts (Clark, Gibbons, Fawcett, & Scheftner, 1989; Forman et al., 2004; Joiner et al., 2005; Ostamo & Lonnqvist, 2001). This has been confirmed in numerous studies. In one particularly impressive study referred to as the "kitchen sink" study (after the paper's title: "Four Studies on How Past and Current Suicidality Relate Even When 'Everything but the Kitchen Sink' Is Covaried"), Joiner and colleagues (2005) conducted a series of analyses on four separate populations with varying degrees of suicide risk to determine if the magnitude of the relationship between past suicidal behaviors and current suicidal symptoms or future suicidal behaviors would hold even when a staggering list of well-established suicide risk factors was simultaneously considered: age, sex, functional impairment level, hopelessness, depression, personality disorder diagnosis, psychosis, problem-solving impairment, current suicide ideation, family history of depression, and family history of suicide. In all cases, past suicidal behavior maintained a robust relationship with current or future suicide risk that was not significantly diminished even when these other variables were factored in. When these researchers repeated their procedures with the other suicide risk factors, no other variable (not even hopelessness) demonstrated the ability to maintain the magnitude of their relationship with suicidality in the presence of other risk factors.

These results provide a powerful demonstration of the "resilience" of past suicidal behaviors in predicting current and future suicide risk even in the presence of an impressive array of covariates and unambiguously highlight the importance of assessing for past suicidal behaviors when conducting risk assessments. No other risk factor for suicide has yet been identified that shares this unique characteristic. As such, history of suicide is a critical component of the BHC's risk assessment and should be evaluated as early as possible in the risk assessment to obtain the information that will most significantly drive their eventual risk formulation and clinical response.

When asking about past suicidal behaviors, BHCs should again implement appropriate sequencing and wording of questions to reduce the patient's discomfort in talking about suicide and to enhance the likelihood of obtaining an accurate historical report. This can be accomplished by gradually increasing the intensity and specificity of each question:

- Have you ever had thoughts of suicide like this before?
- Have you ever tried to kill yourself before?

By first asking about suicide ideation, which the patient has already endorsed and begun to discuss, the BHC can begin the historical review on "familiar ground." Regardless of the patient's response to the question about past suicide ideation, the BHC should ask about past suicide attempts, since previous suicidal behavior (not suicide ideation) is the target variable for assessment. In this context, although questioning about past suicide ideation serves a clinical purpose (i.e., frequency of previous suicidal episodes), it more importantly serves as a bridge to a higher level and more emotionally intense component of the risk assessment. If the patient responds negatively, the BHC should follow up with a third question that directly probes for specific methods of self-harm, preparatory or rehearsal behaviors, and suicide attempts that may have occurred in the past:

- So you've never cut yourself, burned yourself, held a gun to your head, taken more pills than you should, or tried to kill yourself in any other way?

This third and highly specific question in response to a denial of past suicidal behavior is important for a number of reasons and warrants further discussion. First, patients will occasionally withhold information about their suicidal thoughts and behaviors but will respond honestly if directly asked (Rudd et al., 2001). Consider the patient who, for the past few weeks, has driven to an isolated location on four occasions and held a loaded gun to his head but after several minutes puts the gun down and drives home and never mentions these actions to his wife or anyone else. When asked if he has ever tried to kill himself before, he might answer negatively because he has not yet pulled the trigger and therefore not yet "tried" to kill himself. When asked about specific methods and preparatory behaviors, however, he is much more likely to admit to this highly dangerous behavior because although he does not necessarily want to disclose his actions, he also does not necessarily want to lie. Second, asking about suicidal history in a repeated and increasingly specific manner minimizes the likelihood of missing episodes that the patient has inadvertently dismissed or overlooked. This often occurs among patients with repeated instances of suicidal episodes or self-harm behaviors, as well as among patients who have forgotten about instances in the distant past. In these cases, the highly specific question can prompt or jumpstart memories of relevant episodes. Finally, listing off multiple methods for self-harm and suicide further demonstrates to the patient that the BHC is comfortable discussing such issues in detail, which increases the likelihood of self-disclosure.

Screen for Multiple Attempter Status and Assess Attempt History

In most cases, patients will not report a history of past suicidal behaviors, in which case, the BHC should move to assessing the current suicidal episode. In the event of a positive endorsement, however, the BHC should quickly screen for multiple attempter status and obtain some basic information about key past attempts. Identifying multiple attempters (i.e., patients with two or more previous suicide attempts) is important because this subpopulation is at much greater risk for suicide than nonmultiple attempters (i.e., patients with zero or one previous suicide attempt) (Rudd, 2006). Multiple attempters tend to be chronically suicidal, with frequent suicidal episodes that are easily triggered and maintained over time. If a patient endorses previous suicidal behaviors, the BHC should therefore ask how often and when these behaviors occurred. When working with multiple attempters, it is useful to identify patterns in behavior and intent over time. This can understandably be a daunting prospect within the primary care setting, especially with patients who report a very high frequency of past attempts. For many multiple attempters, it is simply not feasible for BHCs to conduct a thorough assessment of each and every suicidal episode that has occurred in their lives. The BHC's goal therefore should not be to obtain a detailed history of every suicide-related behavior that has ever occurred but rather to establish a snapshot of the patient's behavioral pattern and intent over time in order to better understand the patient's current risk and to map out the general trajectory of suicidal behaviors over time.

This snapshot of the patient's suicidal history can be achieved by starting with the first episode, then jumping forward in time to the "worst" or "most serious" episode, then moving forward again to the current episode. BHCs can begin the historical assessment by asking patients to briefly describe the first attempt: "Tell me a little bit about the first time you tried to kill yourself. What's the story of what happened there?" Asking patients to "tell the story" of the suicide attempt as opposed to asking a series of questions to uncover details of the attempt (akin to an interrogation) is a collaborative strategy the BHC can use to enhance patient honesty and mitigate fears about self-disclosure. As the patient begins to relate the story of their first suicide attempt, the BHC should pay attention to several key features of the suicidal episode: when it occurred, methodology, context or location of the attempt, and intended or desired outcome. These variables provide BHCs with information about the "facts" of the suicidal episode that can guide management strategies and possible interventions. For example, does the patient attempt suicide when alone and the likelihood of rescue is low or does the attempt occur in a situation with high probability of survival (e.g., taking a handful of medication then immediately telling someone who is also in the house)? Identifying contextual variables also provides clues as to the types of situations that are likely to trigger suicidal behavior (e.g., relationship failures, arguments with family, job stressors) and are critical for developing management strategies and interventions. Developing a crisis response plan, for instance, in which a suicidal patient seeks out support during a crisis from a family member whose critical and abusive behavior contributes to suicidal thinking and urges is unlikely to be effective.

Assessing for these features of each episode is also important because they serve as indicators of behavioral intent. The behavioral intent associated with each episode should be assessed for two reasons. First, understanding the behavioral intent associated with each episode enables the BHC to more accurately classify the behavior as a suicide attempt or self-harm—an important differential, given the scientific evidence supporting increased risk for suicide associated with previous suicide attempts as compared with self-harm. Second, suicidal intent is considered one of the most important and robust predictors of suicidal behavior. There are two dimensions of suicidal intent for BHCs to assess: subjective and objective. Subjective intent entails what the patient reports to have been the motivation underlying the behavior. The BHC can clarify subjective suicidal intent by asking the patient one or more questions such as:

- Did you hope you would die, or did you hope something else would happen?
- What did you hope would happen when you [method]?
- Did you expect to die as a result of [method]?

The objective dimension of suicidal intent includes circumstantial features of the episode, such as isolation, likelihood of intervention, and preparation for the attempt and/or death. If the patient does not relate these details as part of their description of the suicide attempt, BHCs can quickly assess for these variables with clarifying questions such as:

- Where were you when you [method]?
- When did this occur?
- Did you practice or rehearse [method] in any way or prepare for your death at all?

These objective indicators of suicidal intent differentiate fatal from nonfatal suicide attempts (Beck et al., 1974) and predict eventual death by suicide (Beck, Brown, & Steer, 1989; Harriss et al., 2005; Hawton & Harriss, 2006). Suicidal intent is an important variable for nonfatal suicidal behaviors as well, based on findings that suicide attempters with high levels of suicidal intent are very similar to individuals who die by suicide (Lester, Beck, & Mitchell, 1979). In general, objective indicators of intent are better predictors of death by suicide than subjective indicators (Beck, Brown, & Steer, 1989), indicating that BHCs should place more emphasis and weight on situational or objective features of past episodes than a patient's self-report of behavioral intent. BHCs should additionally probe patients about their reactions to surviving these suicide attempts by asking a question such as, "Afterward, were you glad to be alive or disappointed that you weren't dead?" Gauging a patient's survival reaction is a brief and straightforward method for determining suicidal intent and is an empirically supported method for estimating risk of reattempt. Suicide attempters who report disappointment about survival (i.e., wishing they had died) following an attempt are significantly more likely to attempt suicide again than those who were glad to be alive (Henriques, Wenzel, Brown, & Beck, 2005).

Upon concluding the assessment for the first suicide attempt, the BHC should transition to the patient's "worst point" suicide attempt: "Next I'd like to talk about the time you most wanted to kill yourself and attempted suicide. When was that worst point in your life? Tell me the story about that suicide attempt." The reason for jumping ahead to the worst-point suicide attempt even if this skips other suicidal episodes or attempts is because the worst-point suicidal episode is much more strongly associated with future suicidal behavior than current suicidal crises among patients with multiple suicidal episodes (Joiner et al., 2003). Specifically asking about the patient's worst-point suicide attempt is therefore a useful and efficient strategy for maximizing risk assessment decisions with chronically suicidal patients.

BHCs should repeat the assessment steps described earlier to obtain information about methodology and objective indicators of intent during the worst-point suicidal episode before transitioning to the assessment of the current suicidal episode. In some cases, the patient will indicate that the worst-point episode is the same episode as the first suicide attempt or current crisis (e.g., "The first time was the worst time" or "Right now is the most suicidal I've ever felt"). If this arises, BHCs should simply note this and ask patients to identify and describe the second worst suicidal episode in their lives. Once the assessment of the worst-point suicide attempt is complete, the BHC transitions to the current suicidal episode: "Next I'd like to talk a little bit more about what's been going on recently with your suicidal thoughts and feelings. You said you've been thinking about [content of suicide ideation]. Could you tell me a little bit more about what you've been thinking?"

Having confirmed the presence of suicide ideation, the BHC briefly assesses for Mary's past suicidal behaviors:

B: Have you ever had thoughts like this before, or is this the first time you've ever thought about killing yourself?

M: It's not the first time.

B: When's the first time in your life you thought about killing yourself?

M: It was a long time ago, like in high school.

B: Have there been any other times?

M: A bunch of times. It just comes and goes when things are going really badly in life.

B: Have there ever been any times in your life when you've intentionally injured yourself?

M: Yeah, a few times.

B: And how many of these times would you say you were trying to kill yourself or hoping you would die?

M: Maybe seven times.

B: Let's start with the first time you tried to kill yourself. Tell me the story about what happened.

At this point, Mary described an incident around the age of 15 in which she used a razor to cut her wrists following an argument with her mother, whom she described as highly critical and demeaning. She made this attempt in the bathroom while her parents were downstairs. She locked the door, filled the bathtub with water, broke open her razor to pull out the blade, got into the bathtub, and sliced her wrists several times with the blade. Upon questioning by the BHC, Mary reported that she had imagined herself dying in the bathtub, although now she doubts that she really wanted to die. After several minutes, her bleeding stopped and she decided that she was "just being stupid" and wrapped up her wrist. Mary reported wearing long sleeves for approximately a week to hide the wounds. When asked if she was glad to be alive or wished she were dead afterward, Mary answered:

M: I'm not really sure, but I don't think I really wanted to die. I didn't wish I had died, but I don't know that I was exactly glad to be alive.

B: Okay, I understand. Let's jump forward in time a bit. You said you attempted suicide about seven times in your life. I want you to think about the time you felt the worst, when you most wanted to kill yourself.

M: Okay.

B: When was that worst time in your life that you tried to kill yourself?

M: About 2 years ago.

B: I'd like you tell me the story about that time 2 years ago.

Mary described a period of several months in which she experienced a significant depressive episode. She felt that her husband was disconnected from her and seemed indifferent about her and therefore experienced intense loneliness. At the peak of her distress, Mary took "a handful" of over-the-counter sleep medications and prescription pain killers, hoping she would "fall asleep and just not wake up." She took the pills at night after her husband had fallen asleep, then got into bed next to her husband and fell asleep. When she did not wake up in the morning, her husband called an ambulance to transport her to the hospital, where she was treated and then admitted to the inpatient unit for 2 weeks. When asked about her reaction to surviving this attempt, Mary answered:

M: I didn't feel anything. I guess I was disappointed.

B: I see. Well I appreciate you sharing that with me; it must have been difficult to talk about.

M: It wasn't so bad. I've never really talked about this before.

B: Well I'm glad you're able to talk about it now. Why don't we spend a little bit of time now talking about what's been going on recently to make you want to kill yourself.

M: Okay.

In this segment, the BHC skillfully obtains a brief history of Mary's suicidal history by engaging her in a conversation about two critical suicide attempts in her history. He does not interrogate or interview Mary but rather facilitates a guided discussion that quickly and efficiently obtains the most relevant clinical information needed and smoothly transitions from one point in time to another.

Assess the Current Suicidal Episode

As can be seen in the discussion up to this point, the structure of suicidal symptoms is multidimensional in nature, with different factors demonstrating differing magnitudes of association with suicidal behaviors. When considering current suicidal episodes, similar patterns emerge in the scientific literature. As a specific example, Joiner, Rudd, and Rajab (1997) showed that current suicidal symptoms can be explained by two primary dimensions termed "resolved plans and preparation" and "suicidal desire and ideation." Resolved plans and preparation consist of subjective courage to attempt suicide, availability of means and opportunity for an attempt, specificity of plan for attempt, preparatory and rehearsal behavior, duration of suicidal ideation, and intensity of suicidal ideation. Suicidal desire and ideation, in contrast, consist of a lack of reasons for living, wish for death, frequency of suicidal ideation, desire and expectancy for a suicide attempt, lack of deterrents to attempt, and suicidal communication. Similar two-factor structures for current suicidal symptoms have been reported in several other studies (Beck, Brown, & Steer, 1997; Joiner et al., 2003; Mieczkowski et al., 1993), indicating that this is a reasonable method for understanding varying dimensions of suicide risk. Although the presence of both symptom dimensions are of clinical concern, the resolved plans and preparation factor is more significantly related to recent and future suicide attempts than the suicidal desire and ideation factor (Joiner, Rudd, & Rajab, 1997; Joiner et al., 2003). BHCs seeking to maximize accuracy in their risk assessments within the temporal and situational constraints of the primary care setting should therefore emphasize these symptoms and dimensions of current suicidal episodes.

The relative importance of the resolved plans and preparation factor as compared with the suicidal desire and ideation factor is due to the relationship of these factors to the two dimensions of suicidal intent. As suicidal intent emerges during the suicidal crisis, the patient spends an increasing amount of time thinking about the specifics of suicide and how to accomplish the act. As noted earlier, objective indicators of intent include behaviors such as taking precautions against discovery, preparing for death, and rehearsing or practicing the method; these behaviors overlap with the construct of resolved plan and preparation. Components of suicidal desire and ideation (e.g., desire for death, expectations about suicide), however, overlap with the subjective indicators of intent that are much less robustly associated with suicidal behaviors. Focusing on resolved plans and preparation is therefore a preferable method for assessing suicide risk because it incorporates an assessment of the patient's level of suicidal intent. As part of the risk assessment, BHCs should aim to elicit information about the presence of a specific plan, the intensity of current suicide ideation, preparatory or rehearsal behaviors, and access to lethal means.

Assess for the Presence of a Specific Plan

Once the patient has transitioned to an account of the current suicidal episode, the BHC should determine if the patient has started to formulate a specific plan to kill themselves by asking questions such as "Have you thought about how you might kill yourself? Do you know how or when you intend to do this?" Eliciting information about the suicide plan or "blueprint for suicide" can provide critical clues for risk management. For example, a patient who plans to shoot himself with his personal handgun should have firearms restriction enacted as a risk management precaution. Similarly, a patient who plans to overdose on medications should have her medications monitored and should only be prescribed nonlethal amounts of medications. In general, patients with well-thought-out and highly specific plans are at much greater risk for suicide than those who have not considered the details of the intended act because planning generally entails mental rehearsal of the act (e.g., "I see myself doing it after I get home from work"), which serves to escalate the patient's fearlessness about death and their capability for engaging in the act.

It is not uncommon for patients to be reluctant to disclose the details about their suicide plan due to fear of being hospitalized or otherwise thwarted in their intentions. This reluctance could signal greater levels of suicide risk (American Psychiatric Association, 2003) and therefore warrants a brief discussion. BHCs assessing patients reluctant to provide detailed information about their suicide plan should resist the temptation to confront this resistance and attempt to "pry" these details out of the patient. Instead, BHCs should seek to maintain a collaborative stance by moving on with the risk assessment in order to elicit additional information that might be less "threatening" to the patient. The BHC should continue to build a collaborative alliance with the patient then return to the issue of specific plans later in the interview. Asking a patient to describe their expectations about the consequences of honest disclosure (e.g., "What do you think might happen if you were to tell me the specifics of your plan?" or "How do you think I'll respond if you tell me fully what you've been thinking about?") is a useful strategy for quickly identifying the source of the patient's hesitation and any barriers to full disclosure.

If, for instance, the patient is afraid that the BHC will automatically recommend hospitalization following disclosure of specific plans (a common fear for many suicidal patients, especially those who have disclosed suicide risk in the past and have been referred for hospitalization as a result), the BHC can engage the patient in a discussion of how and when such a decision is made, which provides a natural transition for the BHC to discuss steps that can be taken to reduce the likelihood of this disposition.

Assess the Intensity of Suicide Ideation

Suicide ideation can be measured according to multiple dimensions, the most common of which are frequency (how often the thoughts occur), intensity (how severe the thoughts are experienced), and duration (how long the thoughts last). Importantly, these three dimensions of suicidal thinking relate differentially to suicidal behaviors. Frequency of suicide ideation has consistently been linked with the suicidal desire and ideation factor (Beck, Brown, & Steer, 1997; Joiner, Rudd, & Rajab, 1997; Joiner et al., 2003; Mieczkowski et al., 1993), whereas intensity of suicide ideation is associated with the resolved plans and preparation factor (Joiner, Rudd, & Rajab, 1997). Duration of suicide ideation has also been found to relate more strongly with the suicidal desire and ideation factor in some studies (Beck, Brown, & Steer, 1997; Joiner et al., 2003) and more strongly to the resolved plans and preparation factor in others (Joiner, Rudd, & Rajab, 1997). This suggests that of these three dimensions of suicidal thinking, it is the severity or intensity of these suicidal thoughts that are most relevant to suicidal behaviors and therefore should be emphasized.

This research has important implications for suicide screening procedures in primary care (and any other clinical setting) that warrant particular attention by BHCs. Most suicide screening methods ask patients to report or indicate the frequency with which they experience thoughts of suicide. Frequency of suicide ideation loads onto the suicidal desire and ideation factor of suicidal symptoms (Beck, Brown, & Steer, 1997; Joiner, Rudd, & Rajab, 1997;

Joiner et al., 2003), whereas the intensity dimension of suicide ideation loads onto the more pernicious resolved plans and preparation factor (Joiner, Rudd, & Rajab, 1997). Consistent with the purpose of screening to maximize detection at the expense of specificity, measuring frequency of suicide ideation might be an ideal approach to suicide screening, although as a part of the more refined risk assessment process, BHCs should be sure to emphasize the intensity of suicide ideation. To demonstrate the clinical difference between the frequency and intensity dimensions of suicide ideation, consider the following two cases:

- John reports thinking about suicide "only once per day" while working alone on the night shift. During this daily episode, he spends "hours at a time" thinking about shooting himself with his firearm, during which "I can't think about anything else; it's all-consuming."
- Dave reports thinking about suicide "off and on all day, every day" for the past few years, typically when he gets frustrated or angry. "They're just passing thoughts that only last a second or two," he adds.

If using a suicide screener that measures frequency of suicide ideation, it is quite possible that Dave will score higher than John since Dave has more frequent discrete episodes of suicide ideation. However, when we consider the intensity dimension of suicide ideation, it is clear that John is at much greater risk for suicide than Dave. BHCs must understand the distinction between frequency and intensity of suicide ideation and be able to accurately assess each.

Assess for the Presence of Preparatory or Rehearsal Behaviors

Perhaps the most indisputable indicators of elevated suicidal intent are preparing for death and rehearsing suicidal acts. Preparing for death can entail activities such as settling final financial or legal issues, making funeral arrangements, writing a suicide note, purchasing a gun, or hoarding medications. Rehearsal behaviors are even more pernicious and include "practice" activities such as driving to the site of the planned suicide, tying knots and weighting ropes, holding a firearm to one's head, counting medications, or aborting suicide attempts at the last minute. The reason these behaviors are so dangerous is because they serve to develop the individual's capability for lethal self-injury through acquired fearlessness about death and increased tolerance to pain (Joiner, 2005). The fact that intensity of suicide ideation is related so highly to the resolved plans and preparation factor is accounted for by the mental rehearsal that underlies both constructs. As suicide ideation becomes more intense, the suicidal individual finds it increasingly difficult to disengage from these thought processes (as in the case of John briefly presented in the previous section). This repeated mental rehearsal of the suicide attempt results in overlearning of the sequence of steps required to enact the action. Through preparation and rehearsal, suicidal individuals increase their courage and competency to carry out suicidal acts. BHCs should therefore assess for the presence of preparatory or rehearsal behaviors by asking, "Have you practiced [method] in any way, or have you done anything to prepare for your death?"

Access to Lethal Means

Up to this point, the discussion of suicide risk assessment has focused primarily on the nature of the patient's suicidal thinking, especially as it relates to the concept of suicidal intent. Because of the clear and consistent link between suicidal intent and eventual suicidal behaviors, many BHCs understandably spend most of the time in their risk assessments attempting to gauge the severity of intent, quite possibly due at least in part to the considerable amount of attention given to intent in the literature. An interesting and notable caveat to some of the research on the relationship between suicidal intent and death by suicide has demonstrated conflicting results, however, arguably due to the confounding variable of availability of means. Some studies have found that intent has little relationship with the lethality of a suicide attempt (Brown, Henriques, Sosdjan, & Beck, 2004; Plutchik et al., 1988; Swahn & Potter, 2001), for example, most likely because many patients have inaccurate expectations about the lethality of their chosen method (Beck, Beck, & Kovacs, 1975; Brown, Henriques, Sosdjan, & Beck, 2004). Availability of means, however, demonstrates a strong association with the lethality of chosen method (Eddleston et al., 2006; Peterson et al., 1985). It is therefore recommended that BHCs routinely ask about access to lethal means of suicide (e.g., "Do you have a firearm at home?" or "How much medication do you have in the medicine cabinet at home?").

Regular and repeated questioning about availability of means over the entire course of care is paramount because suicide attempts almost always occur during short-term peaks in distress. For example, among patients who survived life-threatening suicide attempts, 24% made the decision with 5 minutes preceding the attempt and 70% made the decision within the preceding hour (Simon et al., 2001). Of those who attempt suicide, 90% do not go on to die by suicide at a later time, due in large part to the fact that 75% never make another attempt (Owens, Horrocks, & House, 2002). This low reattempt rate by suicide attempters further supports the notion of suicidal behavior as a response to an acute (vs. chronic) stressor, although it is important to note that a full one quarter of all suicide attempters will eventually reattempt and consequently become multiple attempters.

Data have also supported a strong association between suicide and length of time from firearm purchase, with suicide rates being highest immediately following the purchase of the firearm and declining risk occurring as time passes: 57 times higher during the first week following firearm purchase, declining to 30 times higher during the first month, and 7 times higher after 1 year (Wintemute et al., 1999). These latter statistics not only provide further support for the central role of preparatory behaviors, but also highlight the importance of asking about access to means on a recurrent basis with suicidal patients. Simply put, just because a suicidal patient does not have access to a firearm now does not mean he or she will not gain access to one in the future. Because suicide attempts and death by suicide often occur within the context of an acute period of emotional distress, the removal or limitation of access to lethal means can reduce the probability for a suicide attempt in some cases or in other cases cause the suicidal individual to substitute to a less lethal method. Although means substitution might not seem at first to be an ideal outcome for patients, the fact that reattempt rates remains so low following a first suicide attempt suggests that constraining a suicidal patient's options to only those with low lethality could potentially be a life-saving strategy in both the short and the long term.

Having identified Mary as a multiple attempter and briefly assessing the first and worst-point suicide attempts, the BHC transitions to an assessment of the current suicidal episode:

B: So you told me a little while ago that you've been thinking about just ending it all. Have you thought about how, exactly, you might kill yourself?

M: Yeah. I'd just take a bunch of pills.

B: What kind of pills?

M: Oh, whatever's in my cabinet. I have sleep pills, pain pills, blood pressure pills; probably just taking all of those would do it.

B: When you think about overdosing on your meds, do these thoughts come and go or are they really severe, like you can't stop thinking about it?

M: Well it started off as just an idea, but now I think about it a lot, and it's really bad.

B: If you were to rate the severity of these thoughts from 0 to 10, with 0 being not severe at all and 10 being the most severe you've ever experienced, how would you rate those thoughts?

M: Probably a 6 or 7.

B: And have you thought about when or where you might do this?

M: At home. I usually think about it at night when I'm getting ready to go to bed. Sometimes I'll just sit there and think about it, and the other day, I even went to the bathroom to see how many pills I had.

B: Did you count them or pour them out or anything like that?

M: No, I just kind of shook the bottles and felt how much they weighed.

B: Have you done anything to prepare for your death?

M: No, I don't know that there's much to get ready for.

B: Have you done anything else to practice or get ready for your suicide, like write a note or tell someone about it?

M: No, just that checking the other night.

B: So you have a large amount of meds at home that you could overdose on?

M: Yeah. I have lots of medical problems so I have all sorts of pills.

B: Have you considered any other ways for killing yourself other than taking your meds?

M: No, just the overdosing. That's kind of my thing, I guess.

B: So you haven't thought about shooting yourself or hanging yourself or cutting yourself or any other methods?

M: Oh no. That's all too messy. I want it to be clean and peaceful.

B: Okay. I see.

In this segment, the BHC focuses his risk assessment on those factors that are most useful for estimating the risk level of the current suicidal episode: specificity of planning, intensity of suicide ideation, evidence of rehearsal or preparatory behaviors, and availability of means. The BHC also assesses for additional (especially more lethal) methods of suicide that Mary might be considering currently.

IDENTIFY PROTECTIVE FACTORS

Protective factors, in contrast to risk factors, serve to decrease risk for suicide. Identifying those factors in a patient's life that serve as a "buffer" against suicide or otherwise mitigate risk is a useful strategy for developing management plans and interventions to target suicide risk. In general, protective factors include the patient's personal strengths as well as those features of life that are generally going well. Examples of protective factors include the presence of reasons for living (Linehan et al., 1983; Malone et al., 2000), which might convey a sense of optimism or hope for the future. Strong relationships with family or friends (Turvey et al., 2002; Stravynski & Boyer, 2001), and especially the presence of children in the home (Clark & Fawcett, 1994), have been associated with decreased risk of suicide and align with theoretical work that a sense of belongingness to a social group reduces the desire for suicide (Joiner, 2005).

By determining what factors function to keep the patient alive, the BHC can begin to more fully understand the suicidal crisis and build interventions and strategies that are more likely to be successfully implemented. Transitioning to protective factors within the context of the risk assessment also functions as a "turning point" in the clinical encounter toward a discussion of "what is right in my life" and away from what has up to this point focused primarily on "what is wrong in my life." Facilitating the process of talking about positive aspects of life can be a powerful intervention in and of itself and can potentially elevate the person's mood as the BHC approaches the intervention stage of the encounter. Protective factors can be assessed by asking the patient questions such as:

- Given all that we've talked about, what is it that keeps you alive right now?
- What reasons do you have for living?
- What has prevented you from acting on these thoughts?

It is important to note that, in general, protective factors have much less empirical support than risk factors and BHCs should be cautioned against assuming that the presence of protective factors negates the presence of risk factors. Multiple attempters generally have fewer protective factors and resources to draw upon in times of crisis, which provides at least partial explanation for their increased vulnerability to crises. BHCs might therefore find this stage of the assessment particularly challenging when evaluating multiple attempters. In our experience, however, framing protective factors in terms of "what keeps you alive right now" is an approach that even the most despondent suicidal patient can almost always answer.

Having gained an understanding of Mary's history of suicidal behaviors and the current suicidal episode, the BHC next transitions into the identification of protective factors:

B: You know, Mary, with all this going on in your life and given that you've been thinking so much about how to kill yourself, I'm wondering what it is that keeps you alive? I mean, what stops you from taking those pills?

M: Well I don't want to kill myself. Well, I mean I do, but I guess that's just not how I want it to end, you know? I'd rather live to be old and be happy.

B: So there's a part of you that wants to live.

M: Yeah, I guess so.

B: So tell me what's worth living for. What's going well for you in life?

M: Well there's my dog. I absolutely love him and who would take care of him if I were dead?

B: What's his name?

M: Barney. He's a corgi and he's just the cutest little thing in the world. I love playing with him in the backyard. I should take him to the park or something but I'm too embarrassed to go because I just can't walk because of my weight.

B: So Barney is a reason for you to live and so is playing in the backyard.

M: Yeah. And my husband would miss me, too. He's had to put up with so much of my craziness for years, I'd hate for him to have to deal with this.

B: Sounds like he's really important to you.

M: Yeah, he is.

B: Good. What else keeps you from killing yourself?

M: Well, I guess my religious beliefs, too. I haven't gone to church in years, though.

In this segment of the risk assessment, the BHC begins identifying positive variables in Mary's life that will serve as a foundation for risk management and intervention strategies. Encouraging Mary to discuss these issues further elicits positive emotions that directly counter the dysphoria of the suicidal state.

PUTTING IT ALL TOGETHER

The sequential and hierarchical approach outlined previously provides a useful framework for conducting suicide risk assessments in a manner that fits well within the context of primary care and provides adequate information to make well-informed, empirically based decisions about risk management and treatment. In our clinical experience, this approach is efficient enough to allow adequate time for the development and implementation of appropriate interventions. It is important to emphasize, however, that although this approach is useful and provides a natural flow and organization to the assessment, BHCs should not adhere so rigidly to this exact sequencing that the treatment alliance is compromised. Flexibility in risk assessment is paramount and will significantly enhance the BHC's ability to elicit accurate information from patients. As an example, if a patient would prefer to talk about the current episode before talking about past episodes, then the BHC should "go with the flow" and assess the current episode before assessing past episodes. The key to high-quality risk assessments is obtaining the information necessary for effective management and intervention; the order in which one obtains this information is much less important.

The case of Mary illustrates a number of critical points that warrant discussion. First, routine suicide screening identified a high-risk patient that was previously unknown to be high risk. Some BHCs might argue that this case vignette demonstrates why routine screening should not be conducted in primary care: It "derailed" the BHC from the chief reason for the consult (diabetes), resulting in little if any useful feedback to the PCP regarding the management of this disease. This argument fails to consider appropriate prioritization of health care needs, however. Simply put, if Mary kills herself, she cannot effectively manage her diabetes. Because suicide screening was in place, a previously unrecognized multiple attempter in an acute period of distress was identified and assessed—an important first step to improving her health and well-being. Related to this, this argument assumes that suicide risk is completely independent of all other health issues, which is in sharp contrast to a considerable body of evidence demonstrating that suicidality is associated with increased health complaints and functional impairment. This leads us to the vignette's second key point: the timing of the BHC's questioning about suicide risk.

Although the full transcript of this encounter is not provided, it should be noted that the BHC checked the suicide screening item before the appointment began, but he did not immediately ask about suicide. Instead, the BHC started the appointment as usual by focusing on the requested consult issue: diabetes. Consistent with the hierarchical sequencing of the risk assessment, the BHC begins "on common ground" with the patient and gradually escalates the intensity of the encounter toward the issue of suicide risk. He follows Mary's lead in the encounter until he finds a natural transition point (i.e., Mary's sharply critical self-statements) to shift to the more intense issue of emotional distress. When Mary confirms the presence of emotional distress, the BHC normalizes this experience and shifts to the more intense issue of suicide ideation. In a matter of minutes, the BHC has effectively and smoothly focused the clinical encounter on suicide risk, obtaining buy-in from Mary at each step.

The third key point, and the natural balance to the previous point, is that the BHC did not wait until the final moments of the appointment to ask about suicide risk, but rather raised the issue as soon as possible to allow adequate time for discussion. Delaying suicide risk screening until the end of a clinical encounter is an all-too-common clinical practice that only leads to one of two situations: (1) inadequate time devoted to risk assessment and management or (2) extension of the appointment beyond the schedule's structure, resulting in the BHC falling behind. Screening only works if there is adequate time to conduct an appropriate risk assessment and effectively manage that risk. The most effective BHCs therefore raise suicide risk as soon as possible to maximize the time that can be spent on the issue.

Fourth, the BHC remains calm and completes the assessment even when the patient is reporting very high-risk behaviors. Although it is not possible to convey a sense of "calmness" on the part of the BHC through this written vignette, his continuation of the risk assessment despite Mary's report of high-risk behaviors demonstrates his commitment to fully understanding Mary's situation before making a clinical decision. In the face of this self-report, especially the disclosure of a reasonable suicide plan with access to means and recent rehearsal behavior (i.e., shaking the pill bottles), we would understand why the BHC might choose to discontinue the interview and immediately recommend hospitalization. However, he instead chooses to collect all of the relevant information before making any decisions.

Related to this, the BHC refuses to argue with Mary about suicide and manages his emotional reactions to Mary's disclosures. Because the clinician's primary goal is to prevent death by suicide, it can be very tempting to attempt to "talk the patient out of it." However, this typically only serves to move the patient into a position of justifying or arguing in support of suicide. The BHC's neutral stance and approach during the assessment demonstrates to Mary that suicide is an issue that can be talked about openly and can be understood. The effect this has on Mary is best seen in her disclosure that she has never talked about suicide with anyone before.

When assessing Mary's past history of suicidal behaviors, the BHC identifies and briefly assesses the first, worst-point, and current suicidal episode, providing him with a general sense of the suicidal trajectory over time in a time-efficient manner. Without a doubt, a full assessment of each of Mary's seven suicide attempts would provide useful clinical information. However, to do so would take much greater time than is feasible within the constraints of the primary care setting. By picking these three points in time, in combination with Mary's statements about other attempt episodes, the BHC gains the following clinical information: (1) Mary is as a multiple attempter; (2) Mary generally attempts suicide via medication overdose ranging from low to moderate lethality; (3) the medical severity and lethality of Mary's attempts seem to be increasing over time; (4) she tends to attempt at home before bedtime using readily available means; and (5) suicide attempts seem to occur primarily during depressive episodes. These clues provide important information for the BHC to develop management and intervention strategies specific to Mary.

Sixth, the BHC asks clarifying questions to get specific information about Mary's thoughts, plans, and intentions. Mary's responses are often vague or ambiguous, so the BHC follows up with clarifying questions to improve the precision of the information. For example, when the BHC first asks for past self-injurious behaviors of any type, Mary initially says "a few times." When the BHC follows up with a very specific question about the number of suicide attempts (using the very specific language "trying to kill yourself or hoping you would die"), Mary discloses she has attempted suicide seven times in her life—a very different picture from a "few times." The BHC's effectiveness in improving his precision is due in part to the fact that he used clear, easy-to- understand language that minimized misunderstanding. When asking about suicide attempts, he used the words "kill yourself" or "hoping you would die," not "harm yourself" or "hurt yourself" or other such imprecise terminology. In addition to improving the precision of the assessment, the BHC's ability to use these terms further reinforces the sense that suicide can be discussed openly and honestly.

Finally, during the assessment of protective factors, the BHC does not simply ask Mary to provide a list for the purposes of documentation, but rather engages her in a conversation about these issues. The BHC uses the assessment of protective factors as an intervention in and of itself to elevate her mood and increase cognitive flexibility. When Mary lists her dog as a reason for living, the BHC takes a moment to ask for the dog's name, which personalizes this process and increases Mary's emotional attachment to positive memories (i.e., playing with her dog in the backyard). Mary quickly falls into the habit of negating these positive experiences through self-criticism, but the BHC chooses not to confront these tendencies because this could spark an adversarial stance. Instead, the BHC simply highlights the positive aspect of pet ownership, thus reinforcing and strengthening this memory trace—an important skill for Mary to develop, as will be discussed in subsequent chapters.

CORE COMPETENCIES FOR THE BEHAVIORAL HEALTH CONSULTANT

1. Know those risk and protective factors that have demonstrated the most robust empirical association with suicidal behaviors.
2. Routinely screen all referred patients for suicide risk.
3. Integrate a risk assessment for suicide risk early in the appointment.

4. Elicit suicide ideation, behavior, plans, and intent using a sequential and hierarchical approach to questioning that decreases patient reluctance to discuss suicide and increase accurate self-disclosure.
5. Remain calm and complete the entire suicide risk assessment before formulating risk management decisions.

CHAPTER 5

Strategies for Managing Suicide Risk in Primary Care

As discussed in previous chapters, suicide risk is best conceptualized as existing on two dimensions: baseline (or chronic) risk, which is an individual's "set point" level of risk when not acutely distressed or dysphoric, and acute risk, which is the short-term dimension of risk that occurs when the suicidal individual is symptomatic and in crisis. Because baseline risk is higher for multiple attempters, acute suicidal episodes become more easily triggered and last for longer periods due to increased vulnerability to suicidal crises. We therefore recommend behavioral health consultants (BHCs) differentiate among four categories of suicide risk outlined in Table 5.1. Using these four categories will assist the BHC in recognizing and considering suicidality from both dimensions of risk and will further aid in the communication of patient risk levels between BHCs and primary care staff. Critically, use of this two-dimensional categorization scheme assists clinic staff in recognizing how suicide risk fluctuates over time—from baseline to acute exacerbation back to baseline—and aids providers in responding appropriately to chronically suicidal patients.

Accurate categorization entails two simple questions, the first of which addresses baseline risk and the second of which addresses acute risk:

1. Is the patient a multiple attempter? If yes, they are categorized as chronic high risk. If no, they are categorized as nonchronic risk.
2. Is the patient symptomatic and in crisis? If yes, they are categorized with the "acute exacerbation" qualifier. If no, they are categorized as baseline.

Categorizing patients in this manner is a simple yet critical step in the assessment of overall suicide risk.

TABLE 5.1
Categories of Suicide Risk

Category	*Criteria*
Baseline	Ideator or single attempter; no significant stressors or prominent symptoms
Acute	Ideator or single attempter; presence of significant stressors and/or prominent symptoms
Chronic high risk	Multiple attempter; no significant stressors or prominent symptoms
Chronic high risk with acute exacerbation	Multiple attempter; presence of significant stressors and/or prominent symptoms

SEVERITY OF SUICIDE RISK

After distinguishing which risk category a suicidal patient falls in, BHCs should next assess the severity of suicide risk in order to guide the most appropriate clinical response. A continuum of suicide risk based on a synthesis of risk factors and protective factors with the four categories of risk is presented in Table 5.2 (cf. Bryan & Rudd, 2006; Rudd, Joiner, & Rajab, 2004), along with implicated clinical responses in a primary care clinic.

It is important to highlight that suicide risk assessment is not a static process, but rather one that varies over time as the factors that impact suicide risk fluctuate in intensity and severity. As such, the process of suicide risk assessment can be complicated by temporal factors in at least two ways. First, identifiable risk periods are inconsistently defined in the literature, such that there is no reliable way to determine how long an acute suicidal episode will endure. Second, chronic suicidality complicates risk estimates in that multiple attempters have a higher baseline risk for suicide to begin with and tend to remain in suicidal crises for much greater periods. We recommend, therefore, that risk assessment be a continuous and routine task throughout the course of patient care.

A distinct risk assessment scheme will ideally translate into straightforward, clinically informed, and effective decisions. Table 5.2 provides a summary of risk levels with indicated clinical responses or options. As suicide risk increases, the indicated clinical response builds off of all clinical responses at lower risk levels. In other words, the clinical response for patients at moderate suicide risk inherently entails those strategies for the mild risk level, and the response for patients at severe suicide risk entails those at the moderate and mild risk levels. Note also that the same clinical features always translate into higher risk levels for multiple attempters due to their lower activation

TABLE 5.2
Continuum of Suicide Risk With Implicated Clinical Response

Risk Level	*Clinical Features*		*Indicated Clinical Response*
	Ideator or Single Attempter	*Multiple Attempter*	
Very low	No identifiable suicidal ideation (baseline risk level)	Not applicable	1. No particular changes in ongoing treatment
Mild	Suicidal ideation of limited intensity and duration, no identifiable plans, no intent, identifiable protective factors	No identifiable suicidal ideation (baseline risk level)	1. No particular changes in ongoing treatment 2. Evaluate any expressed suicidal ideation to monitor change in risk 3. Consider referral to specialty mental health 4. Consider medication treatment
Moderate	Frequent suicidal ideation with moderate intensity and duration, some specific plans, minimal objective markers of intent, limited rehearsal or preparatory behaviors, identifiable protective factors	Suicidal ideation of limited intensity and duration, no identifiable plans, no intent, identifiable protective factors	1. Refer to specialty mental health 2. Increase frequency of contact (in clinic or via telephone) until connected to specialty mental health 3. Develop crisis response plan 4. Frequently reevaluate suicide risk, noting specific changes that reduce or elevate risk 5. Consider medication change if symptomatology worsens or persists 6. Obtain professional consultation as indicated
High	Frequent, intense, and enduring suicidal ideation, specific plans, clear objective markers of intent, rehearsal or preparatory behaviors, few if any protective factors	Frequent suicidal ideation with moderate intensity and duration, some specific plans, minimal objective markers of intent, limited rehearsal or preparatory behaviors, few if any protective factors	1. Consider referral for inpatient hospitalization evaluation (voluntary or involuntary, depending on situation)

thresholds for suicide risk that contribute to their chronic suicidality. As such, the baseline risk level (i.e., the lowest level of risk) for a multiple attempter is higher than that for an ideator or single attempter.

Patients assessed to be at very low risk have no identifiable symptoms of suicidality and, therefore, do not require any particular changes to clinical care. In the presence of suicidal ideation, however, the patient moves into the mild range of risk, which implicates closer monitoring but not necessarily a significant change in overall treatment approach. As noted elsewhere (Bryan, Corso, et al., 2009), patients assessed to be at mild risk for suicide can generally be effectively managed in the primary care setting, but BHCs should nonetheless consider referral to an outpatient mental health specialist for more aggressive treatment, depending on the clinical presentation. BHC interventions for mildly suicidal patients should include typical cognitive-behavioral interventions as well as a possible recommendation for the primary care provider (PCP) to initiate psychopharmacologic treatment.

As suicidal intent begins to emerge, the patient moves from mild to moderate range of suicide risk. The transition to moderate risk that accompanies the presence of suicidal intent is a critical threshold because along with suicidal intent comes the planning and behavioral rehearsal for suicide (i.e., resolved plans and preparations) that indicates increased risk for suicidal behaviors. BHCs should refer patients at moderate risk of suicide to outpatient mental health treatment for specialty care and increase the frequency of monitoring until the patient can be successfully connected to the specialist. BHCs should also assist patients in developing a crisis response plan (CRP; discussed later) at this level of risk and assist the primary care team in supporting the patient's utilization of the plan.

Patients with increasingly intense levels of suicidal symptoms, especially intent, who also have significant deficiencies in protective factors fall within the severe range of suicide risk. At this risk level, a primary task of the BHC is to determine whether to recommend to the PCP that an inpatient evaluation should be made. BHCs should keep in mind that the decision about whether to refer a patient for inpatient evaluation ultimately lies with the PCP, who should initiate this process with the BHC's support.

We return to the case of Mary, introduced in the previous chapter, to demonstrate how risk can be formulated using the framework described.

Mary's risk categorization (Table 5.1) would be chronic high risk with acute overlay due to the fact that she is a multiple attempter and is currently symptomatic with suicidal symptoms. We next turn to the risk continuum (Table 5.2) and use the column for multiple attempters. Because Mary is a multiple attempter, we automatically know that she cannot be classified as "very low" risk. We can further rule out an assignment of "mild" risk because she is clearly not at baseline functioning but rather is symptomatic and actively suicidal. Mary is therefore at "moderate" or "high" risk for suicide. The results of her risk assessment uncover that she is experiencing suicidal ideation of moderate to severe intensity (6 or 7 out of 10 rating, thinks about it while in bed), specific elements of a plan (at home, at night while in bed), objective markers of intent to include preparatory behaviors (went to the bathroom and shook the pill bottle), and the presence of several protective factors (supportive husband, dog).

Based on these clinical features, Mary meets criteria for "high" suicide risk. The indicated clinical response therefore includes consideration for inpatient evaluation plus the clinical responses for all lower levels of risk. In Mary's case, the clinical response would include a referral to specialty mental health, increased frequency of clinical contact, a crisis response plan, consideration of medication treatment, and frequent reevaluation of suicide risk.

The BHC must now consider whether to recommend an inpatient evaluation. To arrive at this determination, the BHC must ultimately make a decision about whether outpatient safety can be maintained. If the answer is no, then an inpatient evaluation should be recommended. If the answer is yes, then the BHC must set into motion those risk management strategies that are judged to be most relevant to the clinical situation. Key questions for a BHC to consider when assessing outpatient safety might include

- Can access to lethal means be secured?
- Is there a supportive other who can assist with securing means?
- Is there a supportive other who can monitor the patient and assist with treatment adherence?
- Can the patient collaboratively formulate and adhere to a crisis response plan (discussed in the next section)?
- How soon can a follow-up appointment be scheduled?

BHCs should keep in mind that the presence of protective factors does not necessary negate risk factors, but certain protective factors (e.g., supportive others) can potentially be mobilized to remove or otherwise restrict the effects of certain risk factors (e.g., access to means).

In the case of Mary, the BHC determined that her husband was able to restrict Mary's access to medications and the PCP agreed to prescribe no more than 7 days of medications at a time to restrict access. Mary's husband was additionally enlisted to ensure she attended all medical appointments and supported the treatment plan via a crisis support plan (discussed later in this chapter). As a result, the BHC determined that a referral for inpatient hospitalization was not indicated at this time and ensured adequate documentation of this decision in Mary's chart.

THE PROBLEM WITH NO-SUICIDE CONTRACTS

Most patients that the BHC assesses will not meet criteria for inpatient treatment and can be effectively treated on an outpatient basis, whether through the primary care clinic or referral to specialty mental health. As such, the BHC needs to follow the risk assessment with interventions to manage risk in the short term. A common clinical practice when working with acutely suicidal patients is to implement a "no-suicide contract" (alternately called "no-harm contracts" or "contracts for safety") as part of treatment. A no-suicide contract is an agreement between the patient and provider in which the patient agrees not to harm or kill themselves when in a suicidal state and to seek out assistance or support (usually from the treating provider) if they does not believe they can honor the agreement. No-suicide contracts commonly include several key elements (Rudd, Mandruskia, & Joiner, 2006):

- An explicit statement agreeing not to harm or kill oneself
- Specific details about the duration of the agreement
- A contingency plan in the event a crisis emerges that would jeopardize the patient's ability to honor the agreement
- The specific responsibilities of both patient and provider

The underlying assumption of the no-suicide contract is that a patient who is unwilling or unable to enter a commitment of self-preservation is at a heightened risk for suicide. Unfortunately, the concept and use of no-suicide contracts has spread widely to health professions outside mental health, notably PCPs and emergency department providers, despite their many problems and limitations. BHCs are likely to find that PCPs will routinely use the concept of a no-suicide contract with suicidal patients, typically in the form of a verbal "contract for safety" in which the PCP asks the suicidal patient to promise to call a health care provider (whether themselves or a mental health specialist) or access another source of social support when thinking about suicide.

Despite widespread use, however, a number of problems exist with no-suicide contracts that warrant discussion. First, no-suicide contracts have no scientific evidence supporting their efficacy as a suicide prevention measure. On the contrary, Rudd et al. (2006) have outlined several sources of evidence that actually speak against their effectiveness in clinical practice. Miller (1999) has also noted that use of the term *contract* is problematic because the language implies concern for the legal aspects of practice more than the clinical process. Miller further argues that such language may limit open and honest communication because patients have nothing to gain by signing a contract but may perceive the agreement as an attempt by the provider to reduce personal responsibility for any bad outcomes in treatment. Because patients commonly view no-suicide contracts as a mechanism to reduce the provider's anxiety, not to meet their clinical needs, they will often sign the contract simply to appease the provider but with little or no intention to honor the agreement.

No-suicide contracts can additionally limit patients' willingness to discuss suicidality because they mistakenly believe that experiencing any form of suicidality is a violation of the contract. When combined with providers' faulty belief that no-suicide contracts will stop or prevent suicide, the resulting absence of communication about suicidality can reduce a provider's vigilance to fluctuations in risk status. Perhaps paradoxically, no-suicide contracts actually increase risk for malpractice findings. The convergence of these points has resulted in professional guidelines recommending against the use of no-suicide contracts.

From the perspective of clinical care within the context of primary care, it is difficult to imagine that during the first meeting with a provider, whether PCP or BHC, a patient would be willing to relinquish the right to self-determination, particularly if the provider has yet to actually produce any tangible or definitive outcome in the treatment exchange (e.g., symptom relief or the necessary skills for effective self-management). One of the potential reasons why no-suicide contracts are violated so frequently is that the patient is unable to make a meaningful commitment to remove suicide as an option forever during a period marked by intense psychological pain and before a meaningful treatment alliance has been established (Drew, 2001). Without question, suicide as an option for reducing emotional distress and suffering will eventually have to be addressed in the patient's treatment. It is most appropriate, however, to address the question after the treatment alliance has been firmly established, the patient has experienced some symptomatic relief, and the patient has developed adequate skills for self-management of crises. The crisis response plan is a simple and empirically supported alternative to the no-suicide contract that BHCs can implement to teach the very self-management skills that suicidal patients often lack.

CRISIS RESPONSE PLAN

Because the suicidal thought process is characterized by impaired problem-solving, absence of cognitive flexibility, and extreme cognitive distortions, patients often need decision-making aids when in a suicidal crisis. The crisis response plan (CRP) is such a decisional aid that outlines a set of specific instructions for the patient to follow during periods of crisis. The CRP is developed collaboratively between the provider and patient and serves several primary purposes (Rudd et al., 2006):

1. Facilitating honest and productive communication between the patient and provider about emotional distress by making it clear what the expectations are for both in terms of how suicidal crises will be addressed.
2. Assisting to establish and maintain a collaborative relationship by identifying the roles and responsibilities of both the patient and provider.
3. Facilitating active involvement of the patient in the treatment process, including readily accessing emergency procedures when and if needed.
4. Enhancing the patient's commitment to the treatment process and living rather than requesting the patient to essentially give up his or her right to die by suicide. Making a commitment to living rather than to not dying sends a very different message to the patient about control and individual responsibility, both explicitly and implicitly. The focus is not on restraining or restricting rights, but rather on enhancing commitment to a treatment process.

When creating a CRP with a suicidal patient, the BHC should adopt a collaborative, "team"-based approach as discussed in Chapter 3. As such, the patient and BHC should both actively generate items for inclusion in the plan. Sitting next to the patient as opposed to sitting across from them is one nonverbal strategy for fostering the collaborative effort. Moving to a position adjacent to the patient is particularly easy for BHCs in primary care who use rolling examination room stools.

Use of a generic, preprinted CRP is discouraged for a number of reasons. First, it does not actively involve patient participation and, therefore, reduces the likelihood of actual skill implementation. Nor does it "customize" the plan to the patient, which might result in the inclusion of steps that are not effective for the individual. Finally, it assumes mastery of skills that a patient might not actually have. With respect to this latter issue, a critical element for the effectiveness of CRPs is for patients to actually possess the ability to use and carry out each step. CRPs should also be easily accessible to the patient (e.g., kept in a pocket or a purse); using 3 × 5 index cards, behavioral prescription pads, or backs of business cards are common formats for CRPs. Alternatively, BHCs can print up blank CRP templates (see Figure 5.1) for ready access in their examination rooms. As can be seen in Figure 5.1, the CRP contains four basic components that will assist the patient in self-managing suicidal crises, each of which will be discussed next.

Step 1: Obtain an initial commitment to treatment. The first step for creating a CRP is to introduce the concept of the CRP and elicit an agreement from the patient to commit to the treatment process. When eliciting the patient's

I will use this crisis response plan when:
Things I will do on my own for 30 minutes:
If that does not work, I will contact other people:
If I am still feeling upset, I will contact a medical professional:

FIGURE 5.1
Crisis response plan template.

commitment to treatment, the BHC should utilize a collaborative approach in which not only does the patient commit to the treatment process, but also the BHC (and the PCP by extension). Using "we" language and asking patients to share their personal experiences when suicidal are two simple and effective techniques for communicating collaborative intent and increasing engagement and participation. For example, BHCs can introduce the concept of a CRP using the following approach:

> *Many times when people are feeling suicidal, it feels unbearable, like it will never end. It can be hard to focus and make decisions when feeling like that. Is that how you feel when thinking about suicide? It can therefore be helpful to have a response plan ready to go in advance, so that when we're feeling like this and having the most difficulty making decisions, we have something handy to help get us through. Let's talk about some steps we can take during those times when you're most upset and thinking about killing yourself; that way we'll be able to help get you through those difficult times*

and start improving your life. Do you think that developing a plan to help get you through those times when you're in the most pain would be helpful?

Strategic questioning and discussion of CRPs couched in terms of making a commitment to living or to improve one's quality of life, in contrast to making a commitment to not kill oneself, can increase a patient's willingness to engage in the treatment process.

Step 2: Identify personal warning signs. A CRP can only be effective if patients can appropriately identify an emerging crisis (i.e., their personal "warning signs"). The next step for creating a CRP is therefore to assist patients in identifying their personal warning signs for suicidal crises. Patients should be asked to list any thoughts, images, emotions, behaviors, physical sensations, or any symptoms or signs that they typically experience when in crisis. In many cases, patients do not possess an adequate level of self-awareness to easily identify their indicators of elevating suicide risk. Limited self-awareness is a critical factor that can sustain suicidal crises over time, especially among chronically suicidal patients, since the inability to detect early indicators of emerging crises directly inhibits the patient's ability to head off escalating levels of distress before decision-making is significantly impaired. BHCs should be aware that the task of identifying personal warning signs can be slowed by this deficiency in awareness. For instance, when asked to identify their personal warning signs, it is not uncommon for suicidal patients to answer, "I don't know." Indeed, one could argue that if patients knew what their personal warning signs for impending crises were, they would be more adept at resolving them. BHCs may therefore need to assist patients in identifying warning signs, such as displaying a list of common warning signs such as the one in Figure 5.2 for patients to review and select from.

As the patient identifies those warning signs that are most relevant to or useful for identifying their personal warning signs, they should be listed on the CRP in the patient's own words.

Step 3: Identify self-management (coping) strategies. Once patients have identified those warning signs that can reliably indicate an emerging crisis, patients should next be assisted in developing activities and strategies that can be utilized in response to these warning signs in order to reduce emotional distress. To foster the ability to self-manage crises and develop mastery of self-regulation skills, these initial coping strategies should include activities that do not require the involvement or assistance of others. These typically involve strategies such as behavioral activation, relaxation, or mindfulness exercises (described in detail in Chapter 6) that work to develop crisis management and emotion regulation skills. To quickly and effectively identify self-management strategies, BHCs can begin by asking patients to consider

Thoughts	"I'm worthless." "It's my fault." "Nobody cares about me." "Things are never going to get any better." "I can't take this anymore." "People would be better off without me." "I can't sit still." "I can't control my thoughts."
Images	Unpleasant memories Flashbacks Seeing yourself dying Mentally replaying uncomfortable events
Emotions	Anger Depression Worry Agitation Guilt
Behaviors	Crying Shaking/trembling Avoiding others Losing your temper Becoming quiet
Physical symptoms	Racing heart Muscle tension or pain Feeling sick to your stomach Headaches Hard time breathing Trouble sleeping Feeling restless or on edge

FIGURE 5.2
Common warning signs preceding suicidal crises.

techniques or activities they have used successfully in the past to feel better during times of emotional distress and then list them on the CRP (e.g., "When feeling highly stressed in the past, what sorts of things helped you to feel better?").

Not surprisingly, patients can struggle to generate self-management strategies. BHCs can facilitate this process by providing a list of possible self-management strategies that can cue the patient's memory of strategies successfully used in the past (see Figure 5.3). BHCs can additionally ask patients to list activities they used to enjoy but no longer engage in regularly (e.g., "What are some things you used to enjoy doing but no longer do?"). Patients frequently discontinue or reduce personally meaningful or enjoyable activities when emotionally distressed, which intensifies their emotional turmoil. Prompting patients to consider and resume these past behaviors can therefore not only reduce emotional distress, but can also undermine beliefs related to

Listening to music
Meditation
Puzzles (e.g., crossword, Sudoku)
Thinking about a positive upcoming event
Reading a book
Thinking about positive memories
Prayer
Looking at pictures of friends
Deep breathing*
Reading spiritual or inspirational material
Reading letters from family members
Reviewing my reasons for living list*
Going for a walk
Exercising
Taking a shower or bath
Eating a favorite food (e.g., ice cream, pizza)
Watching a funny movie
Playing a sport
Cooking

*These are skills/strategies that often must first be taught by a provider for effective utilization.

Note: BHCs should ensure that coping strategies obtain the desired effect and do not inadvertently escalate emotional distress (e.g., reading letters from a parent who was abusive during the patient's childhood, looking at pictures of a spouse who has recently disclosed infidelity or a desire for divorce).

FIGURE 5.3
Common self-management (coping) strategies.

themes of failure (e.g., "I'm a failure because I quit exercising"). Here again, the use of a preexisting list of activities can oftentimes cue a suicidal patient's memory and facilitate the process of CRP development.

For those patients already engaged in treatment, whether with the BHC or with a mental health specialist, BHCs can also reinforce those skills the patient has already learned in treatment (e.g., cognitive restructuring activities, relaxation skills, behavioral activation) by asking the patient to explain how these skills work and are intended to be utilized. Supporting the treatment process is a critical function of the BHC and should be incorporated into interventions and recommendations wherever possible. In the absence of any identifiable self-management strategies that are currently within the patient's mastery, BHCs can briefly teach a coping skill or strategy and then have the patient practice it to demonstrate competency and mastery, consistent with the general approach and model of BHC practice.

Step 4: Contact external sources of support. If self-management strategies are not effective in reducing emotional distress or distracting patients from the distress, the next step is to contact external sources of support, typically family members and/or friends. BHCs should stress that the patient reserves the right to choose whether to inform this individual of the crisis. In other words, the patient does not necessarily need to tell the supportive person that he or she is thinking about suicide but can instead choose to reach out "just to talk" or "just to stop by" as a distraction or a mood elevation technique. If necessary, the BHC and patient can discuss whether informing this supportive person of the crisis would be beneficial. As patients list social supports, the BHC should ask the patient if these individuals have been helpful in the past during times of crisis (e.g., "Do you usually feel better after talking with this person?"), as this can help to differentiate between supportive and potentially iatrogenic significant others. For example, a family member with whom the patient tends to get into arguments leading to increased anger and dysphoria would not be suitable for inclusion on the CRP. Information for accessing health care providers and other crisis services should come last in the CRP. This would entail any current treatment providers (particularly mental health specialists), crisis hotlines, 911, and emergency departments.

Specific names and telephone numbers should be written down on the CRP for each individual identified. Although seemingly trivial, a highly emotionally aroused individual can have difficulty remembering critical information such as telephone numbers or can forget which of their many friends is supposed to be called. Likewise, patients often benefit from rehearsing the steps of contacting health care professionals, such as pushing the correct sequence of numbers to get the appropriate voicemail box. BHCs who provide their contact information to patients as part of the CRP should carefully explain their availability and procedures for returning calls. For example, if the BHC does not routinely answer his/her telephone and only checks voicemail a few times per day, patients should be informed of this up-front so they are prepared for this possibility in the event they call during a crisis. BHCs can even call themselves during the appointment so that patients can hear the voicemail firsthand, which can reduce the possibility of premature hanging up during a crisis. Here again, writing down the specifics of these steps can tremendously benefit a patient in crisis.

Step 5: Review the steps and obtain buy-in. As a final step, the BHC should verbally review each section of the CRP and then ask the patient if there is anything else that should be included. This not only reinforces the collaborative process but also allows for any last-minute additions or modifications that could increase effectiveness. BHCs should then ask the patient to rate the likelihood of using the CRP on a scale of 0 (*not at all likely*) to 10 (*very likely*). If patients rate their likelihood as less than 7 or 8, BHCs should discuss with the patient what barriers would prevent implementation and engage the patient in a conversation to adapt the CRP to increase the likelihood of implementation. A copy of the CRP should be made and maintained in the patient's medical record, and the patient should keep the original copy in a manner that is easily accessed (e.g., in their pocket or purse).

Two completed sample CRPs can be found in Figure 5.4. An important point for BHCs to keep in mind when developing a CRP is whether a patient can actually accomplish the self-management strategies on their own; BHCs should not assume that a patient can competently accomplish a given skill, even if it seems simple or straightforward. In some cases, brief rehearsal of skills or steps during the appointment can provide a quick method for BHCs to gauge the patient's mastery of specific skills.

BHCs should ensure that the patient's PCP and treatment team are aware of any CRPs and should consider keeping a copy in the patient's medical chart where it is readily accessible and easily found. All clinic staff members should be educated about and trained in the use of CRPs, so that consistency in responding to specific suicidal patients can be maximized. Specific strategies for consulting with primary care staff regarding risk management strategies will be discussed later in this chapter.

Sample 1

I will use this crisis response plan when: 1. Wanting to go to sleep and not wake up 2. Thinking about holding a gun to my head 3. Thinking "I can't take it anymore."
Things I will do on my own for 30 minutes: 1. Take slow, deep breaths 2. Think about my upcoming promotion
If that does not work, I will contact other people: 1. Talk to Dave about hobbies to distract myself: xxx-xxxx 2. Talk to Beth about funny memories: xxx-xxxx
If I am still in crisis, I will contact a medical professional: 1. Psychologist: Dr. Wood xxx-xxxx 2. Psychiatrist: Dr. Brown xxx-xxxx 3. Call suicide hotline: 1-800-273-TALK 4. Call 911 or go to ER

Sample 2

I will use this crisis response plan when: 1. Feeling sad 2. Getting angry 3. Thinking "I hate myself"
Things I will do on my own for 30 minutes: 1. Go for a walk with my dogs 2. Watch a comedy TV show 3. Play games online
If that does not work, I will contact other people: 1. Call my spouse using a calling card or chat with her online: xxx-xxx-xxxx 2. Talk to my brother about what is bothering me: xxx-xxxx 3. Go to speak with my chaplain
If I am still in crisis, I will contact a medical professional: 1. Call BHC: Dr. Black xxx-xxxx, press 1, then leave a message with my phone number and the time I called 2. Go to the hospital

FIGURE 5.4
Sample crisis response plans.

MEANS RESTRICTION COUNSELING

As Marsha Linehan (1993) has frequently noted, treatment is not effective with dead patients. To kill oneself, one must have the means for doing so. Because of this very simple and undisputable fact, it makes sense to talk about means restriction as a risk management strategy. Interestingly, means restriction has not received much attention as an intervention for suicidal patients. Although means restriction is often mentioned as a risk management strategy in many treatment texts (e.g., Linehan, 1993; Rudd, Joiner, & Rajab, 2001; Wenzel, Brown, & Beck, 2009) and practice recommendations and guidelines (e.g., APA, 2003; Berman, 2006; Bryan & Rudd, 2006), the extent of the discussion is typically limited to a sentence or a paragraph at most.

In the context of the current discussion, means restriction counseling entails two distinct but interrelated actions, as outlined by the Harvard Injury Control Research Center (n.d.): (1) assessing whether a person at risk for suicide has access to a firearm or other lethal means and (2) working with them and their family and support system to limit their access until they are no longer feeling suicidal. The first component was discussed in the previous chapter on risk assessment. In this section, we will address the second step: means restriction counseling.

The lack of attention to and guidance on means restriction counseling is likely a major factor contributing to the very low numbers of providers who actually ask about access to lethal means and then take steps to reduce this access. The majority of outpatient psychiatrists surveyed in one study, for instance, reported receiving no education or information regarding firearm safety issues, which was proposed as one factor contributing to the finding that only half of outpatient psychiatrists had ever seriously considered assessing access to firearms among patients (Price, Kinnison, Dake, Thompson, & Price, 2007).

Several studies of emergency department personnel—commonly the first source of medical treatment for an individual during or immediately following a suicidal crisis—are similarly illustrative of this issue. For example, in one study, only 28% of emergency department nurses who had provided care to suicidal adolescents within the preceding 6 months educated parents on means restriction during these encounters (Grossman, Dontes, Kruesi, Pennington, & Fendrich, 2003). When parents of adolescent suicide attempters (via deliberate overdose) were interviewed about the treatment received in the emergency department, only 12% of parents with medications at home and none with firearms at home received education or counseling about means restriction (McManus et al., 1997). The numbers do not improve when considering mental health professionals' actions in the emergency department—only 3% of pediatric patients seen in a psychiatric emergency department were assessed for firearm access by psychiatric residents (Giggie, Olvera, & Joshi, 2007).

This low rate of means restriction counseling could potentially be explained by low perceived efficacy of the intervention by health care providers. In the study of outpatient psychiatrists mentioned earlier, Price and colleagues (2007) found that fewer than one-third believed means restriction counseling would result in improved firearms storage or fewer firearms in the patients' homes. These perceptions of limited efficacy are not supported by empirical data, however. In a study of child and adolescent suicide attempters presenting to the emergency department for a medication overdose, 86% of parents who received means restriction counseling during the emergency department visit reported that they had locked up or disposed of medications during a follow-up interview, as compared with only 32% who had not received any means restriction counseling (McManus et al., 1997). Similar outcomes have been reported by Kruesi and colleagues (1999), who found that parents receiving means restriction counseling following pediatric mental health visits in the emergency department were more likely to secure prescription medications (75%) than parents who did not receive means restriction counseling (48%). This study also found that means restriction counseling was associated with greater likelihood of parental action to secure other potential methods of suicide, including over-the-counter medications (48% of counseled vs 22% of not counseled) and firearms (63% of counseled vs 0% of not counseled).

Although these data speak to the effectiveness of means restriction counseling as an intervention for reducing access to potential methods of suicide, they unfortunately do not speak to the effectiveness of means restriction counseling for reducing suicide attempts or deaths by suicide. Indeed, many providers insist that suicidal patients will attempt suicide regardless of means restriction attempts by simply substituting methods. Without a doubt, this is a valid argument, and unfortunately, no data exist to confirm or disconfirm this perspective. However, using this argument as the rationale for not counseling patients and/or family members about means restriction overlooks several important facts about suicidal behaviors:

1. With an 85% fatality rate, self-inflicted gunshot wound is the most frequent method of death by suicide in the United States, accounting for more than half of all suicides (Vyrostek, Annest, & Ryan, 2004). All other suicide attempt methods have much lower fatality rates, suggesting that any means substitution away from gunshot wound will increase the survival rate for a suicide attempt.
2. Approximately 90% of first-time suicide attempters do not eventually die by suicide (Owens et al., 2002). Although 20% to 25% of first-time attempters will eventually make another nonfatal suicide attempt, the overwhelming majority of suicide attempters will never attempt again and do not die by suicide, suggesting that increasing the

odds of surviving a first-time attempt will likely result in decreased rates of death by suicide over time.

Thus, despite the fact that no studies have yet to demonstrate the efficacy of means restriction counseling as an intervention for reducing suicidal behaviors, clear evidence supporting its efficacy for reducing access to lethal methodology is available, which has considerable potential for reducing the likelihood of fatal self-inflicted injury.

BHCs should be mindful that discussions about means restriction have the potential to create an adversarial relationship between the patient and BHC because this intervention directly challenges the patient's capacity to willingly engage in suicidal behaviors whenever he or she desires. By asking the patient to surrender access to the suicide method, whether firearm, medication, or other means, the BHC is effectively asking the patient to give up their chief problem-solving strategy, which can create conflict. Ideally, the BHC has established an effective treatment relationship with the suicidal patient as part of the initial encounter and risk assessment, which should enhance their ability to effectively counsel patients about means restriction. When counseling about means restriction, it is recommended that BHCs routinely assess for the presence of firearms in the home since it is such a highly lethal methodology that results in rapid death and leaves little chance for rescue or intervention. For patients with firearms in the home, BHCs should counsel about means restriction specific to firearms even if the suicidal patient is not considering self-inflicted gunshot wound as their primary suicide method. Although it might seem unnecessary to counsel a patient about a methodology that is not being actively considered, BHCs and patients need to be aware that the mere presence of a firearm in the household significantly increases the chance that a suicide attempt will be fatal.

BHCs should be aware that in the case of gun owners, a request to temporarily remove or otherwise restrict access to firearms might be met with considerable resistance by patients with strong political or social beliefs related to firearm possession. As noted in previous chapters, the BHC should avoid arguing with the patient about whether they can kill themselves but instead emphasize a commitment to the shared goal of alleviating the patient's suffering. The BHC should therefore first reaffirm their commitment to the patient's well-being by realigning with the patient's stated goals and objectives to manage or reduce their suffering and then discuss means restriction as one method for ensuring adequate safety to accomplish this goal. BHCs should be careful not to minimize the personal sense of sacrifice that gun owners might feel when asked to temporarily restrict their access to firearms. In all cases, BHCs should strive to maintain a teamwork mentality with suicidal patients and/or their caregivers in order to maximize safety of at-risk patients. Tips and critical points for means restriction counseling adapted from the Harvard Injury Control Research Center (n.d.) are presented in Table 5.3.

BHCs should also consult with PCPs about restricting access to medications by recommending they prescribe only nonlethal amounts of medication. BHCs can suggest, for example, that PCPs prescribe only a 7-day supply of medication with a required follow-up for refill instead of a standard 30-day supply. Required follow-ups can be scheduled with the BHC, who can reassess risk and treatment adherence, provide additional interventions as needed, and update risk management recommendations to the PCP, who can then refill the prescription appropriately. This process can be repeated as often as needed until the PCP and BHC determine the patient's suicidal crisis has resolved and routine prescribing patterns can be resumed. In the case of Mary first introduced in the previous chapter, this collaborative PCP-BHC approach was implemented as a part of her treatment and risk management plan. The PCP specifically altered his prescriptions such that Mary could only receive several days of pain medication at a time and had to return to the clinic each week to obtain refills. During these follow-up visits, Mary met with the BHC, who assessed for adherence to behavioral and pharmacologic treatments and monitored progress in accessing specialty mental health care.

TABLE 5.3

Tips and Critical Points for Means Restriction Counseling on Firearms

- Presence of a firearm in the home increases the chance that a suicide attempt will be fatal.
- Because suicidal desire can increase very rapidly, restricting access to lethal means can reduce the likelihood of bad outcomes in a crisis.
- Recommend removing firearms and other lethal means.
- Wherever possible enlist the support of a significant other.
- Ensure to ask about the presence of multiple firearms in multiple locations. In the case of joint custody situations for child or adolescent patients, ensure firearms are secured in all homes where the patient might reside.
- The safest option is to completely remove the firearm from the home until the situation improves.
- If complete removal is unacceptable, securing firearms with the following measures is a less safe alternative:
  1. Unloaded
  2. In a tamper-proof safe designed for firearms storage
  3. Lock ammunition separately or remove completely from home
  4. Ensure keys or combinations to locks are inaccessible to at-risk individuals
- Hiding unlocked firearms is discouraged since they can be found by at-risk individuals.

COORDINATING CARE WITH PRIMARY CARE STAFF AND FAMILY MEMBERS

Once patients are identified as being elevated in risk for suicide, BHCs should notify PCPs to discuss strategies for treatment and risk management. This coordination is imperative so PCPs can make safe and effective decisions about medication issues (e.g., prescribing only nonlethal amounts and dosages of drugs). Antidepressant medications should also be considered if initiation of pharmacotherapy can contribute to symptom management or relief. Widespread concerns about antidepressant use following the Food and Drug Administration's black box warning on antidepressant labels have contributed to a decrease in antidepressant prescriptions (see, e.g., Kurian et al., 2007) despite overwhelming scientific evidence that antidepressant treatment is associated with decreased suicide rates (Bostwick, 2006; Gibbons et al., 2007). Antidepressants appear to have a particularly positive effect when obtained in primary care clinics or connected with initiation of outpatient psychotherapy (Simon & Savarino, 2007).

Consultation with PCPs about antidepressant use will be discussed thoroughly in Chapter 8, but it is important to note at this point that BHCs are positioned to play a critically important role in educating PCPs about the research on antidepressants and suicide and in assisting with short-term monitoring of clinical response and suicide risk immediately following initiation of, or dosage changes in, antidepressant medication. Arguably, the most significant impact a BHC can have in the management of suicide risk among patients in primary care is to support PCPs in immediately initiating indicated psychiatric treatments, whether pharmacologic or behavioral, for suicide risk and associated features.

Family members (and nonfamily sources of social support) can additionally play a valuable role in effective risk management, as they can often provide observation or information that the patient might not report. For example, when developing CRPs, family members might be aware of indicators of emerging crises that the patient has not considered or recognized. Family members can additionally be informed of crisis response procedures and treatment recommendations to reinforce appropriate and effective use. BHCs can provide tips and recommendations to family members to reduce the possibility of inadvertently triggering suicidal behaviors, such as fostering overdependence or overreliance on external crisis management skills at the expense of internal self-regulatory skills. Family members who provide an inappropriate amount and type of attention and concern during suicidal crises could potentially increase the frequency and/or intensity of these episodes if the patient develops the perception that social support can be obtained via suicidality. Taking the time to briefly explain risk management and treatment recommendations to family members can therefore increase the likelihood of effective utilization and reduce the chance of iatrogenic effects.

Involvement of family members can also be valuable when it comes to monitoring clinical response to interventions, especially antidepressant treatment. This is particularly relevant for adolescent and young adult patients, who have been specifically identified as a subpopulation of concern for potential clinical worsening in the early phase of antidepressant treatment. Educating parents or other family members about observable signs and symptoms associated with clinical worsening (e.g., agitation, worsening insomnia, increased irritability) and providing directions for appropriately responding to these changes (i.e., supporting treatment recommendations and immediately contacting the health care provider) can increase the chances of detecting clinical declines and identifying more effective treatments much earlier. In all cases, involvement of family members in the treatment process should always be accomplished consistent with general medical standards related to confidentiality and in collaboration with the patient, who ultimately should determine which family members to involve and the extent of their involvement. One particular method for involving family members (or other sources of social support) is the crisis support plan (CSP).

CRISIS SUPPORT PLAN

The crisis support plan (CSP) is a risk management strategy similar to the CRP that explicitly incorporates the involvement and support of a significant other in the suicidal patient's life. The CSP is designed to increase the likelihood of patient adherence to risk management strategies and treatment recommendations and to enhance social connectedness between the suicidal patient and a significant other. Like the CRP, the CSP is developed collaboratively among the BHC, the patient, and the identified significant other and serves several primary purposes:

1. Facilitating the process of restricting access to lethal means by enlisting the aid of a supportive other willing to secure potential methods for suicide.
2. Facilitating active involvement of a supportive other in the treatment process, to include providing support during crises and enacting emergency procedures when and if needed.
3. Enhancing the patient's sense of connectedness and social support.

Because the CSP is a collaborative effort between three parties, it can only be accomplished when a supportive other is available to participate during the appointment. In some cases, the patient will have a family member or friend accompanying them to the appointment, which lends itself to easy implementation of this intervention. When patients are attending the medical appointment alone, the BHC can request that a supportive other be brought to a follow-up appointment in order to complete this intervention at a future date.

There are no limits or restrictions on which supportive others can complete a CSP with the patient or how many supportive others to be identified. In some cases, identification of a problematic source of social support contributing to the patient's emotional distress can actually be ideal for a CSP since this intervention directly targets and fosters social connectedness. For example, a suicidal patient's indifferent or disengaged spouse might be selected for the CSP in order to increase involvement and investment in the patient's treatment and care, which can contribute to an enhanced sense of social support. Similar to CRPs, CSPs involve an active commitment to the treatment from both the patient and the supportive other. BHCs can create blank CSP templates (see Figure 5.5) for ready access and completion in their examination rooms. As can be seen in Figure 5.5, the CSP is much more predetermined than a CRP, since the expectations and roles of the supportive other tend to be more consistent across cases. However, this is not to suggest that CSPs should not be individually tailored to each unique case; patients and supportive others should customize the plan as appropriate to maximize its likelihood for successful use.

Step 1: Educate the supportive other. The first step for creating a CSP is to educate the supportive other on the patient's current risk level and risk management plan. BHCs should discuss suicide risk using the same framework and model used to discuss suicide risk with the patient (i.e., the suicidal mode and functional model of suicide) to ensure a consistent and shared understanding of the problem between both parties. Educating the supportive other about suicide in the presence of the suicidal patient also serves to enhance learning for the suicidal patient by reviewing the constructs and information an additional time.

BHCs should include the suicidal patient in this educational step by asking the patient to elaborate or explain key concepts. For example, when explaining the concept of suicidal beliefs, the BHC might ask the patient to provide specific examples of thoughts or beliefs central to the suicidal mode: "Can you describe some of those thoughts we talked about that contribute to your desire for suicide?" Involving the suicidal patient in the education process reinforces the collaborative process and enables the suicidal patient to actively describe their unique experience to the supportive other. BHCs should also be sure to explain suicidality as an attempt to solve problems and alleviate emotional distress (i.e., the functional model of suicidal behaviors). The

Patient's Name: ________________________________ Date: __________

I understand that suicide risk is to be taken very seriously. I want to help ______________ ________ find new ways to manage stress in times of crisis. I realize there are no guarantees about how crises resolve, and that we are all making reasonable efforts to maintain safety for everyone. In some cases hospitalization may be necessary.

Things I can do to assist ________________________________:

1. Provide encouragement and support in the following ways:
   -
   -
   -
2. Help ________________________________ follow his/her crisis response plan.
3. Ensure a safe environment by doing the following:
   - REMOVE all firearms and ammunition
   - REMOVE or LOCK UP:
     - All knives, razors, and other sharp objects
     - All prescription and over-the-counter drugs (including vitamins and aspirin)
     - All alcohol, illegal drugs, and any related paraphernalia
   - Make sure someone is available to provide personal support and monitor the patient at all times during a crisis and afterwards as needed.
   - Pay attention to the patient's stated method of suicide/self-injury/intent to harm others and restrict access to vehicle, ropes, flammables, etc., as appropriate.
   - Limit/restrict access to vehicle/car keys as appropriate.
   - Identify people who might increase risk for the patient, and minimize their contact with the patient.
   - Provide access to things the patient identifies as helpful and encourage choices and behaviors that promote health, such as good nutrition, exercise, and rest.

If I am unable to continue to provide these supports, or if I believe that the crisis response plan is not helpful or sufficient, I will contact the patient's treatment provider to express my concerns.

If I believe ________________________________ is a danger to self or others, I agree to:

- Call his/her mental health treatment provider: [insert phone number]
- Help ________________________________ get to a hospital
- Call 911

I agree to follow this plan until ______________________

______________	______________	______________
Support signature	Patient signature	Provider signature

FIGURE 5.5
Sample crisis support plan.

supportive other should additionally be informed of risk management strategies that have already been discussed and/or implemented, especially the CRP. The educational component of this intervention can typically be accomplished in less than 5 minutes.

Once the supportive other has been educated about suicidality, the BHC should introduce the CSP to the suicidal patient and the supportive other as a strategy designed to improve patient safety and maximize treatment outcomes. For example, the BHC might introduce the concept of a CSP using the following approach:

> *Our plan is to find other ways in which we can help to solve these problems and reduce emotional distress that don't require suicide as on option. We've already started to identify some alternative solutions. What would really help us out is some additional support from you to make sure our plan is used effectively and to make sure the environment remains safe long enough for us to determine if the plan is actually going to work. Would you be willing to work with us to figure out how you can best help us to accomplish our goals?*

Just as in the case of a CRP, strategic questioning and discussion of the CSP as a process for maximizing safety and assisting the suicidal patient in accomplishing the identified treatment goals, as opposed to asking the supportive other to be responsible for the life or death of the suicidal patient, can increase the supportive other's willingness to play an active role in the patient's treatment. It is critical for the BHC to recognize that the CSP is not asking the supportive other to be responsible for the patient's life or death since this infringes upon the patient's autonomy and the simple fact that the patient is ultimately responsible for this outcome. Rather, the CSP asks the supportive other to be responsible for maximizing safety and supporting the treatment plan, not to completely eliminate risk, which is impossible.

Step 2: Identify helpful supportive actions. Once the rationale for the CSP has been provided and buy-in obtained from the supportive other, the next step is to identify specific actions the supportive other can take to help the suicidal patient. The BHC should facilitate a conversation between the suicidal patient and the supportive other to identify these specific actions. This dialogue is a critical method for empowering the suicidal patient to voice their needs and expectations of the supportive other. The BHC's primary role in this process is to assist the suicidal patient in verbalizing these needs and expectations in terms that are behaviorally oriented, achievable, and consistent with overall treatment goals. For example, a request to "be there for me" is too vague and subjective to be of practical use to the supportive other (e.g., What does it mean to "be there for me"? Does "being there for me" change depending on the situation? What if the supportive other defines "being there for me" differently from the patient?). Vague, nonspecific responses such as these are common from suicidal patients, who often struggle to translate their needs into behaviorally defined actions.

BHCs can facilitate this process using the downward arrow technique. In the downward arrow technique, originally designed to assist patients in identifying core beliefs that underlie automatic thoughts, the provider asks the patient to explain what the thought means about the patient. Using the previous example (i.e., a request to "be there for me"), the BHC can use a similar approach to define these vague needs into more specific behavioral terms (e.g., "If your supportive other were there for you, what would that look like? What would he/she be doing? What would I see him/her doing to tell me that he/she is there for you?"). Such questioning can lead to the identification of actions such as "turn off the TV and talk with me when I am crying" or "go on a walk with me," both of which are clear and unambiguous, thus making them easier to accomplish.

Because the CSP is a collaborative process, the BHC should ensure that both parties are actively involved in its development by facilitating any negotiations between the patient and the supportive other regarding these actions. The BHC should elicit the supportive other's commitment to these actions and willingness to carry them out: "Do these seem like reasonable actions you can take to help [patient's name]?" Any actions that are unacceptable to the supportive other or judged by the supportive other to be too difficult to accomplish should not be included, and alternatives should be discussed.

The CSP should additionally elicit the supportive other's commitment to the patient's personalized CRP, which requires the CRP to be reviewed as a group. The suicidal patient should take the lead in informing the supportive other about the steps to be taken during a crisis. Ideally, the supportive actions identified in the CSP will overlap with the steps from the patient's CRP. Obtaining the supportive other's commitment to the appropriate use of the CRP is critical, as supportive others can intervene prematurely by providing external sources of support before the suicidal patient has the opportunity to implement self-management strategies, which is antithetical to the goal of teaching the patient self-management skills. BHCs should ensure that supportive others understand how to assist patients in using self-management strategies as their first steps for crisis management. For example, the supportive other might offer to do relaxation exercises with the patient for 10 to 15 minutes, go for a walk with the patient, or remind the patient where their survival kit is located.

Step 3: Provide means restriction counseling. The next step of the CSP is to provide the same means restriction counseling to the supportive other that was provided to the patient and specifically review procedures and actions to take in order to maximize the patient's safety. BHCs can be particularly helpful in problem-solving barriers to effective means restriction (e.g., where to temporarily store firearms or medications) and help provide a balanced and reasonable approach to means restriction, such as identifying when and under what circumstances restricting access to vehicles and common but potentially lethal household objects (e.g., knives, cords, chemicals) should be accomplished. As discussed previously, the BHC should be sure to ask about firearms access in all cases regardless of the methodology being considered by the patient and stress the importance of limiting access to this highly fatal method.

Step 4: Review emergency procedures and obtain buy-in. The final section of the CSP includes several steps for the supportive other to take in the event of an emergency or imminent risk. The BHC should review these steps with the supportive other and answer any questions the supportive other might have about how to determine when the emergency procedures should be activated. BHCs should be sure to include the telephone number for the patient's specialty mental health provider (e.g., psychologist, psychiatrist, other therapist). If the patient does not have a specialty mental health care provider, the BHC can include his or her number in this section. Just as in the CRP, BHCs who provide their contact information to supportive others as part of the CSP should carefully explain their availability, procedures for returning calls, frequency of checking voicemail, and so forth so that supportive others have accurate expectations about the BHC's typical response in the event they call during a crisis.

As a final step, the BHC should verbally review each section of the CSP and ask both the patient and the supportive other if there is anything else that should be included. BHCs should then ask the supportive other to rate the likelihood of following the CSP on a scale of 0 (*not at all likely*) to 10 (*very likely*). Supportive others rating their likelihood as less than 7 or 8 should be engaged in a conversation about barriers to adherence so that adaptations can be made to increase the likelihood of implementation. Once a final CSP is agreed upon, the BHC should help the patient and supportive other agree on the duration of the CSP, at which time the plan will be reviewed for possible modifications or renewal. Three copies of the CSP should then be made: one for the patient's medical record, one for the patient, and one for the supportive other.

CORE COMPETENCIES FOR THE BEHAVIORAL HEALTH CONSULTANT

1. Accurately categorize patients according to baseline and acute risk dimensions and appropriately match clinical decisions with the results of the risk assessment.

2. Refer patients at moderate or higher risk for suicide to specialty mental health.
3. Consider referral for inpatient evaluation for patients at severe risk for suicide.
4. Explain the rationale for the CRP and collaboratively create a plan with patients at moderate or higher risk for suicide.
5. Routinely screen for the presence of firearms in the home and counsel patients on restricting access to lethal means.
6. Assist patients in connecting with specialty mental health care.
7. Coordinate care with PCPs and family members and use crisis support plans were appropriate.

CHAPTER 6

Brief Interventions for Suicidal Patients

Within primary care, the treatment process typically unfolds in a series of fairly uniform steps. First, the patient presents with a complaint or concern of some kind. Next, the primary care provider (PCP) conducts an assessment that usually includes a physical examination and the ordering of indicated tests. After the assessment, the PCP makes a diagnosis, provides some form of intervention, and then finally decides on a disposition and follow-up plan that might include referral to a specialist.

This formula is generally followed for any presenting complaint ranging from routine to more complex. In the case of a common cold, for example, the patient might report symptoms such as a runny nose, cough, congestion, and fatigue. As part of their assessment, the PCP will perform a series of routine procedures such as listening to the patient's respiration, checking their ears and nose, and taking the patient's temperature to rule in and rule out likely candidates for the symptom presentation. Upon determining that the patient is suffering from the common cold, the PCP might recommend interventions such as over-the-counter decongestants or pain relievers and counsel the patient on increased fluid intake and rest. The PCP might conclude by recommending follow-up in 7 to 10 days if symptoms do not improve.

A similar approach would be utilized even for more complex or emergent presentations, such as myocardial infarction. A patient reporting chest pain, shortness of breath, sweating, nausea, and a pressure in the chest would likely have their blood pressure checked, their temperature taken, and an electrocardiogram completed (if available). If the result of this evaluation points to a likely heart attack, the PCP would probably initiate some form of treatment to manage the care while making arrangements to transport the patient to an emergency department for a higher level of care. For instance, they might implement any combination of the following: having the patient lie down and administering antihypertensives to control blood pressure, β-blockers to slow heart rate to control tachycardia, or diuretics to improve breathlessness and reduce central blood volume (cf. Hunt et al., 2001). Upon arrival of an ambulance, the patient would then be immediately transferred to the higher level of care.

Contrast this to the typical approach taken when a suicidal patient presents to primary care. Such a patient might present to the clinic reporting depressed mood, agitation, insomnia, and a sense of hopelessness, but this does not necessarily mean they will be assessed for suicide risk. In such cases, the patient might be started on an antidepressant and instructed to follow-up in 4 to 6 weeks or sooner "as needed." If a patient discloses suicide ideation, intent, or planning, the patient will likely be directed to contact an outpatient mental health professional for treatment and might be provided a list of possible mental health specialists. Alternatively, it is quite possible that the patient will be directed to the local emergency department for an evaluation. The patient might then be told to follow-up "as needed" in the future. In this scenario, which is all too common in primary care, steps in the sequence of care are typically skipped. In the first iteration of this scenario, a full assessment is skipped and suicide risk is consequently missed, which leads to a missed opportunity for a suicide-focused intervention. In the second iteration, the intervention step is passed over and a dispositional decision is made immediately. In both cases, no intervention specific to suicide is provided.

Based on our experience working in and consulting with primary care teams, suicide risk is the presenting complaint that most consistently results in no intervention of any kind, in sharp contrast to the general practice model of primary care, which typically provides some form of intervention even for highly complex cases that cannot be adequately treated in the primary care system, and at the very least, PCPs will continue to manage the patient's care until the patient can be connected with the more appropriate level of specialty care. Contributing to this alarming lack of intervention and management efforts for suicidal patients is the pervasive and faulty assumption that effective interventions for suicidal patients are too time-consuming or too elaborate for the primary care context. Suicide-specific interventions can be quite simple and straightforward, however, and are actually quite similar in form to many techniques used in primary care to target other health issues. Several empirically supported interventions that are easy to effectively adapt and transport to primary care will be described in this chapter.

COMMON ELEMENTS IN EFFECTIVE TREATMENTS FOR SUICIDALITY

Before discussing specific interventions for suicide risk, it is useful to briefly review the scientific basis for existing treatments that have been designed for the purpose of preventing suicidal behaviors. Unfortunately, the research base for this issue is quite limited relative to our knowledge base for treating other psychiatric and behavioral problems (e.g., depression), which explains at least in part the diversity of opinions regarding whether suicide can actually be prevented or treated. Although treatment studies might report suicidal behaviors as an outcome variable, very few studies have been conducted to explicitly target suicidal behavior as the primary outcome variable. Even when treatments are developed and found effective, they are rarely disseminated to the wider mental health and medical communities (Comtois & Linehan, 2006). Providers therefore have limited guidance on how to develop and implement effective treatment plans. Although efficacious and effective treatments for suicidal behaviors—whether biological (i.e., psychotropic medications) or psychological in orientation—are desperately needed, this is not to suggest that effective treatments have not been identified. The focus of this chapter will be on psychological or behavioral treatments rather than psychotropic medications. Consultation regarding antidepressant medications will be addressed in Chapter 8.

There are a large number of uncontrolled studies of treatments for suicidal individuals ranging from case studies to large-sample longitudinal follow-up studies, but these types of studies cannot provide causal information about the effectiveness of a treatment and are therefore not considered here. Of 53 clinical trials (i.e., including both a treatment and comparison group without requiring randomization) targeting suicidality that we identified for review, the majority (n = 28, 53%) were cognitive-behavioral in orientation. None of the treatments reporting outcomes indicate they might be potentially harmful as compared with the comparison treatment conditions, although it is possible that such iatrogenic treatments exist but have not been published. When considering treatment for suicidality, it is important to consider the broad variability in both the patient populations targeted (e.g., suicide ideators, suicide attempters, multiple attempters) and treatment goals (i.e., reducing suicidal thoughts, attempts, and/or associated symptoms). Although these variables are often lumped under the umbrella of "suicidality," they can be quite distinct behavioral and psychological phenomena, which add to the complexity of interpreting results and identifying patterns and common elements for effective treatments. Another problem that complicates interpretation is the exclusion of suicidal patients from many treatment studies, with estimates that up to 45% of treatment efficacy trials exclude suicidal patients (Linehan, 1997).

When talking about treatment outcomes for suicidality, we can consider not only which treatments work but also what they have in common that might help us understand why they work. Although dismantling studies, which would definitely answer these questions, have yet to be conducted, enough data currently exist to identify patterns and trends to inform clinical practice. Unfortunately, because of inadequate data, we cannot conclude whether psychological treatments have enduring effects over the long term, since the longest follow-up period available in the 53 identified clinical trials is 24 months, with an average follow-up length of 10 months. Such limited follow-up timeframes are inadequate to address questions about enduring impact, limiting us to conclude with any amount of certainty that psychological and behavioral treatments can only delay suicide for up to a few years following treatment.

Perhaps of greatest concern to the behavioral health consultant (BHC) is whether we can identify similarities across psychological treatments demonstrated to be effective that would lead to clear strategies for practice. To date, there have been no clinical trials targeting suicidality in primary care clinics, which requires us to consider the broader treatment literature to distill existing findings and modify existing treatments into practical interventions for use within the primary care setting. To practice with an evidence-based approach, it is therefore important to look for similarities across clinical trials to focus on those areas that hold the most promise for effective treatment and intervention. We will therefore consider two primary questions:

1. Are there identifiable common elements across treatments that work at reducing subsequent suicide attempt rates?
2. What are the specific techniques used in these studies and how can they be translated to the primary care setting?

Based on a review of clinical trials for suicidality, Rudd (2009) has identified a number of common elements of effective treatments for suicidality. These elements represent general principles underlying the treatment but are not specific techniques or interventions. Clear patterns in technique can be seen as well across clinical trials, however, and will be discussed later.

Theoretical Models Easily Translated to Clinical Work

All of the effective treatments are based on clearly articulated, well-defined, and easily understandable theoretical models that are founded on empirical research. Given that most of the clinical trials are based on cognitive-behavioral theory, common features across the models should not be surprising. In general, effective treatments are based on models that identify thoughts, emotional processing, and associated behavioral responses that are viewed as interdependent and critical to understanding the motivation to die and associated symptoms. Changing the suicidal process ultimately requires alteration of these interrelated features. Critically, in effective treatments, patients find the models easy to understand in terms of these thoughts, emotions, and behaviors associated with suicide risk. Effective treatments make it easy to explain to patients in understandable language why they have tried or are thinking about killing themselves. Simple and easy-to-understand models of suicidality contribute to treatment effectiveness because they lend themselves to easy skills development, contributing to reduced symptom severity, which in turn contributes to decreased risk and fewer subsequent suicide attempts.

Treatment Fidelity

In all of the treatments found to be effective, treatment fidelity is a central factor. Treatment fidelity translates to providers being trained to a predetermined minimum level of competence and supervised throughout this training and early treatment delivery until mastery is achieved, thereby minimizing behavioral drift. Although each individual treatment varies in how it accomplished this fidelity, several consistencies can be seen. First, a sizable portion of effective treatments are protocol-driven, with a clear sequence and hierarchy of treatment targets. The terms *sequence* and *protocol-driven* should not be mistaken for *fixed* or *rigid*, however, which is a common misattribution by many providers. Rather, protocol-driven treatments specify in advance which problems or issues should be targeted first and in which order to maximize success in subsequent stages of treatment.

Related to this, effective treatments place the reduction of suicidal behavior as a central and primary focus of treatment rather than placing the peripheral or associated symptoms (e.g., psychiatric symptoms, hopelessness, relationship problems) as the primary focus. Effective psychological treatments view suicidality, at least to some degree, as independent of psychiatric diagnosis. As such, although each treatment might contain only a finite number of specified interventions and techniques that are determined in advance, the order of their application is generally not rigidly prescribed (i.e., intervention X occurs in session 1, intervention Y occurs in session 2, intervention Z occurs in session 3). Instead, these interventions are applied in a flexible manner that directly targets suicidality as it uniquely manifests in the individual patient. Interventions are therefore conducted to develop specific competencies within the suicidal patient, with progress through subsequent phases of treatment being contingent upon patient mastery of earlier competencies. Ensuring providers consistently target suicidality as a primary treatment outcome clearly seems to lend itself to positive changes and treatment effectiveness.

Patient Adherence

Effective treatments directly target nonadherence to treatment in a predetermined and consistent fashion. Because treatment can only be effective if the patient is actively involved and invested in it, adherence must be a central and primary focus for intervention, with clear plans for what a provider should to do if nonadherence emerges. Just as suicidality needs to be a primary target of treatment, so must motivation and investment in care be prioritized. When motivation, investment, and involvement in treatment drop, these issues should become a primary treatment target until effectively resolved.

Targeting Identifiable Skills

Effective treatments target clearly identifiable skill sets that are based on its theoretical model of suicidality (e.g., emotion regulation, anger management, problem solving, interpersonal relationships, cognitive distortions). The model therefore drives the treatment process, with interventions selected to specifically target skill deficiencies that contribute to and sustain the suicidal crisis. In effective treatments, patients understand what is "wrong" and "what to do about it" in order to reduce suicidal thinking and behaviors. Critically, patients are explicitly taught how to develop the skills, practice the skills as a part of treatment, receive feedback and reinforcement to gradually shape and enhance skill mastery, and are assisted in generalizing these skills in increasingly complex and varied situations.

Personal Responsibility

Effective treatments place considerable emphasis on the suicidal patient's self-reliance, self-awareness, self-control, and personal responsibility for choices and behaviors, based on a philosophy that if a patient develops appropriate skills, the emotional distress and upset associated with problems in life will diminish along with associated suicidal urges. Consistent with this goal, patients assume a high degree of personal responsibility for their care, including crisis management, because this is assumed to contribute directly to improved adherence and motivation for care. In effective treatments, providers are primarily responsible for maintaining treatment fidelity including appropriate targeting of suicidality, patient nonadherence, and faithful application of interventions.

Easy Access to Treatment and Crisis Services

Effective treatments emphasize the importance of crisis management and access to available emergency services both during and after treatment, with clear delineation of a plan of action in the event of crises. Additionally, effective treatments almost always dedicate time to practicing the skills necessary to effectively resolve crises, which typically includes patients learning how to identify what characterizes a crisis or emergency and how to judiciously and effectively implement a plan in response to crises.

BRIEF INTERVENTIONS FOR SUICIDAL PATIENTS

Having reviewed the common elements or principles of effective psychological treatments for suicidality, we next transition to a description of specific interventions that can be used by BHCs working with suicidal patients in primary care. All of the interventions described in this chapter are pulled directly from empirically supported treatments and are therefore founded upon the treatment principles discussed earlier. Of note is that these interventions are remarkably consistent across effective treatments, although they may go by different names, may receive varying degrees of emphasis, or may be administered with slightly different verbiage or style within each individual treatment protocol. Each of these interventions are feasible within the brief, time-limited primary care context and are consistent with the BHC practice model that places a premium on self-management and skills building.

The interventions described in this section are not presented in any particular manner to suggest superiority of any one strategy over another or to implicate any ideal temporal or sequential ordering of strategies. As such, there are no "better" or "worse" interventions in general. Similarly, given the time limits of the primary care clinic, in most cases, it is typically feasible for a BHC to select only one intervention during any given appointment. Indeed, it is much better for a BHC to implement a single intervention very well than to implement multiple interventions with less fidelity or quality. Given the range of options for intervention, BHCs should therefore select those interventions that flow directly and naturally from the risk assessment and are matched to the unique presentation of the suicidal patient as informed by the underlying model of suicidality. In all cases, the intent of the selected intervention(s) should be the immediate and aggressive targeting of suicidality. BHCs who can rapidly translate assessment data into a case conceptualization based on a clear, empirically supported model of suicidality will therefore be much more effective with suicidal patients.

To demonstrate case conceptualization as a guiding principle for the selection of interventions, we will return to the case of Mary from Chapter 4 and use the suicidal mode as the model for considering her case.

Mary has several predispositions that elevate her baseline risk for suicide, including a history of multiple suicide attempts and recurrent depressive episodes. Early in life, her relationship with her parents was marked by harsh criticism that fostered and reinforced core beliefs of self-hate and being unlovable. During depressive periods, Mary experiences intensification of self-critical thoughts arising from these core beliefs. She also experiences worsening of sleep disturbances associated with headaches, back pain, and fatigue secondary to muscle tension. These thoughts and physical symptoms magnify her depressed mood and fuel her desire to overdose on medications as a strategy for managing these uncomfortable feelings and thoughts. As she thinks about overdosing more and more, she perceives a loss of control over her thoughts and begins ruminating about death and becomes increasingly pessimistic about the future. When she starts preparing for an overdose (e.g., counting pills, shaking the pill bottle) she experiences a calmness and reduction in rumination, which reinforces her suicidal thinking and behaviors as a coping strategy.

Over the years, her suicidal episodes have intensified, further supporting the inherently reinforcing nature of her behavioral pattern and demonstrating a "need for more" to achieve the desired calming effect. This has resulted in increasingly lethal behaviors. Mary's suicidal belief system also reduces the salience of the protective factors in her life. When suicidal, she minimizes the importance of the positive factors in her life (e.g., the amount of enjoyment she experiences with her dog, or the extent of her compassion for him) and decreases the frequency with which she engages in meaningful activities (e.g., attending church services). When distressed, she struggles to recall specific positive events in her life, but easily calls to mind negative events or expected outcomes.

As demonstrated by the case of Mary, suicidal episodes are marked by activation of multiple systems of the suicidal mode, providing many different potential targets for intervention. BHCs working from a simple model of suicidal behaviors are well-positioned to select and administer interventions to directly deactivate the various systems of the suicidal mode in order to efficiently resolve the suicidal crisis.

Coping Cards

Suicidal patients commonly have distorted beliefs and self-perceptions that contribute to emotional distress and suicidal symptoms such as a hopelessness, perceived burdensomeness, feeling of being unlovable, or worthlessness

TABLE 6.1
Common Suicidal Beliefs

Hopelessness
- "No one can help me."
- "Nothing will work."
- "It's no use."

Perceived burdensomeness
- "The world would be better off without me."
- "People would be happier without me around."
- "I make things worse for people."

Thwarted belongingness
- "No one cares about me."
- "I'm an outsider."
- "I have no one to turn to."

Feeling of being unlovable
- "I am unworthy of love."
- "I don't deserve any respect."

Unbearability
- "I can't stand this anymore."
- "I can't take this."
- "This is more than I can handle."

Worthlessness/self-hate
- "I'm a failure."
- "I can never be forgiven for what I've done."
- "I'm a horrible person."
- "I am beyond hope."

(see Table 6.1 for common suicidal beliefs). These thought processes can be directly targeted via cognitive interventions to systematically deconstruct the suicidal belief system via two interrelated processes. The first process entails a "distancing" from the suicidal beliefs through recognition of these beliefs for what they actually are: mental activity, not reality (e.g., when thinking "I'm such a screw-up," responding with "I'm not really a screw-up, that's just my depression talking and I don't have to listen to it"). The ability to cognitively "distance" themselves from the suicidal belief system improves the suicidal patient's ability to respond to these thoughts in more adaptive ways.

The second process entails the ability to respond differently to typical triggers of suicidal beliefs, whether these triggers are thoughts, emotions, or environmental situations. These alternative response patterns can include countering a suicidal thought with a more adaptive or positive thought (e.g., when thinking "I can't take this anymore" countering with "I can take this because I'm a strong person") or engaging in an activity that defies the suicidal urge (which will be discussed in detail in the "Behavioral Activation" section). Deactivation of the suicidal belief system is critical because these thought processes sustain and intensify negative emotional states, interfere with protective factors, and increase the motivation to engage in suicidal behaviors in response to emotional distress.

Coping cards are a simple strategy for teaching and reinforcing the skills required to respond to suicidal thoughts in more adaptive ways. Coping cards can be created using 3 × 5 index cards that the patient can carry with them in a pocket, purse, or backpack or keep nearby in a desk drawer or on a refrigerator. On the front side of the coping card, the suicidal or maladaptive belief should be written down in the patient's exact words. These thoughts and beliefs are generally identified during the risk assessment process. On the reverse side, a more adaptive response is written. Wherever possible, the patient should write on the cards themselves (instead of the BHC writing on the cards) to fully engage them in the process and truly create a coping card that is "in the patient's own words." The patient is then directed to read the coping card both at regularly scheduled times during the day and as needed. Coping cards should be read on a regular basis even when the patient is not feeling suicidal so that overlearning occurs, resulting in increased internalization and automatic processing of the adaptive response. Coping cards should additionally be read by the patient as needed whenever they notice themselves thinking the suicidal or maladaptive belief (e.g., during suicidal crises or other periods of emotional distress) to directly apply the skill to the target problem of suicidality. Coping cards can take several forms, depending on the specific needs of the patient, and the two most common forms being a direct counterpoint to suicidal beliefs and a cue for engaging in alternative coping behaviors. Sample coping cards are displayed in Figure 6.1.

As seen in these examples, coping cards can be flexibly applied as an intervention for a wide range of suicidal presentations. In cards A and B, maladaptive beliefs are targeted for deactivation by identifying alternative responses or counterpoints to the suicidal beliefs. A patient using these cards would be instructed to review the cards at least three times per day at scheduled intervals (e.g., during meals, in between classes, during smoke breaks at work) and whenever they notice themselves thinking the maladaptive thoughts.

In cards C and D, however, adaptive sequences of actions to maladaptive thoughts are identified to enhance behavioral responses to the suicidal belief system. Note that cards C and D are similar to the crisis response plan in that they list highly specific, concrete steps to be taken in response to a triggering situation with a recognition for the cognitive constriction and impaired cognitive flexibility that is characteristic of the suicidal state. These cards additionally break down the desired response pattern into very small, discrete steps that are each very easy to achieve. Breaking down longer behavioral chains into sequences of discrete steps can reduce the sense of complexity

	Front	Back
(A)	I can't take this anymore.	This is only temporary, and I can endure.
(B)	I screw everything up. I'm a failure.	Mistakes happen. It's okay to make mistakes. I can figure this out.
(C)	I don't want to get out of bed.	1. Get up and stand next to the bed. 2. Count to 10. 3. Decide whether to get back into bed.
(D)	I can't do anything when I'm thinking about suicide.	1. Set a time limit for doing the activity (5–30 minutes). 2. Do the activity for the full length of time *even if suicidal.* 3. After doing the activity for the time limit, decide whether to continue it.

FIGURE 6.1
Sample coping cards.

and the feeling of being overwhelmed that suicidal patients often experience during an acute crisis.

In general, it is recommended that patients not be provided with more than two or three coping cards at any given time in order to focus their attention onto a smaller set of skills. This increased focus can accelerate skill mastery. Related to this, BHCs should not develop new coping cards until the patient demonstrates adequate mastery of earlier cards. One clue indicating skill mastery is patient report of acquired automaticity of the adaptive response (e.g., "I don't even need to pull out the card anymore because I can just say it to myself now. I can hear myself saying it without using the card."). As the BHC and patient collaboratively develop additional coping cards over the course of subsequent follow-ups, the BHC should encourage the patient to continue rehearsing previously mastered coping cards in order to ensure the learned response does not degrade prematurely.

A common obstacle arising during the coping card intervention is the patient's difficulty in identifying adaptive responses to suicidal beliefs and maladaptive thoughts. Indeed, if suicidal individuals could adequately respond to suicidal beliefs and thoughts, they would probably not be suicidal in the first place. The difficulties that many suicidal patients have in generating adaptive responses, combined with the time demands of the primary care setting, can tempt the BHC to generate solutions on behalf of the patient, but this undermines the core treatment philosophy of emphasizing the patient's personal responsibility and the development of self-management skills. Enabling the suicidal patient to develop their own solutions is critical for treatment effectiveness; BHCs must therefore resist the temptation to do the patient's work. When confronted with this barrier to coping card completion, the BHC can assist the patient in developing adaptive responses to suicidal and maladaptive beliefs and thoughts by asking questions common to cognitive therapy approaches:

- What is the evidence that this belief is true? What is the evidence that it is not true?
- What other explanations could there be for this?
- What would you tell a friend who was saying these things?

Patients might additionally report that the adaptive responses are not believable (e.g., "But I don't really think that I'm a worthwhile person"), which can potentially reduce adherence to the intervention. The sense that an adaptive response is not believable is simply a function of inadequate reinforcement of the response up to this point in the patient's life. BHCs should encourage patients to complete the task anyway, even if they do not yet believe in the adaptive response, since repeated rehearsal of the adaptive response will nonetheless contribute to learning. As the adaptive responses become "more familiar" to the patient, their belief in the response will emerge.

Survival Kit/Hope Box

The "survival kit" (alternatively termed the "hope box" intervention by Brown, Wenzel, & Beck, 2009) is another brief intervention designed primarily to target the affective system of the suicidal mode. The purpose of the survival kit is to centralize tangible objects that can prime positive emotional states and elicit thoughts that counter the suicidal belief system. Survival kits can be created using any form of a container (e.g., shoe box, manila envelope, tackle box) in which objects having positive associations can be stored. Objects commonly placed in survival kits include pictures of vacations, inspirational quotes, scripture passages, trinkets or souvenirs from important events, letters from loved ones, and family photos. Patients can decorate the survival kits if they so choose; this can be a particularly useful strategy for engaging adolescents in the task. The specific content of a survival kit has no bounds and can vary considerably from patient to patient. Key to the selection of objects to be included in the survival kit is the ability of the object to prime a positive emotional experience, thereby reducing the intensity of aversive emotions sustaining the suicidal state. BHCs should therefore require patients to bring in their survival kits to a follow-up appointment for review. When a patient returns to a follow-up appointment with their survival kit, BHCs can simply ask the patient to briefly "tell me the story" of each object. This reduces the likelihood that patients will select objects that trigger or sustain suicidal states, such as pictures of a "loving" parent who also abused the patient or love letters from an intimate partner with whom the patient recently separated or broke up.

As the patient explains their rationale for including each object in the survival kit, the BHC should be mindful of the patient's emotional state and ask follow-up questions to further elicit positive emotions. For example, when "telling the story" of a picture from a family vacation at the beach, the suicidal patient might simply explain that she included the picture "because that was a fun trip" without providing any additional information or detail. This lack of detail is an interesting and unique feature of suicidal patients that seems to inhibit positive emotional states and effective problem solving (Williams, Barnhofer, Crane, & Duggan, 2006). The BHC should therefore follow up with questions such as "What specifically made it fun? What was the best part of the trip? Why did you choose to go to the beach? Who went with you? Can you describe to me how the ocean sounded or smelled?" Similar questions can be asked about trinkets, souvenirs, or other heirlooms:

"How did you get this object? What does this object mean to you personally? Why have you kept this object for all these years?" Such follow-up questions strengthen the intensity of the memory trace and heighten the emotional engagement associated with the objects. By eliciting positive emotions, the hope kit intervention provides a direct functional alternative to suicidality for emotional relief: Instead of reducing negative emotions and/or increasing positive emotions with suicidality, the patient can achieve the same outcome by using their survival kit.

Although primarily an intervention targeting the affective system of the suicidal mode, the survival kit also functions to undermine suicidal and maladaptive thoughts and beliefs by enhancing the patient's sense of mastery over the suicidal state. Being able to self-generate positive emotions and/or reduce the intensity of aversive emotions during suicidal crises counters the sense of hopelessness and intolerability of the suicidal state. In effect, suicidal patients learn that something can be done to manage suicidal thoughts and feelings. Furthermore, suicidal people are generally less skilled at identifying toxic relationships and situations that reinforce poor self-image and fuel suicidal states. In those cases where the suicidal patients select objects for their survival kit that are judged to be inappropriate or unhelpful, the review of the survival kit's content with the BHC provides an opportunity to learn how to better discriminate among those people, events, and experiences that contribute to or mitigate distress.

Two common barriers to the survival kit intervention are difficulty in identifying objects for inclusion in the survival kit and selecting objects that are inadvertently iatrogenic. In cases where a suicidal patient struggles to identify objects to be included in the survival kit, the BHC should return to the protective factors identified in the risk assessment for guidance. In Mary's case, her pet dog and her husband were identified as protective factors. The BHC might therefore ask Mary what sorts of reminders of her dog and her husband could be included in the survival kit:

> *"Other people have found it useful to include things such as pictures, books, or magazines about their pets, an old dog tag or leash you might still have, a card sprayed with your husband's cologne, or a picture from your wedding. These are just a few examples of some reminders, but we can include whatever you'd like. What sorts of things can we put in your survival kit that will remind you of your dog and your husband?"*

As seen in this example, when facilitating the process of survival kit creation, BHCs can provide a menu of possible options geared to activate the patient's thinking. In all cases, the patient should select each object themselves even if it consists only of choosing their favorites from the BHC's menu.

In cases where patients include potentially iatrogenic objects, BHCs should facilitate a process through which the patient gains an understanding of the maladaptive qualities of the object. As noted previously, the inability to accurately identify toxic persons and situations is a notable skills deficit that sustains suicidality over time. However, simply telling a suicidal patient that a particular person or situation is toxic does not contribute to skill development. The BHC can facilitate appropriate skill development by engaging the patient in a line of Socratic questioning to guide the patient to this understanding:

- When you think about this object what goes through your mind or what do you feel?
- Do you feel better or worse when you think about these things?
- Do these thoughts or feelings make you desire suicide more or less?

Oftentimes, BHCs will find that patients will report both positive and negative emotions associated with these iatrogenic objects. In the case of a photo of an abusive family member, for example, a patient might verbalize feelings of love or compassion for the abuser mixed with anger, hatred, or rejection. In such cases, the question about whether to include a particular object can be complex and confusing for the suicidal patient. The ultimate question to be answered is whether the object functions to reinforce or reduce suicidality. If the object reinforces suicidality in any way, even if it also potentially reduces suicidality, it should not be included in the survival kit and an alternative should be identified.

Reasons for Living List

The reasons for living list is an intervention similar to both the coping card and survival kit interventions. Its primary target is the cognitive system of the suicidal mode, although it additionally operates on the affective system. Specifically, the reasons for living list is designed to increase cognitive flexibility and fluidity while reducing cognitive rigidity. As noted in previous chapters, suicidal individuals generally report fewer reasons for living overall as compared with nonsuicidal individuals (Strosahl, Chiles, & Linehan, 1992), and when these reasons for living are listed, suicidal individuals report fewer reasons related to future plans, goals, and hopes (Nademin, Jobes, Downing, & Mann, 2005).

This deficiency in future-oriented reasons for living is a critical feature of the suicidal mode's cognitive system because reasons for living serve to buffer an individual against hopelessness in the face of adversity and situational stress. Suicidal individuals anticipate fewer specific positive events will occur in the future than nonsuicidal individuals, but suicidal and nonsuicidal individuals are able to list comparable numbers of future negative events (MacLeod, Rose, & Williams, 1993). This indicates that deficits in forward planning are not global among suicidal individuals, but limited only to desirable outcomes. Suicidal individuals also judge the probability of negative events as more likely than nonsuicidal individuals and demonstrate difficulty in generating reasons for why these negative events might not happen (MacLeod & Tarbuck, 1994).

Interestingly, suicidal individuals and nonsuicidal individuals can list the same number of reasons for why a negative event might not happen, but suicidal individuals take longer to generate the first reason, thus demonstrating significantly reduced cognitive fluidity (MacLeod & Tarbuck, 1994). Once suicidal individuals are able to think about reasons for why negative events might not happen, however, levels of hopelessness significantly drop (MacLeod & Tarbuck, 1994). These data suggest that, although suicidal individuals do not necessarily anticipate more negative outcomes per se, when a negative outcome is possible, suicidal individuals overestimate its likelihood because of an inability to quickly think about positive aspects of themselves or the situation that would prevent the outcome from happening. Consider the implications of these findings: when in a crisis and overestimating the likelihood of a negative outcome in life, it is more important for the suicidal individual to rapidly call to mind any reason for living, even if it is only one reason, than to take a long time to list off many reasons for living. During a crisis, speed matters. Strengthening the suicidal patient's capacity for rapidly identifying reasons why a negative outcome such as suicide might not occur is therefore a useful intervention. The reasons for living list directly fosters this skill.

The reasons for living list flows naturally from the protective factors portion of the risk assessment and should be tied directly to the responses of the patient in that segment of the clinical encounter. Like coping cards, the reasons for living list can be created using 3 × 5 index cards that the patient can easily carry with them in their pocket, purse, or backpack or keep in an easily accessible location such as a drawer. On the index card are listed the patient's identified reasons for living. These might include people (e.g., family, friends, coworkers), meaningful activities (e.g., camping, favorite vacation spots, playing with children, cooking, movies), dreams or aspirations (e.g., graduating from college, promotions, retirement), ideals or values (e.g., love for others, not wanting to hurt loved ones), or any other factors that serve to reduce the desire for suicide and increase the desire for life.

Wherever possible, the patient should write the list themselves. The patient is then directed to read the reasons for living list both at regularly scheduled times during the day and as needed. The importance of reviewing the list on a regular basis, even when the patient is feeling relatively calm should be stressed by the BHC because the automization resulting from overlearning is the very essence of cognitive fluidity. Patients should also be directed to write additional reasons for living on the list as they are identified in daily life. As this list expands and grows, the patient's sense of the meaningful aspects of their life shifts dramatically. Suicidal patients also begin to develop the ability to pay attention to positive aspects of their lives instead focusing excessively on the negative aspects of life.

Cognitive constriction can often become very evident as a result of the reasons for living list intervention. This constriction frequently manifests in the form of cognitive "shortcuts" or overgeneralizations when attempting to generate reasons for living. For example, a suicidal patient might report that "family" is their only reason for living; being able to identify only one reasons for living (or a few) can be discouraging to the patient and reinforce perceptions of isolation, worthlessness, feeling of being unlovable, and other core suicidal beliefs. Overgeneralized responses such as "family," "friends," "work," "pets," or "religious beliefs" typically collapse many reasons for living into a single, broad category that masks the true extent of the positive features in the patient's life.

Consider the case of a patient who reports "family" as the only reason for living. The response "family" glosses over the many specific details that contribute to the concept of "family" as a reason for living, such as relationships with individual family members, specific memories with family members, or planned activities the patient might be looking forward to. In other words, the suicidal patient takes a cognitive shortcut by combining all the various aspects of "family" into an overgeneralized concept that loses the emotional salience associated with specific events, relationships, and memories (Williams, Barnhofer, Crane, & Duggan, 2006). The BHC can teach the patient to overcome this tendency by asking pointed questions designed to focus the patient on specific instances of family life that have positive emotional associations. For example, the BHC might ask patients one or more of the following questions:

- What are the names of your family members?
- What types of things have you done with that family member that you enjoy?
- When is the next time you plan on seeing this person? What will you do together?

Such questions can effectively and very rapidly "convert" an reasons for living list with only a single item to a list with many items.

Strategic questioning in combination with active listening can also provide clues to reasons for living in other areas of life. The second and third sample questions noted earlier not only focus on family relationships but also tap directly into enjoyable and meaningful activities that also serve as reasons for living. Consider the following exchange with Mary, who reported that her only reasons for living were her pet dog (Barney) and her husband:

MARY [M]: Only Barney and my husband. That's all I can think of. That's pathetic.

BHC [B]: Well, that's a good start. Tell me more about Barney. Why is he one of your reasons for living? What do you like to do with him?

M: (smiles) Well, I like playing with him in the backyard, and we used to go to the dog park a lot, but we don't do that anymore because I'm tired.

B: So you like to be outside?

M: Yeah. Especially when it's sunny and warm.

B: What do you like to do when it's sunny and warm?

M: Well, I used to go for walks a lot more…

B: With Barney?

M: Yeah, but also without him. I would just go for a walk just to go for a walk.

B: And you enjoyed that?

M: Yes. And I used to have this garden in my backyard that I would take care of. I grew herbs in one section, and then just some flowers in another section. I would grow the herbs and then use them when I was cooking. The backyard used to smell so wonderful with that garden.

B: Oh really? Are you a chef?

M: (laughs) No, I wouldn't say that, but I would cook. I loved having dinner parties and cooking big meals.

B: You liked cooking for others?

M: Oh, yes. I would attend cooking classes to get recipes and practice the dishes, then I'd usually cook it once for my husband to make sure I got it right, then we'd plan a party and I'd cook it for everyone.

B: Wow, that's impressive.

M: I guess.

B: You know, it sounds like you really liked doing those things. You really got animated just now telling me about it.

M: Yeah, I guess I did. I suppose I miss doing all those things.

B: Is it safe to say, then, that sunny weather, going for walks, the smell of your garden, cooking, and dinner parties are additional reasons for living?

M: I guess so, but I don't really do that anymore.

B: Well, we can talk about that next. Right now let's just focus on figuring out what reasons you have for living. Should we add these things to the list, and then we can talk about how you aren't doing them anymore?

M: Yeah, that's a good idea.

B: Great. I'm wondering also who you typically invited to these dinner parties?

M: Oh, usually just some friends.

B: What are their names?

M: Well, there's Bill and Marcy, and James and Ruth. Oh, and Beth and Mike.

B: Would you say that Bill, Marcy, James, Ruth, Beth, and Mike are also reasons for living?

M: (smiles) Oh, definitely.

B: Okay then let's add them to the list, too. Looks like our list has increased from 2 items to 11. I guess there are more reasons for living than we originally thought, huh?

M: Yeah, I guess so. I had forgotten about those things.

In the span of a few minutes, the BHC has effectively used targeted questions to increase Mary's capacity to think flexibly about her reasons for living and has elicited a positive emotional state by enhancing her ability to reappraise memories and life events from a new perspective. The BHC has also set up the encounter to seamlessly move into another empirically supported intervention designed to increase Mary's engagement in valued and meaningful activities (i.e., behavioral activation, to be discussed in the next section). Finally, the BHC has modeled for the patient the process of identifying additional reasons for living and adding them to the reasons for living list, which increases the likelihood that the patient will adhere to this recommendation and intervention.

When attempting to create an reasons for living list, the BHC might find that patients report being unable to think of reasons for living. This barrier is likely to arise during the protective factors section of the risk assessment when the BHC first probes for the presence of reasons for living. In our experience, this barrier most commonly arises in response to the BHC's use of the language "reasons for living" (e.g., "What are your reasons for living?") because, to many suicidal patients, the state of being suicidal is assumed to necessitate an absence of reasons for living. Yet the simple fact that the patient is still alive despite their suicidal desire indicates the presence of at least some reason(s) for living; if there were absolutely no reasons for living, the patient would probably be dead. The BHC should call attention to this seeming contradiction in order to increase the patient's cognitive flexibility and shift their perspective of their suicidal experience. Furthermore, instead of asking suicidal patients, "What reasons do you have for living?" the BHC might instead ask, "Why have you not killed yourself up this point? What keeps you alive?" The alternate wording more directly probes for the information of interest—that is, the identification of those factors that stall or otherwise prevent suicidal behaviors from occurring—and can therefore be a useful strategy for circumventing cognitive rigidity.

Behavioral Activation

Behavioral activation is a treatment originally developed for depression based on dismantling studies of cognitive therapy in which the behavioral activation components of cognitive therapy performed as well in isolation as the full cognitive therapy package. These results have been found both in terms of the acute treatment of depression and the prevention of relapse over a 2-year follow-up (Gortner, Gollan, Dobson, & Jacobson, 1998; Jacobson, Dobson, Truax, Addis, & Koerner, 1996). behavioral activation focuses on reengaging depressed people with inherently rewarding activities in life that counter the patterns of avoidance and withdrawal maintaining emotional distress and contributing to functional impairment. These avoidance and withdrawal patterns function as strategies to cope with situations characterized by low levels of positive reinforcement or high levels of aversiveness (Jacobson, Martell, & Dimidjian, 2001). Because these avoidance patterns work to reduce emotional distress in the short term (i.e., negative reinforcement), they tend to be self-sustaining, although over the long-term, these avoidance patterns contribute to functional impairment. Because avoidance patterns similarly underlie suicidal behaviors, behavioral activation can be a useful intervention for undermining avoidance patterns and increasing the frequency and intensity of inherently rewarding activities in a patient's life.

Suicidal patients often verbalize a desire to "feel better," but as a treatment target, this can be vague and difficult to accomplish (e.g., What does "feel better" mean? "Feel better" in which situations? "Feel better" for how long? How do we know "feel better" has been achieved?). behavioral activation therefore focuses on setting short-term behavior change goals and delineating the steps required to achieve these goals, the assumption being that by achieving specific behavior changes the patient will accomplish the less well-defined outcome of "feeling better." The BHC serves as the patient's coach by setting realistic and attainable goals and by encouraging the patient to reach these goals.

Early behavioral activation interventions are typically designed to undermine the avoidance patterns that disrupt daily functioning. Such interventions might include increased exercise, engagement in hobbies, or participation in social activities. In cases of more severely distressed patients, behavioral activation plans might be much more basic or fundamental: showering in the morning, putting on make-up, changing out of pajamas, getting out of bed, cooking a meal. When developing behavioral activation plans, the BHC should follow a series of steps to maximize success: conduct a functional analysis, collaboratively identify desired behavioral alternatives, and set realistic goals.

Step 1: Conduct a Functional Analysis

The functional analysis is a central strategy to BHC practice and should therefore be familiar to most BHCs. In the functional analysis, the BHC and patient work together to identify the variables that contribute to and sustain avoidant behavioral patterns. In the case of suicidal patients, the avoidant behavioral pattern of interest is suicidality. Dimensions typically included in the functional analysis should focus on the contextual or situational variables associated with the avoidance pattern (in this case suicidality):

- Timing and location (e.g., "Are there situations in which you find yourself thinking about suicide most often? When you are suicidal, what is typically going on?")
- Frequency (e.g., "How often do you think about suicide? What percentage of the time would you say you become suicidal after an argument with your spouse?")
- Associated situational factors (e.g., "What typically happens immediately before you think about suicide? What happens after you think about suicide?)
- Duration and course of onset (e.g., "How long ago did you first notice yourself thinking about suicide? Did your suicidal desire become intense very quickly, or did it develop slowly over time?")
- Impact on life functioning (e.g., "When you become suicidal, how does that affect what you are doing or what you would like to be doing?")

As is evident in these sample questions, the functional analysis overlaps considerably with the risk assessment. In this sense, the risk assessment can be seen as a functional analysis of the patient's suicidality.

Step 2: Collaboratively Identify Desired Behavioral Alternatives

Behaviors and activities to be included in the behavior change plan should be relevant to the suicidal mode and easy for the patient to implement. Behaviors should therefore be selected for their ability to reduce negative emotions, increase positive emotions, challenge or defy suicidal thoughts or beliefs, or reduce aversive physical symptoms or experiences. For example, Mary has discontinued taking her dog for a walk, which intensifies her depression and sustains her beliefs of worthlessness and personal failure. She notes

TABLE 6.2
Common Behavioral Activation Strategies

___ Go jog
___ Go to a movie theater and watch whatever is playing
___ Ride your bike
___ Play solitaire
___ Play video games
___ Go to your local playground and join a game being played
___ Create your own website
___ Create your own online blog
___ Join an Internet dating service
___ Get out of your house, even if you just sit outside
___ Sell something you don't want on the Internet
___ Go online to chat
___ Visit your favorite websites
___ Go borrow a friend's dog and take it to the park
___ Give your pet a bath
___ Do yoga, tai chi, or Pilates, or take classes to learn
___ Go outside and watch the birds and other animals
___ Stretch all your muscles
___ Find something funny to do, like reading the Sunday comics
___ Go play something you can do by yourself if no one else is around
___ Visit crazy websites and start keeping a list of them
___ Watch television
___ Go for a swim
___ Listen to the radio
___ Go hiking
___ Go to a sporting event, like a baseball or football game
___ Do something exciting, like surfing, rock climbing, or skiing
___ Get a massage
___ Play a game with a friend
___ Talk to a friend on the telephone
___ Exercise
___ Lift weights
___ Cook your favorite dish or meal
___ Go out and visit a friend
___ Cook a recipe you've never tried before
___ Invite a friend to come to your home
___ Take a cooking class
___ Text message your friends
___ Go out for something to eat
___ Organize a party
___ Go outside and play with your pet
___ Go for a long walk in a park or someplace else that's peaceful
___ Watch a funny movie

that, in the past, this activity provided a sense of vigor and energy, but since discontinuing it, she feels more fatigued and exhausted. These details suggest that resuming this activity could impact four separate systems of the suicidal mode: behavioral (by increasing meaningful activities), cognitive (by countering beliefs of worthlessness and failure), emotional (by eliciting feelings of joy and satisfaction), and physical (by increasing energy). There are no limits to the behavioral alternatives that can be used in behavioral activation, which as an intervention provides a considerable amount of flexibility for BHCs and patients. Common behavioral activation activities are listed in Table 6.2, although this list is far from comprehensive.

When developing a behavior change plan, BHCs should maintain a collaborative stance with the suicidal patient and facilitate the patient's ability to identify their own targets for behavior change. For suicidal patients struggling to identify appropriate behavioral alternatives, the BHC can provide the list of possible activities in Table 6.2 or verbally list possible alternatives. A useful strategy for identifying relevant behaviors is to ask patients about activities they used to engage in before the onset of suicidality (e.g., "What are some things you used to enjoy doing that you don't do anymore?"). Whichever method the BHC uses to generate potential behavioral alternatives, the patient should be directed to choose the few options from many that seem most feasible and most directly related to the suicidality.

Step 3: Set Achievable Goals

Once alternatives have been chosen, the BHC should assist the patient in setting a behavioral activation plan to achieve these goals. To be achievable, behavioral activation plans should be specific, measurable, and realistic. For example, "increasing exercise" is not an achievable behavioral activation goal because it is too vague and cannot be easily measured (what constitutes an "increase" and which activities are considered "exercise"?). In contrast, consider the goal "walk around the neighborhood with my husband for 15 minutes on Monday, Wednesday, and Friday." This latter goal is very specific, and adherence can be easily measured. The extent to which this goal is realistic, however, might vary from patient to patient. For some patients, walking three times per week is a reasonable threshold to accomplish, whereas for others it is simply too high a standard. BHCs should therefore assess the patient's likelihood to achieve the goal by assessing motivation level and potential barriers. BHCs can assess motivation level by asking the patient to rate the likelihood of following the behavioral activation plan on a scale of 0 (*not at all*) to 10 (*very likely*). If patients rate their likelihood as less than 7 or 8, BHCs should renegotiate the plan with the patient to establish new goals that are more likely to be achieved.

BHCs should also take the time to identify and problem-solve potential barriers to successful behavioral activation plan achievement, even if the patient rates their motivation to achieve the plan very high, as this provides an opportunity to model and shape cognitive flexibility and problem solving skills. Potential barriers to behavioral activation plan achievement can include external situational factors (e.g., weather prevents going for a walk, unexpected meetings at work interfere with lunch plans, friends canceling plans at the last minute) or internal experiences (e.g., increased depression, intensification of suicide ideation, illness). Achievement of behavioral activation plans can also be stalled simply by the fact that new behaviors take time to learn and become automatic. A common barrier for exercise goals, for example, is forgetting to pack a gym bag with a change of clothes in the morning before going to work. BHCs should help patients to anticipate these common barriers and plan in advance to overcome them (e.g., packing the gym bag the night before and placing it in front of the door to the garage so it is not forgotten). Breaking a plan down into constituent "subgoals" can significantly increase the likelihood of accomplishment.

Perhaps the most common obstacle to completing a behavioral activation plan is the suicidal patient with severe anhedonia and/or very low motivation to change their behavior—a common feature of the suicidal belief system. Such patients will commonly verbalize the perception that they "can't" engage in the behavior plan due to some feature of their distress (e.g., "I'm too tired," "I can't even get out of bed to shower," "I just don't feel like it") or alternatively will insist that the behavioral activation plan will not work (e.g., "Going for a walk is not going to help," "This won't work"). In such cases, the BHC should avoid arguing with the patient, but rather sidestep these barriers by engaging the patient in behavioral "experiments." Specifically, the BHC should shift their stated goal away from the establishment of enduring behavioral patterns toward the simple initiation of any level of the target behavior. In other words, engaging in the behavior to any small degree becomes the desired goal rather than the development of a new habit. Consider the following exchange between Mary and the BHC, who have just discussed establishing a behavioral activation plan to walk her dog once per week for 15 minutes. When asked to rate the likelihood of following this plan, Mary rated herself as 4 out of 10:

BHC [B]: What gets in the way of you walking your dog on the weekend? What would prevent you from rating yourself at an 8 or 9 or 10?

MARY [M]: I just can't do it. It's been too long and I can't walk that much anymore.

B: If you don't think you can walk for 15 minutes, what would be a more realistic goal to set? 10 minutes? 5 minutes?

M: Zero minutes. I can't walk at all.

B: Wait a minute. How did you get into the clinic today?

M: What do you mean?

B: I mean how did you get inside the clinic today if you can't walk at all? Didn't you walk from your car to the clinic door?

M: Well, it's not that I can't walk at all. It's just that I haven't walked my dog in a long time and it's hard to get up the energy to do it.

B: Oh, okay. So you can walk for at least a few minutes, but it's difficult to do.

M: Yeah.

B: So how about we try an experiment then. Instead of walking your dog every weekend for the rest of your life, how about we just have you walk the dog this weekend only and let's see how that goes. Then we can meet again and determine if we need to change that plan or keep going with it. Does that sound like a reasonable idea?

M: Sure. I can do it once.

B: Okay. So on a scale of 0 to 10, how likely are you to walk your dog just once for 15 minutes this weekend?

M: 9.

B: Okay, great. Let's write that down.

In this vignette, when Mary initially reports a low likelihood in achieving the goal of walking her dog, the BHC attempts to renegotiate the terms with her to identify a more achievable goal (i.e., 5 or 10 minutes instead of 15 minutes). However, Mary continues to reject the plan based on the faulty assumption that she cannot engage in the behavior at all. The BHC quickly calls attention to the maladaptive belief (i.e., "I can't walk at all") and uses humor to provide a cognitive intervention to point out the extreme rigidity of this position, thereby shifting Mary's perception. He then reframes the task by contrasting the specific plan (going for a walk one time on the weekend) with an extreme plan (walking the dog every weekend for the rest of Mary's life) in order to increase the perceived achievability of the task. This succeeds in shifting Mary's self-reported likelihood of walking her dog, which is the first step in initiating a more robust and comprehensive behavioral activation plan.

Relaxation Exercises

Relaxation exercises are frequently used strategies designed to manage physiological arousal associated with acute emotional distress. Relaxation exercises can be quickly and easily taught in the primary care setting and are oftentimes referred to as the "bread and butter" of BHC practice since it is a core psychological skill affecting a wide range of health problems (e.g., anxiety, stress, insomnia, headaches, chronic pain, blood pressure, gastrointestinal complaints). Many different relaxation protocols exist (e.g., diaphragmatic breathing, autogenic relaxation, guided imagery), none of which are particularly better or worse than others. In all approaches, the central component is the intentional reduction of bodily tension, which leads to decreased physiological arousal in opposition to the stress response, which is typically experienced as calming or soothing. Relaxation techniques have demonstrated efficacy for reducing emotional distress, depression, and anxiety (Jain et al., 2007; Leubbert, Dahme, & Hasenbring, 2001; Stetter & Kupper, 2002), suggesting that these interventions operate indirectly on the emotional system via the physical system of the suicidal mode. The positive impact of relaxation on sleep regulation might be particularly important for the treatment and management of suicidal patients, given the importance of sleep disturbance as a perpetuating factor for suicide risk (e.g., Agargun, Kara, & Solmaz, 1997; Bernert, Joiner, Cukrowicz, Schmidt, & Krakow, 2005; Goldstein, Bridge, & Brent, 2008). Wherever possible, BHCs should have patients practice relaxation skills during the appointment to enable the BHC ample opportunity to coach the patient or address any problems. Furthermore, patients who practice relaxation during the appointment obtain immediate experiential success that overcomes the hurdle of initiating a new behavior plan. A sample script for brief diaphragmatic breathing can be found in Figure 6.2.

BHCs should allow patients to practice the relaxation exercise for at least 3 minutes during the appointment, which is usually sufficient for a relaxation effect to be noticeable by the typical patient. Following the end of the relaxation exercise BHCs should engage patients in a discussion designed to increase self-awareness of the relaxation effects:

- What did you notice changing inside your body while you did that exercise?
- What did you notice about your shoulders while you were breathing slowly?
- What happened to your heart rate as we did this relaxation?

Pointed questions such as these are designed to increase the patient's attention to their capacity to manage internal experiences. Because many suicidal patients are deficient in self-monitoring and self-awareness, use of these directive questions can "cut to the chase" and save the BHC considerable time in accomplishing this critical task, in contrast to more indirect questions that can confuse patients who have not yet developed self-awareness skills (e.g., "What was that like?"). Upon demonstration of skill mastery, BHCs should then work collabora-

Go ahead and get yourself settled into your seat in a comfortable position with both feet on the floor and your hands resting in your lap. If you feel comfortable closing your eyes while doing this activity, go ahead and close them. If you'd prefer to keep your eyes open, that's fine, just fix your gaze on a point on the wall or the floor so that you're eyes aren't wandering around while we do this. I want you to begin by taking a slow, deep breath in, and then very slowly breathing out. Good. And repeat that: a slow, deep breath in, and then a very slow breath out. Very good. I want you to repeat this slow, rhythmic, deep breathing at this pace, and while you breathe in this way, I'm just going to help you to relax even more.

As you're breathing in, I want you to notice how the air feels as it enters your body and fills you up, and then notice how the air feels as it leaves your body and you deflate. As you breathe out this next time I want you to let your shoulders slump, sort of like they have weights attached to them pulling them down. Good. Notice also how you might experience a sinking sensation, sort of like gravity is increasing and you're sinking into the seat. Good. Let yourself relax, sort of like you're going limp in your seat and release the tension in your shoulders, your arms, your chest, and your legs. Good. Notice how you're heart rate slows down as you do this breathing as you become more relaxed and calm. Very good. Now let's just sit here for another minute or so, continuing to breathe slowly and deeply, and releasing even more tension from our muscles. [Sit in silence for 1 to 3 minutes, depending on time constraints.]

And now I want you to take just two more very deep, very slow breaths, and when you're ready you can open up your eyes again.

FIGURE 6.2
Sample brief relaxation script.

tively with the patient to schedule regular times during the day when relaxation can be practiced using the guidelines discussed as a part of behavioral activation planning (i.e., specific, measurable, and realistic). For example, prescribing relaxation "three times each day after breakfast, lunch, and dinner for 5 minutes" is much more achievable than prescribing relaxation "three times per day."

Many relaxation protocols recommend patients engage in the relaxation skills for periods that can extend up to 15 or 20 minutes (or even hours). Aside from the impracticality of such a time-intensive intervention in a primary care setting, many suicidal patients lack cognitive and emotional resources to engage in the relaxation task for longer than a few minutes. Asking patients to engage in relaxation exercises for longer than they are able can result in frustration and disengagement from treatment and should therefore be avoided. If patients discontinue relaxation exercises prematurely, BHCs should work to determine the causes for this and modify the intervention appropriately. In many cases, the patient simply cannot sustain attention for longer than a very brief period, in which case the BHC should recommend shorter periods of relaxation practice. BHCs should be alert, however, for the possibility of task interference by cognitive and/or affective experiences. While engaged in relaxation exercises, coping strategies typically used by suicidal patients such as mental distraction are often reduced, which can result in increased experience of aversive stimuli such as emotional distress, self-critical statements, or racing thoughts. Discontinuing the relaxation task can serve as an avoidant response in such cases. Although the ultimate goal is to reduce avoidant response patterns, pushing the patient to move beyond their available resources can be iatrogenic. If premature termination of relaxation appears to be related to avoidance of aversive internal experiences, the BHC might consider adding a mindfulness-based intervention (described in the next section) to augment the relaxation.

Mindfulness Exercises

Mindfulness exercises consist of a series of strategies and techniques designed to both focus attention on the present moment without judgment and to observe rather than react to thoughts and emotions. This tendency to react in maladaptive ways to thoughts and emotions is a function of cognitive reactivity, which occurs with greater magnitude among suicidal individuals. Cognitive reactivity is the process by which small changes in mood activate beliefs and thoughts present during previous aversive mood states (e.g., depression, anxiety, anger, shame) that lie dormant during periods of normal mood states (Ingram, Miranda, & Segal, 1998). In the context of fluid vulnerability theory, the suicidal belief system becomes activated during periods of emotional distress, then deactivates when the person's distress resolves. The suicidal belief system can be reactivated at a later time in the presence of mood fluctuations. This heightened cognitive reactivity is particularly pronounced among suicidal patients and can contribute to significant impairment in problem solving. Research with depressed individuals has demonstrated that following negative mood induction, problem-solving deterioration is seen only among those patients with a history of suicidal ideation, not among depressed patients with no previous suicidal ideation or among nondepressed controls (Williams, Barnhofer, Crane, & Beck, 2005). During normal mood states, in contrast, all three groups perform equivalently in terms of problem-solving effectiveness, suggesting that the impaired problem-solving impairment seen in suicidal individuals is particularly related to emotional distress.

Mindfulness directly targets this cognitive vulnerability by strengthening the individual's ability to respond to thoughts and emotions with less reactivity; mindfulness therefore acts primarily on the suicidal mode's cognitive system. This is accomplished through cultivation of present-moment awareness and focused attention, such that adaptive responses can be effectively generated and implemented in the presence of emotional distress and suicidal beliefs and thoughts. Mindfulness often appears very similar to relaxation, which has led some to propose that the observed improvements in mood disturbance and distress associated with mindfulness might be due to a relaxation response (Benson, 1975). Research demonstrating similar positive effects of mindfulness and relaxation on overall distress reduction has further supported this claim that the two techniques are actually the same (Jain et al., 2007; Kabat-Zinn et al., 1992; Speca, Carlson, Goodey, & Angen, 2000; Stetter & Kupper, 2002).

Although the forms of mindfulness and relaxation initially appear similar, the two techniques have different targets and proposed mechanisms of action. Relaxation exercises, as noted in the previous section, impact emotional distress indirectly through changes in physiological arousal (i.e., decreased sympathetic arousal and increased parasympathetic activity), whereas mindfulness exercises impact emotional distress indirectly through changes in cognitive processing. In fact, relaxation and mindfulness have been found to be equally effective at reducing emotional distress, but mindfulness additionally contributes to more marked reductions in ruminative thoughts and behaviors than relaxation (Jain et al., 2007). Critically, the observed reductions in ruminative thoughts mediate the relationship between mindfulness exercises and changes in emotional distress, suggesting that mindfulness improves emotional distress by changing cognitive processes. Relaxation does not, however, demonstrate this same relationship, suggesting that its positive effects on emotional distress differ from that of mindfulness. Jain et al. (2007) also reported another notable difference between mindfulness and relaxation: Large improvements in positive emotions were associated with mindfulness, whereas only a small improvement was associated with relaxation. These data suggest that mindfulness and relaxation, although similar on the surface, operate in very different ways.

Treatments incorporating mindfulness techniques have contributed to significant reductions in suicidal ideation (Katz, Cox, Gunasekara, & Miller, 2004; Miklowitz et al., 2009) and suicidal behaviors (Katz et al., 2004; Linehan, Comtois, & Korslund, 2004), most likely through the mechanism of reduced cognitive reactivity (Lynch, Chapman, Rosenthal, Kuo, & Linehan, 2006). A wide range of mindfulness exercises have been developed and written about (e.g., Hayes & Smith, 2005; Linehan, 1993; Williams et al., 2006), none of which are necessarily any better than others, resulting in considerable flexibility for the BHC.

Sample scripts for two basic mindfulness exercises can be found in Figure 6.3. In the first script ("sensory focus"), the BHC facilitates increased awareness of sensory experiences to introduce and foster basic attention regulation skills. The second script ("conveyer belt") outlines a somewhat more complex task designed to teach the patient how to observe thoughts and internal experiences without judgment and to refocus their attention in the presence of distressing mental experiences.

Mindfulness techniques can be easily combined with relaxation strategies or cognitive techniques (e.g., coping cards) to target multiple systems simultaneously. For example, the BHC might begin an intervention with a basic relaxation exercise to reduce physiological arousal. Then incorporate a mindfulness task to facilitate the patient's awareness of the relaxation response (e.g., focusing on heart rate, paying attention to muscle tension). Alternatively, the BHC might direct the patient to increase awareness of suicidal beliefs and maladaptive thoughts while engaged in the relaxation exercise and notice how it is possible to remain calm and relaxed while having distressing thoughts. Once skill mastery has been demonstrated during the appointment, the BHC should collaboratively establish a plan for the patient to practice mindfulness skills on a regular basis.

Consider the following exchange between Mary and the BHC following the conveyer belt mindfulness intervention, noting the similarities with and the differences from the follow-up questions recommended for relaxation exercises:

BHC [B]: What did you notice happening inside your body while we did that activity?

CSC [M]: I was breathing slowly.

B: What else did you notice?

M: I felt more relaxed.

B: In what part of your body did you notice that relaxation sensation?

M: My shoulders and my chest, and my arms felt heavier. My heart rate also slowed down.

B: Good. Now did you notice that you were still having bothersome thoughts while we did that?

M: Yes, I was thinking about how fat I am and then I thought about taking the pills.

B: Well, what was different about those thoughts this time as compared with all the other times you've thought those things?

M: Well, they didn't seem so bad this time, like not as overwhelming.

B: And you noticed the calmness in your shoulders, chest, arms, and heart while thinking these things?

M: Yeah, I guess so.

B: So you can have bothersome thoughts and remain relaxed and calm at the same time.

M: Yeah. I didn't think that was possible.

In this vignette, the BHC followed a combined relaxation/mindfulness intervention with strategic questions designed to further augment Mary's mindful self-awareness and counter the belief that aversive thoughts and experiences cannot be tolerated.

Suicidal patients with high cognitive reactivity struggle with sustaining attention and focus over extended periods and therefore might struggle with mindfulness exercises. This can be particularly true for patients who routinely utilize avoidance strategies in response to traumatic memories. Some mindfulness-based treatments incorporate lengthy mindfulness sessions with high frequency (e.g., daily meditation sessions up to 60 minutes in duration;

Sensory Focus

Go ahead and get yourself settled into your seat in a comfortable position with both feet on the floor and your hands resting in your lap. If you feel comfortable closing your eyes while doing this activity, go ahead and close them. If you'd prefer to keep your eyes open, that's fine, just fix your gaze on a point on the wall or the floor so that your eyes aren't wandering around while we do this. I want you to begin by taking a slow, deep breath in, and then very slowly breathing out. Good. And repeat that: a slow, deep breath in, and then a very slow breath out. Very good. I want you to repeat this slow, rhythmic, deep breathing at this pace, and while you breathe in this way I'm going to give you some directions to help you pay attention to some different sensations.

First, I want you to pay attention to the sensation of breathing. I want you to notice how the air feels as you slowly breathe in and fill up, then notice how that air feels as it leaves your body and you deflate. Breathe in and fill up, and breathe out and deflate. Notice how your chest expands and then deflates.

Next, I want you to take just a moment to pay attention to the sense of sound. Pay attention to all the sounds that you can hear right now, even those that you might not typically pay attention to or you might ignore. [Sit in silence for several seconds.] Notice all the sounds of the clinic in the background that you didn't notice before. [Sit in silence for several seconds.] And now return your attention back to your breathing, slow and deep, in and out.

Next, I want you to pay attention to the sensation of touch. Notice what it feels like to sit in your chair. [Sit in silence for several seconds.] Notice the sensation of wearing your glasses [watch/shoes/necklace]. Notice how its weight feels resting on the bridge of your nose and how the arms feel wrapped around your ears. [Sit in silence for several seconds.] Notice the sensation of your hands resting on your legs. [Sit in silence for several seconds.] And return again to your breathing, in and out.

Now just take a few moments to continue focusing your attention on whatever sensations you might experience in your body, just noticing them for a few moments then returning your attention to your breathing. Again and again, always returning to your breathing, over and over again. [Sit in silence for several seconds up to one minute.]

And now I'd like for you to take just two more deep, slow breaths, and when you're ready you can open up your eyes again.

FIGURE 6.3
Sample brief mindfulness scripts.

Conveyer belt

Go ahead and get yourself settled into your seat in a comfortable position with both feet on the floor and your hands resting in your lap. If you feel comfortable closing your eyes while doing this activity, go ahead and close them. If you'd prefer to keep your eyes open, that's fine, just fix your gaze on a point on the wall or the floor so that your eyes aren't wandering around while we do this. I want you to begin by taking a slow, deep breath in, and then very slowly breathing out. Good. And repeat that: a slow, deep breath in, and then a very slow breath out. Very good. I want you to repeat this slow, rhythmic, deep breathing at this pace, and while you breathe in this way I'm going to give you some directions to help you pay attention to some different experiences.

First, I want you to pay attention to the sensation of breathing. I want you to notice how the air feels as you slowly breathe in and fill up, then notice how that air feels as it leaves your body and you deflate. Breathe in and fill up, and breathe out and deflate. Notice how your chest expands and then deflates.

Next, I want you to take just a moment to pay attention to the sense of sound. Pay attention to all the sounds that you can hear right now, even those that you might not typically pay attention to or you might ignore. [Sit in silence for several seconds.] Notice all the sounds of the clinic in the background that you didn't notice before. [Sit in silence for several seconds.] And now return your attention back to your breathing, slow and deep, in and out.

Next, I want you to imagine a conveyer belt in your mind. Take a moment to look at this conveyer belt moving through your mind, from one side to another. Next I want you to imagine that your thoughts are on top of this conveyer belt, moving past you through your mind. Sometimes we have thoughts that are like pictures or images in our head. Place these images on the conveyer belt and watch them move past you. When they've moved past you return your attention to your breathing and the sense of sound. Sometimes we have thoughts that are like words or sentences, like someone is talking. Place these sayings on the conveyer belt and watch them move past you as well, and when they've moved past, you return your attention to your breathing and the sounds. You might notice that some of the thoughts that move past you on the conveyer belt come back into your mind. That's okay, just place them back on the conveyer belt and watch them again, and then return your attention to your breathing and the sounds.

Take a moment to think about something that bothers you or a problem in life, and notice your thoughts about that problem moving past you on the conveyer belt, and then return your attention to your breathing and the sounds. Probably these bothersome thoughts will come back again. Just put them on that conveyer belt again and watch them move past another time, and then return to your breathing and the sounds. You can repeat this over and over as many times as you need to, always returning to your breathing and the sounds. Just watching your thoughts and ideas moving past you on the conveyer belt, every time returning your attention back to your breathing and the sounds, again and again and again. [Sit in silence for several seconds up to one minute.]

And now I'd like for you to take just two more deep, slow breaths, and when you're ready you can open up your eyes again.

FIGURE 6.3
(continued)

Kabat-Zinn, 1990; Segal, Williams, & Teasdale, 2002), but such sustained engagement in mindfulness activities can be very difficult, if not impossible, for many suicidal patients. BHCs should therefore prescribe only what the patient can realistically accomplish to gain a sense of mastery and accomplishment and then gradually increase the intensity of the intervention to further develop mindfulness skills. Patients (and providers) can mistakenly assume that only very time-intensive periods of mindfulness will be beneficial, although there are no data to support this assumption. Thirty seconds of mindfulness is better than none and lays the foundation for 45 seconds, 60 seconds, and increasingly longer periods of mindfulness implementation. This brief, mastery-based approach to mindfulness acquisition is a well-established treatment approach and is a component of efficacious suicide-focused treatments such as dialectical behavior therapy (Linehan, 1993) and is very conducive to the primary care setting.

CORE COMPETENCIES FOR THE BEHAVIORAL HEALTH CONSULTANT

1. Implement interventions based on empirically supported treatment modalities.
2. Match interventions to relevant suicidal mode systems in order to optimally deactivate the suicidal crisis.
3. Practice skills with patients during the appointment to ensure mastery and collaboratively develop specific and realistic behavior plans to reinforce skills use in daily life.
4. Assist patients in troubleshooting common problems and barriers to effective skills implementation.

CHAPTER 7

Preparing for Crises

When considering effective management of suicidal patients, providers typically think only of those actions that occur during the clinical encounter: suicide risk assessment procedures and intervention techniques. Much less considered but arguably just as important as these in-session actions are those steps taken by the provider (and the clinic at large) before suicidal crises occur to set a culture and climate that is prepared for effective work with suicidal patients. Because working with patients in crisis can be anxiety-provoking for providers, setting the conditions by which suicidal crises can be more easily and effectively responded to can reduce provider stress and improve decision-making. During a crisis is not the time the behavioral health consultant (BHC) wants to be figuring out what steps should be taken to transport a patient for inpatient evaluation. Similarly, BHCs do not want to find out that a suicidal patient did not show up for a scheduled appointment 3 days later. Primary care providers (PCPs) likewise want to know before they prescribe a 90-day supply of medications that a patient is a multiple suicide attempter.

Planning ahead and establishing basic clinic procedures designed to improve monitoring and management of suicidal patients can therefore function to (1) increase provider confidence in their ability to manage suicidal patients, (2) increase provider confidence in his or her colleagues' ability to manage suicidal patients, (3) improve consistency in care within a provider over time, (4) improve consistency in care across multiple providers within a single clinic, and (5) reduce the likelihood of error through repetition over time and decreased anxiety. In addition to improved clinical care for patients, each of these factors contributes to enhanced professional and legal protection for individual providers and the clinic as a whole because staff members who are adequately prepared to respond to suicidal patients are much more likely to meet and maintain standards of care.

When preparing for crises, it is recommended that any procedures or expectations adopted by the primary care clinic be standardized across all providers and staff members so that consistency can be achieved across the entire team and the benefits discussed earlier can be fully realized. Preparing for crises include a range of informal and formal activities that can be facilitated by the BHC, including standardization of clinical terminology, implementation of tracking and suicide alert systems, developing procedures for monitoring patients referred to specialty settings, and coordinating procedures with inpatient facilities in the event hospitalization is desired. In this chapter, several preparatory activities designed to reduce the likelihood of patients "falling through the cracks" will be discussed. Some of these activities will be quite easy to implement and are generally applicable to all clinics (e.g., standardization of clinical terminology), whereas others will vary depending on local laws and/or settings (e.g., procedures for transporting patients). In all cases, BHCs should work with the primary care team to determine which strategies and techniques would best prepare their team for suicidal crises.

STANDARDIZED CLINICAL TERMINOLOGY FOR SUICIDE-RELATED BEHAVIORS

The issue of inconsistent terminology and language relating to suicidality has received considerable attention and discussion within the professional literature, with several groups calling for the adoption of a standardized terminology (e.g., O'Carroll, Berman, Maris, Miscicki, 1996; Silverman et al., 2007). In Chapter 3, we introduced the notion of a standardized clinical terminology for suicide-related behaviors and presented the following terms and definitions:

- *Nonsuicidal morbid ideation or death ideation:* Thoughts in which death is a desired outcome but there is no evidence of self-infliction or suicidal intent. Oftentimes, this is expressed as a wish to die without self-infliction.
- *Suicide ideation:* Thoughts in which self-inflicted death is a desired outcome and which may or may not include a plan but does not involve an explicit attempt. This is often experienced as a "weighing of options" regarding suicide.
- *Suicide threat:* Any interpersonal action, verbal or nonverbal, without a direct self-injurious component, that a reasonable person would interpret as communicating or suggesting that suicidal behavior might occur in the near future.

- *Suicide plan:* A proposed method of carrying out a design that will lead to a potentially self-injurious outcome.
- *Self-harm or nonsuicidal self-injury:* A self-inflicted, potentially injurious behavior for which there is evidence that the person did not intend to kill himself or herself (i.e., had no intent to die). Self-harm may result in no injuries, nonfatal injuries, or death.
- *Suicide attempt:* A self-inflicted, potentially injurious behavior with a nonfatal outcome for which there is evidence of intent to die. Suicide attempts may result in no injuries or nonfatal injuries. Suicide attempts that result in death are classified as suicide.
- *Suicide:* A self-inflicted death for which there is evidence (either explicit or implicit) of intent to die.

We then discussed how accuracy in clinical language can affect clinical care on an individual basis with suicidal patients through its impact on the therapeutic alliance.

From a systemic perspective, standardization of clinical language is also extremely important. The advantages of using standard terminology from a systemic perspective include (a) improved clarity, precision, and consistency of a single provider's practice both over time and across patients, (b) improved consistency of communication between providers, (c) improved clarity in documentation, (d) elimination of inaccurate and potentially damaging language from our vocabulary, and (e) elimination of the unrealistic goal to predict suicide (as opposed to assessing risk) through recognition of the complexity and variability of suicidal intent in determining ultimate clinical outcome. These points are especially pertinent to clinics with multiple providers and staff, where standardized terminology could significantly minimize the likelihood for miscommunication and error among the various members of the primary care team, since everyone is using the same terms and definitions to describe certain behavioral patterns.

Practically speaking, adoption of a standardized terminology means that when one provider or staff member (whether BHC, PCP, nurse, or other support staff) notes that a patient recently "self-harmed" via cutting himself or herself, all other staff members immediately understand how this behavioral pattern differs from a suicide attempt via cutting. Perhaps an even more salient practical illustration of the value of standardized language is the differentiation of nonsuicidal morbid ideation from suicide ideation, each of which has a very different level of indicated clinical response. BHCs should therefore assist the primary care team in adopting a standardized terminology for suicide-related phenomena and support the consistent use of this terminology in everyday clinical and administrative work.

"WARM HAND-OFF" POLICIES

The "warm hand-off" is a common practice within integrated primary care clinics in which the PCP directly introduces the patient to the BHC at the time of the patient's medical visit. The two primary purposes of the warm hand-off is to establish an initial face-to-face contact between the patient and the BHC and to transfer to the BHC the trust and working alliance that is already shared by the PCP and patient. Typically, the BHC meets with the patient at that time, but scheduling limitations on the part of both the patient and the BHC might preclude an immediate encounter. Many BHCs report that the warm hand-off reduces the likelihood of a no-show. When working with suicidal patients, warm hand-offs should be made whenever possible so there is a direct transfer of responsibility from one provider to another and the patient does not fall through the cracks. The importance of this direct transfer of care can be seen in a practical case vignette that mirrors incidents in many primary care clinics:

During his appointment with his PCP, John reported recent onset of suicide ideation with planning and objective indicators of intent (purchasing a gun, writing suicide notes, intense periods of suicidal thoughts while lying in bed) following his wife's revelation of an affair and subsequent filing for divorce. The PCP conducted a brief assessment and suggested John meet with the BHC. The PCP walked to the BHC's office, but the BHC was out of his office at the moment, so the PCP directed John to take a seat in the waiting room until the BHC was available. The PCP instructed his nurse to find the BHC and update him about the case while he met with the next patient. After 15 minutes, the BHC returned to his office and the nurse filled him in on the situation. The BHC went to the waiting room to meet with John but discovered that John was longer there, and no staff members knew where he went. After several minutes of searching, the nurse called John's cell phone number and discovered that John had left the clinic because he thought he had been forgotten about.

The case of John's premature departure highlights the value of warm hand-offs for high-risk cases and illustrates several issues for consideration when developing procedures and policies about transferring suicidal patients from one provider to another.

Clinics should consider instituting a warm hand-off policy for 100% of suicidal patients, whether the hand-off is going from PCP to BHC or from BHC to PCP (or any other combination of primary care staff). When a provider is meeting with a patient at the time a warm hand-off is desired, providers should be able to interrupt the current medical appointment to initiate the warm hand-off. If the BHC is in with a patient, for example, the PCP should knock on the door and ask the BHC to step out momentarily so the PCP can directly inform the BHC about the case. This does not mean the BHC has to discontinue the current medical appointment right then and there to see the suicidal patient. It just means that an introduction will be made to ensure a direct provider-to-provider transfer is initiated.

Because it is not realistic to assume that the BHC will be immediately available for every suicidal case, however, clinics should also establish policies about how to monitor suicidal patients while waiting to be seen by a provider. In the clinical vignette, John should have been placed in an area where he could be directly monitored by medical staff aware of his risk status and not distracted by other tasks. Seating John in an examination room across from the nurse's station, for instance, might have been a useful alternative.

It is similarly unrealistic to assume that the BHC will always be physically present in or near his or her office (perhaps because they went to lunch, are in the bathroom, are working with a PCP in an examination room). Clinics should therefore consider methods for easily contacting the BHC in emergent cases, such as via pager or cell phone. In these cases, clinic staff need to be aware that they will have to implement monitoring procedures while they wait for the BHC to become available. Finally, clinics should have a "plan B" in place when the BHC is completely unavailable (e.g., on vacation, sick). Outlining who PCPs or other clinic staff can contact for consultation regarding high-risk cases when the BHC is gone can relieve a considerable amount of apprehension on the part of the PCPs and ensure that BHCs have the opportunity for self-care.

BHCs should consult with primary care teams in the development and institution of these warm hand-off policies and contingencies to facilitate patient care and reduce the likelihood of risk management problems illustrated in the case of John. Warm hand-off policies substantially enhance accountability for patient care and support a team-based approach to suicide risk management.

TRACKING PROCEDURES FOR HIGH-RISK PATIENTS

Keeping track of suicidal patients over time can often be a challenging task for primary care teams, especially in clinics with multiple providers. The ability to effectively monitor and track suicidal patients is critical for safe and effective risk management, as provider incontinuity increases the likelihood of patients "falling through the cracks." Consider as an example the case of Mary, whom we have been following throughout the past few chapters.

Mary is a multiple attempter who has repeatedly overdosed on sleep and pain medications. Her general utilization pattern is to book acute appointments for emergent needs but generally does not consistently or reliably attend scheduled follow-up appointments. Although her PCP can usually meet with her for these acute appointments, in a large clinic with multiple providers, she cannot always meet with him because she typically accepts an appointment with whichever PCP has the next available appointment instead of waiting a little longer to meet with her assigned PCP. It is therefore quite possible that other providers less familiar with her history might prescribe a potentially lethal amount of pain or sleep medications.

As can be easily seen in Mary's case, instituting a system for tracking her (as well as other patients identified as having elevated suicide risk) over time would greatly improve her care, reduce the likelihood of adverse events, and enhance risk management for the clinic as a whole.

One tracking strategy widely used by many outpatient mental health clinics, especially those with multiple mental health providers, is the "high-risk log." The high-risk log is a centralized document that lists all patients assessed to be at elevated risk for suicide. Patients are added to the high-risk log when they reach a predetermined minimum threshold for risk and are removed when they meet predetermined criteria for crisis resolution. Brief, pertinent clinical information that is updated regularly for each case is also maintained on the high-risk log (see Figure 7.1 for a sample high-risk log). Although originally created in outpatient mental health clinics to aid in the monitoring of high-risk patients, the high-risk log can easily be transported to the primary care clinic, where it can be particularly useful due to primary care's much higher patient volume with less frequent and consistent follow-up. High-risk logs enable improved follow-up for suicidal patients who do not show up for appointments and facilitate appropriate "triaging" of cases such that patients with greater need are prioritized over patients with lower risk and need. Such logs also encourage teamwork by all members of the primary care team and can facilitate documentation of management and care.

In general, high-risk logs offer protection for the patient, the provider, and, ultimately, the clinic because they categorize patients by their ongoing level of risk, thus facilitating and documenting clinical decision-making (Wingate, Joiner, Walker, Rudd, & Jobes, 2004). This continuous risk-tracking procedure is useful for managing suicidal behavior because it aids the clinic in monitoring those patients who are at risk for suicide, provides a safety net in the event that the patient's assigned provider is unavailable, and facilitates professional consultation and communication among collaborating disciplines. In our BHC practice, we have found the high-risk log to be an invaluable tool for tracking suicidal patients. Implementing a high-risk log is simple and straightforward and consists of a few critical steps.

Patient Info	PCP	Next Appointment	Clinical Information	Date Added	Adding Provider
Mary Q. 54 y/o F	Dr. Adams	Jun 15	**Chronic risk w/ acute overlay:** Multiple attempter, several OD via sleep/pain meds, recurrent depression, current depressive episode, recent prep behaviors, meds in the home, not currently in specialty MH tx [Jun 8]	Jun 8	Dr. Psych and Dr. Adams
John Doe 16 y/o M	Dr. Brown	Jun 20	**Acute**: Ideator, recent breakup with girlfriend, thinking about OTC med OD, depressed mood, took "handful" of Benadryl "just to see how it would feel" but not suicide attempt, parents secured meds at home [May 15] SSRI med f/u with BHC, SI reduced [May 23] Phone f/u by nurse, no SI in past 3 days, outpatient psychotherapy started with Dr. Zed [Jun 1]	May 15	Dr. Brown and Dr. Psych
Jane Doe 21 y/o F	Dr. Smith	Jun 20	**Acute:** Single attempter, academic stressors, attempted suicide via SSRI OD on May 31, possible bipolar disorder, access to meds at home, wishes she had died after last attempt, plan to re-attempt by taking more meds with alcohol, high agitation and insomnia, psychiatry appt in 4 wks [Jun 2] Med f/u and refill with BHC, no change in SI, intent, plan [Jun 7] Med f/u and refill with BHC, using CRP, decreased SI intensity [Jun 13]	Jun 2	Dr. Psych and Dr. Smith

FIGURE 7.1
Sample high-risk log.

Steps in Implementing a High-Risk Log

Step 1: Define the Minimum Threshold for Adding a Patient to the High-Risk Log

The first step in developing and implementing a high-risk log as an effective risk management procedure is to define what is meant by "high risk" since the operationalization and definition of this construct ultimately drives how the high-risk log will be used clinically and administratively. For example, many outpatient mental health clinics using high-risk logs set "moderate risk" as the minimum level of risk for inclusion of a patient on the log. In other words, if a provider assesses a patient to be at moderate risk or higher for suicide using the clinic's accepted definition of "moderate" risk (see Chapter 5), then the provider is required by clinic policy to add the patient to the high-risk log. Other clinics choose to use "mild" risk as the threshold for adding a patient to the high-risk log.

There is no absolute right or wrong way to define when to add a patient to the high-risk log since the notion of "high risk" will likely vary depending on the nature of the specific population served by the clinic. Community health clinics with an empanelment characterized primarily by low-income populations with multiple comorbidities and limited access to social and medical resources will likely establish a different threshold for high-risk log inclusion than a family medicine clinic serving middle- to upper-class adults who are comparatively "healthy." Likewise, a pediatric or adolescent clinic's criteria for inclusion might differ from an internal medicine clinic serving primarily older adults.

This is not to suggest that the notion of risk is completely arbitrary. As discussed previously, factors such as multiple attempter status, behavioral rehearsal of suicide or preparatory behaviors, and intensity of suicidal ideation are critical determinants of risk that will remain central to determine risk across all patient groups. Each clinic must, however, consider its context and the population it serves to identify the most appropriate approach for effectively using a high-risk log. In general, it is recommended that clinics choosing to use high-risk logs establish an inclusion threshold of "moderate" risk since this is the level of risk in which suicidal intent begins to emerge and the likelihood of suicide risk becomes much more pronounced. This is especially true for multiple attempters, who can easily shift from lower to higher levels of risk very rapidly. BHCs are well positioned to assist the primary care team in considering those contextual factors that can affect successful use of a high-risk log and should therefore play a central role in establishing the clinic's criteria for adding and removing patients.

Step 2: Define the Criteria for Removing a Patient From the High-Risk Log

In our experience, high-risk logs fail most often for two primary reasons: first, because providers and administrators do not adequately operationalize the criteria by which a suicidal episode is judged to be "resolved" and, second, because providers and administrators are reluctant to remove patients once they have been classified as "high risk." The first factor is simply the result of inadequate planning and is easily remedied by developing criteria for high-risk resolution. The second factor is a bit more complex, however, as it stems from anxiety and fear about litigation and can therefore be more difficult to correct. In both cases, the result is a high-risk log that grows in size because no one is ever removed; the high-risk log consequently loses any clinical utility. For a high-risk log to be clinically useful as a method for tracking high-risk patients, there must be a built-in mechanism by which patients are no longer considered high risk, and are removed.

How a clinic defines "resolution" of suicidality warranting removal of a patient from the high-risk log will necessarily vary by the clinic population, since "high risk" can mean very different things in different clinics. Criteria for removing a patient from the high-risk log should at a minimum be the same the criteria for adding a patient to the log. For example, if a particular family medicine clinic decides to add patients to the high-risk log when meeting the predetermined definition of "moderate" risk, then patients should not be removed until, at the very least, they no longer meet criteria for moderate or higher risk (i.e., when classified as "mild" risk). In other words, the criteria for adding a patient to the list are the same as the criteria for removing a patient from the list. Because suicide risk can fluctuate within relatively short periods, criteria for removing a patient from the high-risk log should additionally entail a temporal dimension (e.g., length of time below the threshold for high risk). The addition of a temporal criterion ensures that resolution of suicide risk is reasonably stable over time.

Although there is no empirical evidence yet available to guide the operationalization of "resolution" from a temporal standpoint, a common practice in outpatient mental health settings is to define "resolution" as three consecutive weekly appointments with no suicide ideation or planning (e.g., Jobes, 2006). Translated to the primary care clinic, a criterion of 1 month (i.e., the 3-week criterion "rounded up" to a unit that better matches a typical primary care follow-up period) without suicide ideation or planning might be established. This can be assessed by asking the patient if he or she has "thought about suicide at all, even just once, since our appointment last month."

By establishing reasonable criteria by which a patient is no longer considered to warrant increased monitoring, BHCs can ensure the primary care team effectively utilizes the high-risk log as a tool for improving clinical management as opposed to simply being a tool for managing provider anxiety and fear. Furthermore, consistently following sound practice procedures provides a high level of legal protection in the event of adverse events.

Step 3: Determining Who Manages the High-Risk Log

The next step for successful utilization of the high-risk log involves integrating administrative oversight with clinical practice. A single staff member (with one or more alternates or back-ups) should be responsible for maintaining and updating the high-risk log, as well as ensuring effective communication of these updates with all primary care staff members. When adding, removing, or in any other way modifying a patient's status, providers should inform the log manager to make the change. Centralizing responsibility for managing the high-risk log minimizes the likelihood of errors being made by multiple providers or staff members. It also places someone in charge of overseeing risk management to reduce the chances of clinical or administrative oversight. Although the log manager can be any member of the primary care team, it is generally advisable to assign this task to the support staff so that providers (including the BHC) do not lose clinical contact time. The log manager can meet regularly with the BHC and a small team of providers to staff cases in order to ensure high-risk patients are being adequately managed.

Step 4: Using the High-Risk Log Effectively

Log managers should update all clinic staff frequently regarding changes in suicidal patients' risk levels and status and should ensure that supplemental tracking procedures (e.g., chart alert systems described in the next section) are up-to-date as well. High-risk logs should be easily available to any clinical staff with direct patient contact, including telephone triage staff and administrative staff in charge of checking patients in and booking appointments. This latter group is most likely to identify missed appointments or receive calls from suicidal patients seeking to cancel or reschedule booked appointments and therefore needs to be regularly updated on patient status. Front desk and triage staff members should notify providers when patients on the high-risk log call to cancel or reschedule an appointment or when these patients do not show up for a scheduled appointment. Reasonable efforts to contact patients who cancel or do not show up should be considered and documented in all cases. For example, nurses or other clinic support staff might call high-risk patients within 24 hours of a missed appointment to conduct a brief risk screening, assess treatment adherence, and reschedule the appointment if needed. Being able to quickly identify suicidal patients who miss or call to cancel appointments can minimize disruptions in care continuity, improve overall treatment and patient outcomes, and manage liability risk.

BHCs should plan to develop training programs for primary care staff members to confidently accomplish all of these tasks, including competent suicide risk assessment and ability to effectively interact with and respond to at-risk patients. BHCs should also be prepared to provide ongoing support and consultation to the primary care team to maintain skill level and fidelity over time. Consultation with primary care staff is discussed in detail in Chapter 8.

Types of Chart Alert Systems

Chart alert systems serve as visual cues to "flag" suicidal patients in order to alert providers about elevated risk for suicide. These alert systems can be maintained in or on the medical record to improve awareness of suicide risk for all medical providers and staff who handle the medical chart. When tied directly to the high-risk log, alert systems can assist providers in monitoring fluctuations in suicide risk over time and can help to manage liability risk by reducing the likelihood of clinical errors that could potentially be linked to adverse events. Suicide alert systems are similar in intent and design to allergy alert systems used in many clinical settings to immediately alert providers to known patient allergies, thereby reducing the chance of iatrogenic medical effects. Alert systems can vary depending on the format of the medical charting system, whether paper or electronic.

Paper Chart Alert Systems

For clinics utilizing paper records, alert systems can be as simple as placing a physical indicator on the medical record to visually remind staff of elevated suicide risk upon immediate handling of the chart. This visual cue should be easily modified as clinically indicated. An example of a very simple alert system uses colored Post-it notes: a red Post-it note placed below the patient's name indicates moderate or higher risk (i.e., on the high-risk log) and an orange Post-it note indicates mild risk. For clinics seeking to further refine their tracking system, red Post-it notes can be used to identify high-risk cases, orange can denote moderate risk, and yellow can identify mild risk. These colored Post-it notes should be changed as indicated by high-risk log managers as patients fluctuate in risk level over time. To distinguish chronically suicidal patients, a separate and distinct Post-it note (e.g., green-colored) with the letters "MA" (for multiple attempter) written on it can be permanently affixed to the chart. BHCs should work with clinic staff to determine the optimal level of information required by providers to trigger appropriate clinical responding. At the very least, however, it is recommended that multiple attempters be identified with a distinct alert mechanism to remind providers of the chronic and persistent nature of the multiple attempter's suicide risk.

Electronic Charting Systems

Similar procedures can be developed for clinics utilizing electronic medical records, although the design and implementation of such alert systems will understandably require a greater amount of technological knowledge. Electronic medical records can be programmed to include graphic symbols or processes designating suicide risk level. Visual cues for the electronic charting system might include designing an icon that alerts providers to a patient's suicide risk status when the electronic record is opened up or otherwise accessed. Alternatively, a warning message can be designed to display on the screen when the record is opened. As with paper charting systems, it is recommended that separate icons and warning messages be developed for chronically suicidal patients.

ESTABLISHING PROCESSES FOR COORDINATION OF SERVICES WITH INPATIENT FACILITIES

On occasion, BHCs and PCPs will assess patients whom they believe are at such extreme or imminent risk for suicide that an evaluation for inpatient hospitalization is indicated. Whenever multiple facilities are involved in a patient's care, coordination among all treatment providers is always in the best interest of the patient. Unfortunately, more often than not, communication between inpatient and outpatient facilities can be difficult to achieve, especially when the inpatient facility and primary care clinic are parts of separate organizations.

The challenges associated with coordination between inpatient and outpatient facilities are further complicated by seeming disparities in admission and discharge standards among various inpatient facilities (i.e., hospital A "does not take anyone" vs hospital B, who "admits anyone who walks in"). BHCs and PCPs often express frustration that many patients who are referred and subsequently admitted to inpatient facilities are discharged without the referring provider being notified, which hinders smooth coordination of and transition in care. Adding to providers' frustration is the difficulty that can be experienced in obtaining records of a patient's care while admitted to the inpatient facility. Given that the week immediately following discharge from inpatient care is associated with a dramatic rise in the risk for death by suicide (ranging from an 86- to 375-fold increase, depending on sex and primary psychiatric diagnosis; Qin & Nordentoft, 2005), any barriers to effective transition of care can be problematic. It is therefore recommended that BHCs consult with primary care clinics regarding the establishment of some relatively simple strategies that can facilitate communication between the primary care clinic and the inpatient facility and reduce barriers to transition of care.

Memorandum of Understanding

The primary care clinic might benefit from developing and entering into formal agreements with frequently used inpatient facilities focused on referral and admission procedures, communication between the primary care clinic and the inpatient facility, and coordination in discharge planning. A memorandum of understanding (MOU) can include items related to the release of medical records from the inpatient facility directly to the PCP and/or BHC to ensure timely coordination of care and sharing of clinical information with the primary care team. A template for an MOU can be found in Figure 7.2. As can be seen in this sample, the MOU details procedures for both admission and discharge, including specific agreements regarding the sharing of clinical information. The MOU also clearly delineates the expectations regarding scheduling outpatient follow-up appointments within the first week of discharge. The follow-up appointment is specified as occurring with either an outpatient mental health provider or the primary care team. In general, patients being discharged from inpatient care due to suicide risk should be provided with a firm outpatient follow-up appointment as part of their discharge plan.

The most appropriate level of care following discharge from inpatient care is specialty outpatient mental health. By including the option of follow-up with the BHC in primary care within the first 72 hours of discharge, however, the primary care team can enhance the inpatient facility's options regarding timely follow-up. Patients might also be more likely to initially follow-up in primary care following discharge than to follow-up with an unknown mental health specialist. In these cases, the BHC's primary task is to support the hospital's discharge plan and facilitate the transfer of care to outpatient specialty mental health treatment (whether psychotherapeutic and/or psychopharmacological). The BHC can be a critical player in communication and coordination of care in another key way: Because inpatient mental health providers might feel more comfortable sharing clinical information with another mental

This agreement is entered into by and between the [primary care clinic], hereinafter "the clinic," and [inpatient facility], hereinafter "facility."

The parties acknowledge and agree to the following:

1. When a patient needs transfer from one of the above named facilities to the other above named facilities, the receiving facility agrees to admit the patient as promptly as possible, without regard to race, color, creed, age, sex, handicap, or national origin in accordance with federal and state laws and regulations, provided admission requirements are met and bed space to accommodate the patient is available.

2. Admissions to aforementioned facility:
   - 2.1. The clinic may refer patients directly to the aforementioned facility without waiting for the assessment team to travel to the hospital and assess the individual in question.
   - 2.2. The clinic will send a copy of the assessment performed on the patient.
   - 2.3. The clinic will attempt to obtain signed consent for release of information from the patient using the facility's consent forms prior to transfer to the facility. If this is not possible, the facility will request consent for release of relevant medical information to the clinic. Clinic staff will also request consent to release relevant information from clinic evaluations and treatment to the facility to enhance continuity and collaboration in providing care.
   - 2.4. Following admission, and in the event that consent for release of information is granted, the facility will provide the clinic with information related to diagnosis, clinical status, and nature of treatment being provided, upon request.

3. Discharge from the aforementioned facility:
   - 3.1. At least 24 hours before discharge of referred patients, the facility will contact the clinic (telephone number XXX-XXXX) to notify the clinic of the pending discharge. The facility will arrange a follow-up appointment with a licensed outpatient mental health provider and/or the clinic to occur within 72 hours of discharge.
   - 3.2. Patients will stay the number of days determined by the facility's provider to be clinically necessary.
   - 3.3. A copy of the treatment summary and discharge plan will be provided to patients upon discharge. A second copy will be faxed to the clinic at XXX-XXXX.

FIGURE 7.2
Sample memorandum of understanding.

health provider instead of a PCP, the BHC can serve as the primary point of contact for the inpatient facility during the discharge process.

Release of Medical Information Forms

As mentioned in the MOU, having patients fill out and sign release of medical information forms before hospitalization can be a useful strategy for obtaining a patient's inpatient facility records as quickly as possible following discharge. Even if no formal MOUs are established with inpatient facilities, obtaining copies of these facilities' release forms can be extremely beneficial for BHCs and PCPs. When a patient is assessed to be at high enough risk to warrant an inpatient evaluation, BHCs should ask patient to fill out a release of medical information form while awaiting transport to the inpatient facility. Patients can also sign the primary care clinic's release of information form to share the results of the BHC and other PCPs' risk assessment with the receiving inpatient facility, which can be quite valuable for the inpatient facility's medical provider. The two release of medical information forms (one from primary care and one for the inpatient facility), pertinent medical notes from the BHC and primary care staff, and any other relevant paperwork can be placed in a manila envelope and carried by the patient (or someone escorting the patient) to the inpatient facility, where it should be turned over to the medical staff.

Procedures for Patient Transport

Patients deemed to require inpatient evaluation due to extreme or imminent suicide risk should not be allowed to transport themselves to an inpatient facility for a number of reasons. First, acutely suicidal individuals tend to have impaired mental status, which can affect concentration, decision-making, and problem-solving. Allowing the severely suicidal patient to operate a motor vehicle is therefore dangerous not only for the patient, but also for other drivers or pedestrians in close proximity to the patient. Related to this, motor vehicles can be used as a mechanism for intentional self-injury or suicide; directing patients to drive themselves to inpatient facilities can therefore be very risky from a risk management perspective. A third reason why suicidal patients should not transport themselves to inpatient facilities is for accountability reasons (e.g., What if the patient changes his or her mind on the way to the hospital, or what if he or she gets lost on the way?). When transporting suicidal patients, it is therefore important to have a person responsible for ensuring the patient reaches the destination in a timely and safe manner. BHCs should assist the primary care clinic in developing procedures for transporting suicidal patients to inpatient facilities.

One of the most common and straightforward methods for patient transport is to use a significant other of some kind, whether a family member, spouse, or friend. In some cases, the patient will be accompanied to the primary care appointment by a significant other who can be enlisted for assistance. In other cases, however, it might be necessary for the BHC to facilitate contact with a significant other. For example, a spouse or friend might be called to come to the clinic to pick up the patient for transport. A benefit of calling a significant other is that it activates the patient's social network in support of treatment, which can be a useful treatment strategy. At times, there will be no significant others available to assist with patient transport. In these cases, laws governing the response to and transport of suicidal individuals will vary by area, but in most jurisdictions, the suicidal individual would be transported to the identified medical facility by law enforcement personnel. As discussed earlier in this chapter, BHCs should be knowledgeable about their local laws regarding these issues and be prepared to educate patients about these procedures. Informing patients about each of the steps involved in transporting them to an inpatient facility and any subsequent evaluation can significantly reduce worry or apprehension as these processes unfold.

Emergency Department Discharge Card

When referred for inpatient evaluation, patients' will almost always have their first clinical contact with the inpatient facility's medical staff in an emergency department (ED), which is where the risk assessment to determine whether to admit the patient will likely occur. If a patient is assessed by the attending provider to fall below the threshold for admission and/or if there are insufficient beds available for admission, the patient will likely be discharged from the ED with recommendations to follow-up with an outpatient mental health specialist. In most cases, the patient will not be assisted in booking a mental health appointment, however, under the assumption that the patient will be able to take care of this on their own after leaving the hospital. In addition, no contact with the referring provider is generally made to communicate the decision not to admit the patient. The result is a suicidal patient being discharged from the ED with no intervention or concrete follow-up plan and no notification provided to the primary treating provider (i.e., the PCP and/or BHC). To address this problem, the BHC can use the ED discharge card (see Figure 7.3) to improve the care of suicidal patients who are not admitted to inpatient facilities.

The ED discharge card is a very specific delineation of steps to be taken by a suicidal patient (or the parent of a suicidal child) who has been discharged from the inpatient facility's ED without admission following a referral by the BHC or other member of the primary care team. It can be printed up on half sheets of paper or 3 × 5 index cards and handed to suicidal patients who are being referred to an inpatient facility for further evaluation. Patients should be directed to keep the card in their pocket, purse, bag, or any other easily accessible area.

As can be seen in Figure 7.3, the ED discharge card lists very specific, concrete actions to be taken in the event of discharge without admission. While awaiting transport to the inpatient facility, the BHC should review each step with the patient to ensure the steps are understood. BHCs should explain that the ED discharge card is the procedure to be used if the hospital does not admit the patient for inpatient care. Critically, the BHC should emphasize that the patient should not leave the ED until after he or she has gone through all steps of the ED discharge card.

The patient is first directed to contact the primary care clinic's emergency call (or triage) number. If the clinic does not have an emergency call number, the BHC should work with the primary care team to develop an alternative strategy (e.g., an on-call pager). The on-call provider should be prepared to conduct a brief risk assessment with the patient focusing on availability of means for suicide, mind-altering substances, and social support networks. BHCs should consult with primary care staff to develop a standardized sequencing of questions for this management strategy and be able to provide training to those staff members who will be answering the emergency call number. On-call staff should also be able to access the clinic schedule and book an appointment within the next 24 hours, ideally with the BHC. If no appointment slots are available, suicidal patients should be double booked or instructed to walk-in during lunch or any other open slot during the day. On-call staff should provide a specific appointment date and time to the suicidal patient (i.e., "tomorrow morning at 8:00 AM" instead of "any time tomorrow") and explicitly ask the patient to write the day and time on the ED discharge card, then ask the patient to repeat the day and time back to them to confirm accuracy.

Next, on-call staff should direct the patient to use their crisis response plan (CRP) between now and the scheduled follow-up appointment and highlight that use of the CRP is the standard recommendation and intervention to be used in between appointments. On-call staff should ask patients where the CRP is currently located and to verbally recite the CRP's steps. This step reinforces the importance of the CRP and provides another opportunity for rehearsal, which aids memory and increases the likelihood of adherence.

Following each of these steps, the on-call staff member should then ask the patient to provide a subjective rating of their likelihood to use the CRP between now and the appointment (e.g., "On a scale of 0 to 10, with zero being not at all likely and 10 being a certainty, how likely are you to use your CRP between now and your next appointment to maintain your

You (or your child) have been referred to the emergency department (ED) in order to be evaluated for hospital admission. This means that your level of risk for suicide is currently considered to be elevated and we are concerned about your safety.

If you are discharged from the ED and NOT admitted to the hospital, please follow these steps:

1. Prior to leaving the ED, call the clinic emergency call number (XXX-XXXX) and tell the individual what has happened. They will have some questions for you and may ask you to stay in the ED until they have had a chance to talk with the ED physician about your situation. **Do not leave the ED until the clinic staff member on the telephone gives you permission to leave.** The staff member on call will confirm that you do NOT have access to any method for suicide if you are leaving the ED. They will also confirm you do NOT have access to substances such as alcohol or other drugs.

2. The staff member on call will provide you with a specific day and time for your follow-up appointment in the clinic. This will likely be the next morning. Please do NOT leave the ED without a specific day and time to follow-up in the clinic.

   Write your appointment day/time here: ______________________________

3. Use your crisis response plan until you follow-up in the clinic. This is the plan you developed with your clinic provider, and is what you would normally do between appointments.

4. If you do not feel safe leaving the ED, please tell the staff member on call.

5. **For parents:** Closely monitor and supervise your child until the follow-up appointment. This means your child should not be left alone until the follow-up appointment and should not be allowed to leave you or another identified adult's presence. They should be monitored at all times until the follow-up appointment. The on-call staff member will review with you the importance of removing access to all methods for suicide (and related safety procedures regarding constant observation and access to substances). If you do not believe you can accomplish careful monitoring you need to let the on-call staff member know.

FIGURE 7.3
Emergency department discharge card.

safety?"). Patients who self-rate their confidence level at 7 or higher should be asked one final time to verbally confirm their appointment time, at which point the on-call staff member should provide permission to leave the ED. For patients reporting lower confidence levels, the on-call staff should seek to identify those factors contributing to lowered sense of safety and assist the patient in problem-solving these issues until the patient feels more confident in using the CRP effectively. For parents of referred children, on-call staff should additionally review steps for monitoring their child until the follow-up appointment. Means restriction counseling should be additionally provided to parents of discharged suicidal children.

ASSISTING PATIENTS IN TRANSITIONING TO SPECIALTY MENTAL HEALTH CARE

Patients at moderate or higher risk for suicide should be referred to specialty mental health care since it is in the moderate range of risk that a suicidal patient begins to mentally and behaviorally prepare for their suicide. Patients with this level of risk generally require a much higher intensity and frequency of intervention and monitoring than can be practical for a primary care setting. For patients at mild risk for suicide, management within primary care is feasible, although referral to a specialty mental health setting might nonetheless be considered. Unfortunately, referral to specialty settings does not necessarily mean a patient will actually follow up with a mental health professional; only half of the patients referred to a mental health specialist believe they need the referral in the first place, and of those who do, the majority would prefer to solve the problem themselves (Kessler et al., 2001), with more perceived barriers reported among emotionally distressed patients (Mohr et al., 2010). For the remaining few who do believe they need help and are willing to seek out treatment, the process of accessing mental health services can be a difficult process for patients for a number of reasons.

Patients may be unaware of how to access specialty mental health care, particularly when they have to navigate through what might seem to be a confusing administrative maze of managed care. A common tactic used by many PCPs and BHCs to assist patients is to have preprinted lists of mental health providers available for distribution to patients when a referral is requested or recommended. For a highly distressed individual, however, being directed to choose a mental health provider from a long list of anonymous names can be daunting. Stigma about mental health can increase a patient's anxiety about seeking care and reduce the likelihood of them following through with a referral. Because of their reduced capacity to tolerate emotional distress, suicidal patients in particular can become easily frustrated and give up quickly if their initial efforts to access care are not successful (e.g., mental health providers who do not immediately answer the telephone, are not accepting new patients, or are not covered by the patient's insurance).

These barriers to care do not even begin to address the problem of identifying qualified mental health providers who have the requisite training and experience to competently manage and treat suicidal patients. Training deficiencies in suicide risk assessment and management is quite common, with only a minority of professional training programs offering formal training on the topic (Bongar & Harmatz, 1991; Debski, Spadafore, Jacob, Poole, & Hixson, 2007; Feldman & Freedenthal, 2006; Kleespies et al., 1993) and fewer than half of mental health professionals receiving no more than a few hours of formal training on the topic (Feldman & Freedenthal, 2006; Guy, Brown, & Poelstra, 1990; Reeves, Wheeler, & Bowl, 2004).

In the absence of any widely available, uniform resources for locating mental health providers with sufficient training and experience in managing and treating suicidal patients, BHCs can provide considerable assistance to patients by helping them identify specialty care providers who are covered by their managed care organization and who are most likely to be competent and skilled in treating suicidality. BHCs can assist patients in "narrowing the field" in identifying a mental health specialist by educating them about the following six core features of effective treatment for suicidal behaviors (Rudd, 2009):

1. Effective treatments have clearly articulated, well-defined, and understandable theoretical models that are embedded in empirical research.
2. Effective treatments target suicidality specifically, rather than focus on peripheral symptoms and clinical presentations.
3. Effective treatments target treatment adherence in a specific and consistent fashion.
4. Effective treatments target skill deficiencies (e.g., emotion regulation, anger management, problem solving, interpersonal relationships).
5. Effective treatments emphasize self-reliance and personal responsibility, as opposed to dependency on the treatment provider.
6. Effective treatments emphasize the importance of crisis management and access to available emergency services during and after treatment, with specific and clear plans of action being developed.

The value of networking with local mental health providers therefore cannot be understated, since BHCs familiar with local treatment providers are better positioned to assist patients in connecting with those specialists who provide treatments characterized by the factors above. Patients can likewise benefit from BHCs who teach them how to ask about the services provided by a given mental health provider, which can include role playing the initial contact with a specialist. This might entail rehearsing or practicing questions to ask during an initial telephone call (e.g., inquiring if new patients are being accepted, if the provider accepts the patient's insurance, if any intake paperwork should be completed in advance). The BHC can also educate patients about the typical format of an intake session and follow-up sessions. Each of these strategies can significantly reduce any anxiety or uncertainty a patient might have about initiating treatment.

BHCs should also consider developing transfer policies and procedures for monitoring care while patients are in the process of being transferred to specialty mental health settings. BHCs and PCPs are encouraged to continue regular clinical contact with suicidal patients until the initiation of treatment with specialty mental health can be confirmed. This might entail weekly appointments or "check-ups" over the telephone to reinforce crisis management skill implementation, appropriate use of behavioral interventions, and/or medication adherence. This is especially critical in light of the Food and Drug Administration's (FDA, 2007) recommendation to increase monitoring of patients after the initiation of antidepressant treatment and after changes in doses. Although the PCP and BHC will undoubtedly spearhead such tracking and monitoring, the full primary care team should be used to assist in this task. For example, after adequate training by the BHC, nurses or case managers (depending on specific clinic resources and distribution of duties) can assist in calling patients to determine treatment adherence, identify barriers to accessing mental health services, conduct brief risk assessments, track clinical improvements or worsening, and determine if a patient has scheduled or kept appointments with specialty providers. Nurses can then report these contacts to the PCP or BHC for appropriate clinical decision-making.

Confirmation of a successful transfer of care should be accomplished wherever possible to "close the loop" on high-risk cases. Confirmation of a successful transfer can be obtained in a number of ways, the simplest of which is obtaining an objective indicator of "proof of attendance" from the patient, such as signing a consent form to release information to the specialty mental health provider or providing the primary care team with the specialist's contact information or business card. Even more useful to the primary care team is asking the patient to sign a release for the mental health specialist to communicate directly with the BHC on behalf of the PCP, whether verbally or via written report. In our experience, mental health specialists are much more willing to communicate with a BHC than with a PCP due to shared background and training. Likewise, PCPs tend to prefer that BHCs serve as a liaison between them and mental health specialists since BHCs can "translate" mental health assessment results and treatment recommendations into a language that is easily understood by the PCP. In addition to functioning as a highly valuable risk management process for documenting successful transfer of care, direct communication with the mental health specialist provides an opportunity for PCPs and BHCs to more directly and explicitly support outpatient specialty mental health care.

CORE COMPETENCIES FOR THE BEHAVIORAL HEALTH CONSULTANT

1. Facilitate the implementation of a standardized terminology for suicide-related behaviors across all primary care team members.
2. Assist in the development of tracking and alert systems to aid in the monitoring of high-risk patients and multiple attempters.
3. Implement procedures and policies to coordinate care with inpatient facilities and specialty outpatient mental health settings.

CHAPTER 8

Consulting With Primary Care Staff

One of the most important ways in which a behavioral health consultant (BHC) can impact the health of a very large population is actually not through direct contact with patients, but rather indirectly through consultative and collaborative work with primary care medical providers. BHCs who pursue the goal to modify and enhance routine medical care by primary care providers (PCPs) can have a remarkable effect on a very large number of people. It is during conversations about cases, feedback regarding a BHC's interventions, and "curbside consultations" that the BHC gradually shapes the PCP's clinical thinking and treatment decisions. Over the course of multiple conversations and feedback sessions, the PCP identifies patterns and trends in the BHC's recommendations and starts to adopt these strategies into their standard practice. As the PCP begins utilizing evidence-based behavioral techniques and interventions on their own, they enhance their practice and the health of their patients.

Because the PCP team sees many more patients than any single BHC, implementation of behavioral interventions by PCPs on a regular basis can result in much wider dissemination of behavioral skills across the full spectrum of the population. As an illustration, consider a family medicine clinic that has approximately 20 PCPs managing an empanelment of approximately 45,000 enrollees (this is about the size of the clinic that the lead author worked in). Each PCP meets with an average of 20 to 25 patients per day, for a total of 400 to 500 patient visits per day within the entire clinic, which does not include the many telephone calls to patients made by nurses and administrative team members. A single BHC working in this clinic might see an average of 15 patients per day—a very small percentage of the clinic's total capacity. If, however, the BHC can influence the routine practice of even a fraction of this clinic's PCPs, the total number of patients receiving behavioral health interventions can be dramatically increased from only 15 per day to upward of a few hundred per day. In this way, the BHC indirectly improves the health care of a much larger proportion of the population by influencing the routine clinical practice of PCPs and other clinical team members.

Similarly, the most dramatic and powerful method for improving the care and management of suicidal patients is not through direct contact with the BHC or any other mental health specialist, but rather indirectly through the enhancement of primary care clinical practice. The process of influencing clinical care can take a considerable amount of time and depends heavily on the nature of the relationship that the BHC has with the primary care team members. The BHC should always begin by identifying clinic "champions" for improved behavioral health care. Within any clinic employing multiple providers, the BHC will undoubtedly find variability in PCPs' openness to integrate with consultative services. Some PCPs are very quick to embrace the inclusion of a behavioral health provider and actively seek out frequent consultation and advice. These PCPs provide the overwhelming amount of business for the BHC and are willing to directly ask the BHC for assistance and guidance. They are also the providers who are most likely to consult with the BHC for the full spectrum of behavioral health issues, not just the traditional "psych cases" such as depression or anxiety.

On the other end of the spectrum, the BHC will also encounter PCPs who are less open to integrated behavioral health. These PCPs are more likely to hold a more traditional biomedical perspective of health conditions that does not routinely incorporate behavioral and psychosocial treatment components, and consultations regarding mental health or psychosocial issues are usually obtained from a more narrow psychiatric perspective. Nonetheless, behavioral and psychosocial issues are so prevalent in primary care that biomedical providers cannot avoid them completely and will eventually feel the weight of these issues on their medical practice. Despite their seeming lack of interest in behavioral approaches to health care, most biomedical providers absolutely use behavioral, social, and psychological interventions in at least some aspects of their care and are therefore amenable to influence if the BHC uses the right approach. Robinson and Reiter (2007) discuss strategies for working with biomedical providers in great detail and are a useful for resource for BHCs struggling with this issue.

There are many ways for a BHC to engage PCPs once a strong relationship has been formed. Even with biomedical providers, BHCs who first focus on building a collegial relationship can foster increased interest in what the BHC has to offer, especially in situations where the BHC can reduce workload and burden associated with challenging patients. Building personal, in addition to professional, relationships with PCPs is key to influencing their practice, since personal relationships can directly break down any barriers to and stereotypes about behavioral health providers. BHCs should therefore strive to attend clinic gatherings such as potluck meals, welcome and farewell parties, and drug representative luncheons, as well as social gatherings that occur after work hours. In the same way that a patient-provider relationship is critical to optimal health outcomes, the PCP-BHC relationship is critical to optimal consultation. In this chapter, we will discuss effective consultation with primary care staff in several critical areas related to managing suicidal patients: forming effective treatment alliances with patients, routinely screening for psychosocial health issues including suicidality, prescribing antidepressants for suicidal patients, and determining when to recommend a patient be evaluated for inpatient care.

CONSULTATION ON FORMING EFFECTIVE ALLIANCES WITH PATIENTS

The importance of establishing a strong relationship with the suicidal patient cannot be overstated. Even the best therapeutic techniques are of limited value when an adequate relationship does not exist with the patient. The ability to form an effective alliance with the patient is not a competency applicable only to BHCs, however; it is just as important for PCPs to have this basic skill set as well. Some have argued that a solid therapeutic relationship is not just preferable, but rather essential to successful work with suicidal patients (cf. Maltsberger, 1986; Shneidman, 1981; 1984). It should be noted, however, that such a competency is relevant not only for the issue of suicide risk. The PCP's ability to accurately elicit relevant clinical information in an efficient and effective manner is critical for optimal medical care across all health care issues, including the specific issue of suicide risk. The BHC can play a dramatic role in shaping the behaviors of PCPs to improve their ability to connect with patients and instill the sense of comfort and trust that leads to better outcomes.

Motto (1979) referred to active relatedness to describe provider behavior that facilitated a stable attachment and positive alliance with the patient. In particular, he emphasized availability as the central issue, especially emergency availability, returning telephone calls, and scheduling more frequent appointments when necessary. Perhaps the best-known work on the topic of relationship issues in the treatment of suicidal patients is that of Linehan (1993), who has identified several relational strategies geared toward the type of ongoing and effective long-term relationship with patients that PCPs often seek to establish. During clinical contacts with suicidal patients, Linehan has noted that general provider emotional reactions and behavior in response to suicidality are particularly important. Harmful emotional reactions can include fear, malice, aversion, hate, anxiety, and worry, whereas harmful behaviors include ending appointments prematurely, being late for appointments, and frequently rescheduling appointments. These provider behaviors have been termed *therapy-interfering behaviors* (Linehan, 1993) since they directly undermine the working alliance required for helping patients to improve. Because emotional reactions are largely influenced and shaped by one's preexisting assumptions about suicide, it is critical for PCPs to explore and address personal beliefs and history relevant to suicide before assessing and working with suicidal patients.

The BHC can foster this process by formally or informally identifying any potentially problematic personal beliefs and professional responsibilities related to working with suicidal patients that a PCP might have. Although this education can certainly be accomplished through formal in-service trainings and didactics, the BHC will likely have a much more profound impact by engaging PCPs in one-on-one discussions about suicidality that arise during the course of routine feedback and consultation or even over the break room table or coffee pot. Several questions can help BHCs to engage PCPs in understanding their beliefs about suicide; we also recommend that BHCs take the time to consider these questions for themselves:

1. *Why do people kill themselves?* This question helps the PCP articulate their *personal theory* of suicide and allows the BHC to educate the PCP about an empirically supported, biopsychosocial model of suicide. What is important for the PCP to understand is that their personal beliefs will likely shape their clinical behaviors, such as asking questions about certain clinical areas and potentially neglecting other critical areas. If you discover that much of what a PCP understands about suicide is driven by anecdotal evidence, it may well be a sign that personal beliefs are playing a prominent role.
2. *Is it ever acceptable to die by suicide?* Does the PCP believe that suicide is acceptable in cases of terminal illness? Are there other conditions under which suicide is seen as acceptable? The importance of this question in a medical setting is clear since it is not uncommon for those suffering from medical illnesses to consider suicide. Providing implicit (or explicit) sanction of suicide can be risky with patients who are ambivalent about suicide and are seeking care. Regardless of the PCP's position about the issue, it is vital that the BHC help them to explore and identify their personal stance ahead of time. The BHC might also need to help the PCP separate personal belief from professional obligation, since professional obligations with suicidal patients are sometimes more clear and straightforward than our personal sense of responsibility.
3. *Can suicide be prevented?* This question is important on many different levels because it hints at the PCP's hopefulness—a component of the alliance that is often evident to patients and can influence treatment adherence. BHCs should work to support PCPs who seem overwhelmed

and overworked, as this can manifest itself in negative beliefs and attitudes about a patient's potential for recovery. This question also helps identify the PCP's sense of responsibility in terms of intervention and management, which impacts their likelihood to consult with the BHC.

4. *Do people that access care want to die?* It is important for PCPs to explore their thoughts about those accessing care, especially the seemingly paradoxical question about why those patients who are so hopeless come in for help any way. PCPs need to recognize that accessing care is, in and of itself, an act of hope, even when those presenting are experiencing the most desperate of circumstances. BHCs should teach PCPs to recognize the significance of the simple act of accessing care and the importance of reflecting this back to the patient. Even in cases of persistent and chronic suicidality, continuing to access care is evidence of hope.
5. *What are your individual professional responsibilities with a suicidal patient?* The PCP's answer to this question will help the BHC to understand the steps that are likely to be taken to intervene with and manage suicidal patients. BHCs should help PCPs to understand that their responsibilities are not endless, but rather should be driven by clearly articulated policies and procedures. If PCPs cannot answer this question in simple and straightforward terms, the clinic likely does not have clear expectations, policies, and procedures regarding high-risk patients. The BHC can play an important role in helping to develop these policies and procedures.

Preparing Primary Care Providers for Working With Suicidal Patients

In many ways, establishing and maintaining a relationship with suicidal patients is simplified by the crisis nature of clinical presentation: Expectations and "next steps" tend to be quite clear and basic in crisis situations, although a provider's personal beliefs and emotional state can cloud this process and make it appear much more complex than it really is. From the very first contact the PCP needs to be aware of the patient's level of interpersonal comfort during clinical encounters because suicidal patients tend to withdraw prematurely from evaluations and treatment. This early withdrawal tends not to be because of improvement in symptoms but because of severe psychopathology and related interpersonal dysfunction (Rudd, Joiner, & Rajab, 1995). Suicidal patients often simply cannot tolerate the distress and upset created by the interpersonal contact. As a result, establishing a strong alliance in the initial evaluation with a suicidal patient can be hampered by the severe nature of the psychopathology that might present, so it is important for the BHC to help the PCP in the following areas:

1. *Suicidal patients are likely to have difficulty in interpersonal situations and are likely to have interpersonal skill deficits.* They might have trouble expressing or controlling their emotions, so the goal is to create a safe environment. This can be accomplished by giving the patient time to talk and reinforcing him or her even when anger and hostility emerge. Reinforcing interaction and openness on the part of the patient can be straightforward and simple.
2. *Remember that when suicidal, patients are at a relative worst point in their lives.* They might have trouble communicating clearly due to difficulty concentrating or organizing their thoughts or perhaps because they are crying. Patients in acute suicidal crises often feel powerless and out of control already and need to be reassured to some degree without feeling patronized or dismissed. Being able to sit with a patient who is distress—in contrast to trying to get them to stop crying, for example—communicates comfort and confidence.
3. *Anticipate the possibility of being provoked by suicidal patients.* Especially for chronically suicidal patients, provocative and undercontrolled behavior is oftentimes routine. Respond to provocation by acknowledging the patient's distress in the context of the current crisis and redirect the patient to the task at hand by emphasizing the collaborative nature of the evaluation process.
4. *Recognize that the initial assessment process involves laying the groundwork for ongoing care regardless of whether that care is provided by the primary care team.* All evaluations and assessments are therapeutic exchanges, no matter how the eventual course of care develops. Because patients' willingness to continue in treatment and ongoing care is significantly influenced by the initial evaluation, patients who have a negative experience during the initial evaluation will be more difficult to engage during the next crisis and will be less likely to adhere with treatment recommendations, including referral to specialty mental health settings.

In general, a simple and straightforward formula for working and communicating with suicidal patients is to begin with the patient's stated goal and then structure the evaluation and interventions around this goal. BHCs should teach PCPs how to join patients in identifying realistic, shared health care goals and motivating patients to engage in treatment recommendations. Perhaps most important, however, is for BHCs to assist PCPs in remaining calm and confident when working with highly distressed patients. This can be accomplished by role-playing with the PCP, modeling patient interviewing strategies, and teaching basic stress management techniques. Developing clinical tools to assist and guide PCPs while interacting with suicidal patients (e.g., pocket cards with sample sequencing of questions, decision-making algorithms, etc.) can serve to improve consistency and confidence in clinical practice.

Most importantly, BHCs must encourage PCPs to engage effectively with suicidal patients instead of avoiding them (e.g., by retreating from the examination room to get the BHC as soon as the patient endorses suicidality) in order to improve their clinical skills and competence, which in turn strengthens the PCP's ability to develop and maintain working alliances with patients. Simple and straightforward tips and suggestions that BHCs can provide to PCPs on the issue of working with suicidal patients are provided in Figure 8.1. The simple reality of the matter is that the BHC will not always be available for assistance with high-risk patients; the PCPs must therefore develop mastery of basic alliance-forming strategies when working with suicidal patients.

CONSULTATION ON ROUTINELY SCREENING FOR PSYCHOSOCIAL HEALTH ISSUES AND SUICIDALITY

Given that psychosocial and behavioral factors account for the overwhelming majority of presenting complaints in a primary care clinic, PCPs who are knowledgeable about screening and assessing for these health issues will have a much greater impact on the health of their population. Unfortunately, most PCPs report a general lack of training and experience in these areas. Because suicidal behaviors are a consequence of intense psychological distress, early identification of and intervention with psychosocial health factors can have a tremendous preventative role on the development of a suicidal crisis. Furthermore, specific and pointed screening for suicidality can enhance the detection of those at risk for suicide across all stages of the suicidal state—from the earliest emergence of death as a desired state (i.e., nonsuicidal morbid ideation) to the imminently suicidal (i.e., specific planning with preparatory behavior).

Routine screening for suicide risk within primary care is currently not standard practice. As noted by the U.S. Preventive Services Task Force (USPSTF, 2004, p. 820), "the evidence is insufficient to recommend for or against routine screening by primary care physicians to detect suicide risk in the general population." As a result, the BHC will likely experience initial resistance to recommendations or suggestions that PCPs begin routine screening of patients for suicidality, with the USPSTF's (2004) recommendation typically

Addressing patients' difficulties with interpersonal situations

- "I know it's difficult to talk about such personal issues, particularly with someone you've just met. I appreciate you being willing to do so with me."

Responding to anger and hostility with compassion and understanding

- "It sounds like you've had a very difficult time over the last few weeks. I can see why you would be upset and angry."
- "Thank you for telling me about this even though you're angry."

Reassuring a patient who is in distress

- "Is there anything I can do to help you feel more comfortable and make it easier for you to talk?"
- "Take your time. If you need to just take a few minutes to catch your breath, you can do that."

Responding to provocation

- "I can understand why you'd be so upset. You've had some very painful things happen recently. How about we take five more minutes to talk more about this if you'd like, then I'll need to ask you some questions and get some information so that we can make a decision together about what we can do to help."

Building the evaluation and interventions around a common goal

- "What would you like to be different about what's happening in your life right now?"
- "If you were to feel less depressed, what would be different?"
- "When you decided to come in today, what did you hope I would be able to help you with most?"

Reducing the patient's shame and guilt

- "It's not uncommon for people to think about suicide when feeling depressed and hopeless."
- "I can see how you would think about this given all that has been going on."

FIGURE 8.1
Tips and suggestions for building an effective alliance with a suicidal patient.

being cited by PCPs as the chief reason for opposing implementation of routine screening. Another concern that PCPs often have about routine screening is the very likely prospect of identifying a greater number of suicidal patients, consistent with findings that routine screening with symptom checklists and instruments are associated with increased rates of patient disclosure of suicidal thoughts and behaviors (Bryan, Corso, Rudd, & Cordero, 2008). Understandably, PCPs worry about how to respond appropriately to a potentially larger number of patients identified as elevated in risk for suicide (i.e., "What happens if they say yes?").

It is therefore important that BHCs recognize the possibility that some initial resistance and reticence by PCPs might exist and not to become discouraged by it. The BHC should approach routine screening in an incremental manner, beginning with changes in those processes over which the BHC has the greatest amount of direct influence and control. We therefore recommend that the BHC introduce and implement routine screening for suicide risk in a series of stages that gradually build on each other, beginning with consultation regarding enhanced screening and identification of psychosocial health issues and psychiatric conditions in general. In other words, the BHC's primary goal should be to fundamentally change the manner in which PCPs think about the health care of their patients, such that psychosocial health factors are routinely considered in clinical decision-making. The BHC can accomplish this through ongoing consultation with PCPs and feedback following evaluation and intervention with referred patients. Feedback should be seen by the BHC as an educational process, with each interaction between the BHC and PCP being a "teaching moment" regarding behavioral health issues.

From this perspective, consultation with PCPs regarding patient care can be seen as occurring on two levels. The first level is that of basic content, in which the BHC describes to the PCP the results of a patient evaluation and the specific interventions provided, providing direct feedback and recommendations regarding follow-up care and treatment planning. This level of consultation can generally be summed up as, "This is what I did, and this is what I recommend you do." For example, a BHC providing feedback regarding a depressed patient might provide information to the PCP about the duration and extent of the depression, assistance with diagnostic specificity, information regarding behavioral planning (e.g., increased exercise or enjoyable activities), and recommendations regarding pharmacotherapy.

The second, higher level of consultation is that of shaping clinical practice over time, in which the BHC uses the process of feedback from a specific case as an example of clinical care on a more generalized level. At this level, the BHC approaches the feedback process not only as an opportunity to relay clinical information for one particular case, but also as a mechanism by which to demonstrate fundamental principles about particular health problems and medical treatment that can be generalized across all cases with similar presentations. Again using the example of a depressed patient, the BHC can use feedback as an opportunity to discuss such issues as the relative efficacy of antidepressant medications and cognitive-behavioral interventions, when medications might or might not be indicated, the interaction of depression with various health conditions (e.g., diabetes, hypothyroidism, insomnia), or strategies for eliciting information about mood states from patients. The goal of this second level of consultation is to slowly shape and improve the clinical practice of the PCP over time. As the PCP gains comfort and confidence in assessing and treating psychosocial health conditions, the BHC can begin consulting with the PCP more directly on the issue of suicidality using the same two-level approach to consultation and feedback.

Although BHCs and PCPs will certainly work collaboratively to manage suicidality from the BHC's first day in the clinic, it has been our experience that PCPs will generally be reluctant to change their practice approach to suicidality until they have first established a solid professional relationship with a BHC who has helped them to increase their sense of comfort and clinical confidence with more generalized behavioral health issues. After initial buy-in and trust has been obtained from the PCP, the BHC can generally leverage the PCP to consider more complex and "riskier" clinical issues such as screening for suicide risk. The BHC should first take into consideration the potential impact of a screening process on the routine clinical care of the PCP as well as other clinical staff members. New procedures and processes that add too much work or slow down the efficiency of staff members are not likely to be supported. The BHC must therefore have a good understanding of how the clinic currently functions and its various processes so that a new process can be integrated as seamlessly as possible. Likewise, the process needs to be simple enough that it can be learned and implemented without a great deal of training or preparatory work. The BHC should therefore first identify the preferred method for screening (i.e., verbal questioning, paper-and-pencil screening, etc.).

An example of a process that has worked well in many clinics is paper-and-pencil screening. Upon check-in at the front desk, the patient receives a clipboard with a paper version of the screening device from a staff member who directs the patient to complete the form in the waiting room before the appointment. The front desk staff gives the form to each patient at every appointment check-in regardless of the reason for visit because this approach is simple and easy to remember (i.e., "all patients get the form at every appointment") and does not appreciably increase work demands for the front desk staff or PCPs. For PCPs preferring a verbal screening approach, the BHC should take the time to model methods and approaches for questioning patients in a manner that decreases patient anxiety while increasing the accuracy of honest disclosure. Role-playing clinical encounters with PCPs is a particularly effective strategy for improving clinical interviewing since it enables behavioral rehearsal and practice. Likewise, creating pocket cards for PCPs with sample interview questions can enhance a PCP's sense of confidence during a clinical interview and enhance fidelity over time.

The BHC should suggest piloting the new process for only a limited amount of time (e.g., 1 month), at which point he or she will check in with staff members for feedback and suggestions as to how the process might be improved. For example, front desk clerks might be asked how implementing a screening process would work best for them, and PCPs can be asked if the screening process is easy to use within a routine medical appointment. Obtaining input and feedback from staff members affected by any new process is a critical step for developing a sense of collaboration and respect for the work of all team members, which increases the likelihood for buy-in and adherence to the process. As the new screening process becomes a routine part of the primary care service, clinical decision-making begins to address suicide risk as a routine part of basic medical care. BHCs should reinforce PCPs for implementing routine screening by emphasizing the resulting enhancement of clinical care. In general, the BHC's primary goal at the outset of any new screening process should simply be the demonstration of feasibility in an efficient and easy manner.

Once a screening process has been developed and implemented and has demonstrated feasibility, BHCs should consider gathering data that supports its effectiveness both in terms of efficiency (i.e., it does not add an unreasonable amount of work or time) and incremental value (i.e., it directly improves clinical decision-making and care). Efficiency data might be measured in terms of time spent by front desk clerks in handing out screening devices, answering patients' questions about how to complete the device, and keeping enough copies of the questionnaires available. Ideally, the process will have minimal time demands. To measure incremental value of the screening process, one very simple strategy is to look at the rate of identification of suicidal patients with the new screening process in comparison to the identification rate before the process (which can be accomplished through a review of medical records). As an example of an approach to demonstrating the effectiveness of a suicide screening process, Wintersteen (2008) introduced a standardized set of two suicide screening questions and implemented a 1-hour training program for PCPs, which resulted in a doubling of the rate of inquiry regarding suicide risk and a fourfold increase in the detection of suicidal youths in four primary care clinics.

CONSULTATION ON ANTIDEPRESSANT TREATMENTS FOR SUICIDAL PATIENTS

In 2004, the Food and Drug Administration (FDA) placed a black box warning label targeting suicidal thoughts and behaviors in children and adolescents on all antidepressant drugs, including the entire category of selective serotonin reuptake inhibitor (SSRI) antidepressants. The original intent of the warning label was to alert consumers and health care providers of an increased risk of suicidal thinking and behavior in children and adolescents. Embedded in the label, and potentially lost to consumers and providers alike, is that no deaths occurred in any of the aggregated pediatric trials studied by the FDA. The warning label was subsequently updated in 2007 to include not only children and adolescents, but all patients up to 24 years old. The expanded label also includes information about the benefits of antidepressants with older adults (65 years and older) along with a reminder that psychiatric disorders themselves are the most important cause for suicidality. The complete warning label is available at the following web link: http://www.fda.gov/cder/drug/antidepressants/default.htm. In addition to the label, information is available to health care professionals, patients, and family members in a supplemental medication guide (also available at the same web link) intended to clarify relevant facts and clinical recommendations. BHCs should familiarize themselves with the content of both documents.

Since the warning label appeared there has been considerable discussion and debate in the media and scientific community about its potential impact on mental health treatment. For example, researchers have noted that the volume of prescriptions for children and adolescents has decreased considerably since the warning was issued (Lineberry, Bostwick, Beebe, & Decker, 2007). A significant decrease in the rate of pediatric diagnoses of depression has also been observed (Libby et al., 2007). Specifically, from 1999 to 2004, diagnosis rates for pediatric depression almost doubled (from 3 to 5 per 1000); following the FDA warning label, however, rates returned to 1999 levels, essentially dropping by 70%. Pediatricians and PCPs accounted for the largest reductions in new diagnoses. This same study found that SSRI prescription rates fell below expected trend levels by 58%, one possible interpretation being that fewer parents are willing to seek care for their children given the risks raised by the warning label. Most importantly, and alarmingly, no evidence of increased use of other treatment options such as psychotherapy or psychiatric referral was found.

The rates of pediatric and adolescent depression diagnoses were not the only factors to show a marked difference from prewarning to postwarning label. Since the release of the warning label, an inverse relationship between antidepressant prescription rates and youth suicide rates has also been observed. In the United States, youth suicide rates increased significantly by 14% between 2003 and 2004, while in the Netherlands, a 49% increase in the youth suicide rate was observed. A simultaneous decrease of 22% in SSRI prescription rates for youth was observed in both these nations during that same time period (Gibbons et al., 2007). More recent data available from Canada indicate a more than threefold increase in child and adolescent suicide rates coupled with reductions in rates of antidepressant prescriptions and ambulatory visits for depression since the introduction of the warning label (Katz et al., 2008). These observed decreases in SSRI prescription rates have occurred despite compelling evidence about the efficacy and safety of these medications for children and adolescents (Milin, Walker, & Chow, 2003).

There is also evidence of a "spillover effect" with adults. Valuck and colleagues (2007) found that diagnoses of depression in adults experienced similar and significant reductions since the emergence of the warning label. Using a sample of adults with newly diagnosed depression from a medical claims database, they found the average percentage of adults with new depressive episodes was 88.6% before the warning label and 77.5% afterward, with an annual rate of decline of 7.7% (in contrast to 1.69% before the warning label). They concluded the most likely explanation was a spillover effect in which the warning label's original intent of targeting only those patients 24 years and younger was "spilling over" to adult patients since the warning label's release. Evidence of a potential spillover to the adult population is particularly problematic given that data from FDA and other sources have noted no differences in risk for suicidality among adults older than 24 years when taking antidepressants, along with clear evidence of a significant decline in risk for suicidality among patients older than 65 years who are treated with antidepressants.

Not only have there been "no completed suicides of any subject in any youth antidepressant trial" (Ryan, 2005, p. 938), but some providers and researchers have also argued convincingly that increased SSRI use may actually help *reduce* subsequent suicide rates. Indeed, emerging research does not support claims of increased risk for suicide or suicide attempts after starting treatment with SSRI antidepressants and actually points to decreased risk following initiation (Kahn, Kahn, Kolts, & Brown, 2003; Martinez et al., 2005; Simon et al., 2006). In an innovative study by Simon and Savarino (2007), for example, the incidence of suicide attempts in three outpatient settings (i.e., psychiatry alone, primary care, and combined psychotherapy and psychiatric medication) were tracked over time using a design that differed substantially from previous research studies, in that suicide attempt rates were not only tracked in the months following initiation of an antidepressant, but also tracked during the months preceding antidepressant initiation. The results of this study were quite compelling: The period with the greatest incidence of suicide attempts was actually found to be in the month immediately preceding prescription of the antidepressant, followed by the first month following the prescription, with the incidence of suicide attempts continuing to drop over the course of subsequent months. This pattern was observed across all three outpatient settings including primary care.

This temporal sequencing of relative risk for suicide attempt supports the perspective that patients are prescribed antidepressants because they are at increased risk for suicide, as opposed to becoming more suicidal as a result of the antidepressant. The benefits of adhering to antidepressant treatment for an extended amount of time have also been supported by the literature. Specifically, the likelihood of suicide attempt has been found to decrease for those who are on antidepressant treatment for a minimum duration of 6 months when compared with those on treatment for less than 8 weeks (Valuck, Libby, Sills, Giese, & Allen, 2004). Furthermore, very low rates of SSRI antidepressants found in the toxicology results of suicide deaths indicate that the overwhelming majority of suicide victims are not taking SSRIs at the time of their death (Ryan, 2005).

As noted earlier, of concern are reports that calendar year 2004 witnessed the first increase in suicide rates for adolescents and young adults in more than a decade—approximately 14% to 18% (Gibbons et al., 2007; Hamilton et al., 2005). As Lineberry and colleagues (2007) speculated, these two events—introduction of the warning label and increased suicide rates among teens and young adults—might well be related. In one of the first studies exploring the potential impact of the warning label on clinical practice, these researchers found clearly identifiable changes in day-to-day practice patterns in PCPs, including a decreased willingness to prescribe antidepressants, increased likelihood of referral to a mental health specialist, and a lack of willingness on behalf of patients to accept the medications (Lineberry et al., 2007). The authors concluded that "large numbers of both generalists and non-psychiatric physicians who formerly would have written antidepressant prescriptions themselves are choosing instead to refer patients to psychiatrists or other mental health specialists" (p. 520). This finding is consistent with other (not surprising) research demonstrating that FDA warning labels are linked to decreased prescribing patterns in general (Lasser et al., 2002).

One potential contributing factor to changes in clinical practice might be inaccurate understanding of the black box warning label by PCPs. Cordero, Rudd, Bryan, and Corso (2008) reported that an alarming 91% of PCPs incorrectly believed that deaths by suicide had occurred in the aggregated SSRI clinical trials, although the PCPs in this study did not indicate a decline in the willingness to prescribe. Approximately 90% of these same PCPs indicated that they routinely provided supplemental verbal information of some kind about antidepressants to their patients, which bears further attention in light of PCPs' very high error rate about the aggregated clinical trial results. It is possible that the observed decrease in willingness of patients to accept antidepressant medications might be due to fear inadvertently generated by the warning label in combination with inaccurate education by PCPs regarding the risks and benefits of antidepressant treatment. Interestingly, Cordero and colleagues further reported that the only significant predictor of PCP accuracy was the extent to which the PCP agreed with the warning label, with higher levels of agreement increasing the likelihood for error.

Most alarmingly, not only are fewer antidepressant prescriptions being written, but it appears that effective alternative treatments like psychotherapy are not being pursued. Although PCPs report increased likelihood to refer patients to mental health specialists, the fact that so few patients actually follow through with these referrals raises concerns that fewer patients are receiving treatment of any kind. Indeed, the data support this unfortunate situation: Fewer depressed children and adolescents are receiving a diagnosis of depression and subsequent treatment, whether pharmacological or psychosocial (Libby et al., 2007). As summarized by Pfeffer (2007), "the FDA advisories may have had the unintended effect of discouraging the prescription of antidepressants for pediatric patients and pediatric utilization of antidepressants without compensatory increases in other specific treatments" (p. 843).

Rudd, Cordero, and Bryan (2009) outlined several important facts that are frequently overlooked and often misunderstood about both the initial and revised versions of the black box warning label for antidepressants. First, there were no suicides across 4,400 patients in the pediatric trials (i.e., children and adolescents). Although there were suicides in the adult trials, the adult suicide rates were comparable across both the placebo and clinical arms (FDA, 2007), indicating no increased risk associated with antidepressants. Subsequent reanalysis of the FDA adult data for SSRIs, other antidepressants, and placebo drugs confirmed comparable suicide rates (total $N = 77$) across clinical and placebo arms, evidencing no increase in suicide risk among adults with antidepressant use (Gunnell, Saperia, & Ashby, 2005; Khan et al., 2003).

Second, although statistically significant, the rates of suicidality (defined as suicidal thoughts and behaviors) were low in the aggregated pediatric trial data. In terms of actual numbers ($N = 4,400$), 4% ($n = 176$) of pediatric subjects in the clinical arm and 2% ($n = 88$) in the placebo arm reported suicidal thoughts and/or behaviors, but no deaths occurred. Those patients who received an antidepressant therefore demonstrated a doubling in the relative risk of suicidality (i.e., a 4% risk for suicidality in the clinical arm divided by a 2% risk in the placebo arm)—a number that is often cited and very familiar to health care providers. This relative risk ratio drove the decision to place a black box warning label on all depressant medications. What is often overlooked is that the absolute risk of increased suicidality is only 2% (i.e., a 4% risk in the clinical arm minus a 2% risk in the placebo arm). It is also important to note that "suicidality" was unfortunately broadly defined in these trials and included a wide range of suicidal thoughts and behaviors of varying degrees of severity ranging from nonsuicidal morbid ideation to near-lethal suicide attempts. Because nonsuicidal morbid ideation and near-lethal suicide attempts lie on very distant extremes of the suicide risk continuum, lumping them together (and everything in between) under the unitary construct of "suicidality" obscures the actual nature of risk. The clinical significance of this low suicidality rate, particularly in contrast to overall treatment efficacy of antidepressants (and other psychosocial treatments), is debatable and has received limited attention in the literature.

Third, neither the FDA's warning label nor medication guide provides any age-related data regarding suicide risk, which provides no context for the FDA's findings. This is unfortunate, given that such context is critical to understanding the nature of risk over time and is an important consideration when weighing a decision about treatment. A quick review of suicide rates in the United States can help to provide a basic level of context, however. Specifically, those younger than 24 years are actually at the lowest risk for suicide when compared with older adults. According to the latest data available, the suicide rate (per 100,000) is 0.7 for children 5 to 14 years old, 10.0 for those 15 to 24 years old, 12.4 for those 25 to 34 years old, 14.9 for those 35 to 44 years old, 16.5 for those 45 to 54 years old, 13.9 for those 55 to 64 years old, 12.6 for those 65 to 74 years old, and 16.9 for those older than 75 years (Kung, Hoyert, Xu, & Murphy, 2008).

The general trend for increasing risk with age is confirmed by the observation that "older persons" represented 12.4% of the general population in 2005 but accounted for 16.6% of the suicides, in contrast to the "young," which represented 14.2% of the general population but accounted for 12.9% of the deaths by suicide. The FDA data do not indicate an increased risk for death by suicide for children, adolescents, and young adults taking antidepressants, a finding consistent with what we have known about suicide risk for this group for many years. It is also important to consider data regarding trends in suicidal thinking and behavior. As Kessler and colleagues (2005) have pointed out, data from the National Comorbidity Surveys (1990–1992 and 2001–2003) found no significant changes in suicide ideation or attempt rates during this time period despite the increased rate of antidepressant prescriptions.

Given that as many as 75% of depressed patients pursuing treatment receive medications, the bulk of which are SSRIs prescribed by general medical providers such as PCPs (Olfson et al., 2002), it is imperative that PCPs have an accurate understanding of the black box warning label and the findings of the aggregated antidepressant trials. Because BHCs are often asked to provide consultation regarding the use of antidepressant medications and to assist with medication compliance, as well as frequently being asked questions about medications by both patients and PCPs, BHCs must have a thorough understanding of the nature of the risk for suicidality associated with antidepressant use.

A line of research that might shed some light on the issue of antidepressants and suicidality is the clinical symptom of agitation—for example, physiological restlessness, psychomotor agitation, and racing/crowded thoughts

(Benazzi, 2005; Akiskal & Benazzi, 2005; Rihmer & Kiss, 2002; Rihmer & Pestality, 1999). It appears that the combination of these agitated symptoms in the presence of a depressive episode (i.e., a mixed episode) is a particularly pernicious and lethal combination that accounts for the overwhelming majority of suicidality in mood disorders and is a much stronger predictor of suicidality than depressive symptoms alone (Akiskal & Benazzi, 2005). A more recent study by Benazzi and Akiskal (2006) determined that irritability and psychomotor agitation were the two most predictive symptoms of a mixed depressive state and suggested that the presence of these two symptoms might serve as a "red flag" to any provider considering antidepressant treatment. Rihmer and Akiskal (2006) have argued that any increases in suicidality associated with antidepressants might be due to unrecognized mixed episodes and hypomanic episodes (i.e., bipolar II disorder) in patients, which might require augmentation therapy with benzodiazepines, mood stabilizers, or antipsychotics, in addition to regular clinical follow-up.

As mentioned earlier, the magnitude of the difference in rates of suicidality across the clinical and placebo arms of the aggregated FDA trials for children and adolescents was statistically significant, but the clinical meaningfulness of this difference is certainly open to debate. Furthermore, the observed rates of suicidality are not far from what is common in treatment trials, with rates comparable to placebo (Gunnell, Saperia, & Ashby, 2005; Khan et al., 2003). Although there were suicides in the adult trials, the difference across placebo and clinical conditions was insufficient to claim a drug effect. It is critical for practicing BHCs to be aware that more recent evidence in the literature actually points to a reduction in suicide risk associated with SSRI use, with very low rates of SSRI antidepressants reported in the toxicology results of suicide cases (Ryan, 2005) suggesting that most suicide victims were not taking antidepressants at the time of their deaths. Data are now available that converges in support of marked clinical improvement and lowered risk for suicide following treatment with SSRI medications (Khan et al., 2003; Martinez et al., 2005; Simon, Savarino, Operskalski, & Wang, 2006). The effectiveness of antidepressants is especially pronounced among older persons, who are much less likely to access specialty mental health care. Suicide rates in older persons have been found to decline approximately 10% across both sexes following antidepressant treatment (Erlangsen, Candudas-Romo, & Conwell, 2008). Among adolescents, a markedly lowered risk for suicidality has been found when adolescents continued SSRI treatment for 6 months or longer, as compared with adolescents being treated for less than 2 months (Valuck et al., 2004). It is also critical that BHCs educate PCPs about the benefits and effectiveness of antidepressant treatment, especially when combined with cognitive-behavioral therapies.

The Role of the Behavioral Health Consultant in Antidepressant Prescription Recommendations

Given the very large number of PCPs who report inaccurate knowledge of the content of the black box warning label, BHCs should be proactive in educating PCPs about the risks and benefits of antidepressant use with depressed and suicidal patients. This can be accomplished through a provider in-service training focused on the topic of risk for suicidality associated with antidepressant treatment. BHCs should ensure the topics highlighted in Figure 8.2 are addressed during the training and can provide copies of this information sheet to all primary care staff. Not only should prescribing professionals be targeted in this training, but nurses and other clinical support staff should also be included, since medication questions are often posed to these professionals.

The greatest impact a BHC will have on the clinical practices of the PCP, however, is through routine consultation and feedback on patients. A BHC who is educated about the risks and benefits of antidepressants will be much better positioned to help patients and PCPs choose the most effective combination of treatments, whether pharmacological and/or behavioral. Direct involvement of the BHC in this area can correct errors that might interfere with PCPs' willingness to prescribe antidepressants and patients' willingness to choose and adhere with this treatment option. Involvement of the BHC can additionally ensure that patients receive psychosocial interventions in combination with, or as an alternative to, pharmacological treatments, whether delivered by the BHC or by a mental health specialist.

BHCs can also play a potentially important role in improving the monitoring of patients following the initial phase of medication treatment—an important recommendation included as a part of the warning label. In fact, the recommendation for increased follow-up monitoring was the original intent of the warning label, with the FDA recommending weekly visits following initiation of antidepressants for the first 4 weeks, followed by biweekly visits for the next 4 weeks, followed by a 12-week follow-up visit, and then follow-ups as clinically indicated. Unfortunately, there is no evidence to suggest that the label has had its intended impact, since clinical follow-up patterns after the initiation of an antidepressant have remained unchanged. This should not be too surprising, however, given the demands and context of a primary care clinic, in which weekly monitoring is often difficult to accomplish for most PCPs. BHCs are uniquely positioned to fill this gap and enhance clinical care by conducting follow-up monitoring on behalf of PCPs while simultaneously delivering effective behavioral interventions, thus providing combined care that is generally found to be

1. The FDA black box warning label does not indicate an increased risk for death by suicide but does indicate an increased risk for suicidal thinking and behaviors. This is true for children, adolescents, and young adults.
   a. There were no suicides in the child and adolescent aggregated trials. A doubling in the relative risk for suicidality was observed in the clinical arm (4%) as compared with the placebo arm (2%), which means that for all children in all the trials, a 2% increase is the absolute risk for suicidality.
   b. Although there were suicides in the adult trials, there was no evidence that the medications elevated the risk for death by suicide beyond that seen with placebo. Suicide rates were comparable for adults across the clinical and placebo arms. Numerous studies have since converged with these data.
2. The warning label defines suicidality as heightened risk of suicidal thinking and behaviors, and recommends closer monitoring (i.e., increased frequency of follow-up) during the initial phase of treatment.
   a. Since the warning label's release, there has been no change in clinical follow-up patterns after the initiation of antidepressant treatment.
   b. BHCs can facilitate and conduct follow-up monitoring on behalf of the PCP and can deliver effective psychosocial interventions to augment medication treatment.
3. Emerging evidence indicates that the warning label is contributing to changes in clinical practice patterns.
   a. PCPs are less willing to prescribe antidepressants, and are more likely to refer to mental health specialists. Because only 10% to 25% of primary care patients actually follow through with referrals to mental health specialists, fewer patients are receiving effective treatments.
   b. Depression has been diagnosed less frequently among children and adolescents, and antidepressant prescriptions have declined since the warning label's release. During this same time period, over a threefold increase in suicide rates among children and adolescents have been observed in several countries.
   c. A similar pattern of decreased diagnosis of depression and antidepressant prescription rate has been noted among adult patients. Because the original target of the warning label was only for patients younger than 25 years, only these data suggest an unintended "spillover effect."
4. The warning label notes a decreased risk for suicidality among older patients.
5. Ninety-one percent of PCPs prescribing antidepressants demonstrate errors in their understanding of the risk stated on the warning label, believing that the warning label outlines an increased risk for death by suicide.
   a. Around 90% of PCPs give supplemental verbal information to patients regarding the warning label. Initial data indicate that this information is inaccurate, in that it overestimates risk of death by suicide.
   b. Accurate communication of risk is critical for parents and patients to make informed decisions about effective treatments.
6. Increased risk for suicidality appears to be related to unidentified mixed depressive episodes and/or hypomanic episodes. Irritability and psychomotor agitation should serve as "red flags" for possible mixed depressive episodes.
   a. PCPs and BHCs should implement regular, short-term follow-up with patients demonstrating these symptoms.
   b. Augmenting antidepressant therapy with benzodiazepine, mood stabilizer, or antipsychotic therapies have been recommended for mixed depressive episodes.

FIGURE 8.2

Information sheet on the black box warning label for increased risk of suicidality among antidepressants.

superior to either medication or behavioral therapies alone. Although face-to-face clinical contact is ideal, the FDA notes that telephone contact can be used to monitor patients' clinical status.

CONSULTATION ON INPATIENT HOSPITALIZATION FOR SUICIDAL PATIENTS

It is not uncommon for BHCs to notice that many PCPs respond to suicide risk with an "alarmist" attitude, responding to any mention of suicide with a recommendation for psychiatric hospitalization. PCPs often note that due to their lack of training and experience in working with suicidal patients, they prefer a "better-safe-than-sorry" approach to suicide risk. PCPs and medical providers in general also commonly assume that inpatient hospitalization is the "gold standard" for the treatment of suicidality when, in fact, inpatient hospitalization has never been found to be efficacious in a single clinical trial (Comtois & Linehan, 2006), and its effectiveness has been described as "questionable" by the Institute of Medicine (2002). Hospitalization typically carries with it the added burdens of increased financial costs and social stressors resulting from missed work, inability to take care of personal responsibilities, and possible stigma. In contrast, outpatient psychosocial treatments that specifically target problem-solving strategies and suicidal symptoms and behaviors using a cognitive-behavioral approach demonstrate the greatest level of efficacy (Comtois & Linehan, 2006; Tarrier et al., 2008) and are more effective at retaining the highest-risk patients when compared with inpatient treatment (Rudd et al., 1996).

The BHC plays a critical role in educating PCPs about the judicious and clinically appropriate use of hospitalization to manage suicide risk. Occasionally, extremely high-risk patients will present to the primary care clinic, and further evaluation for hospitalization will be deemed necessary to maintain patient safety. The detailed risk assessment needed to make an accurate determination about hospitalization is generally outside the scope of the BHC, however. As such, very high-risk patients will need to be referred to a local inpatient facility to receive such a detailed evaluation and dispositional decision. With the advent of managed care, however, access to costly inpatient services has been severely restricted both in terms of criteria for admission and duration of care. Because the bar for admission has steadily risen, much to the dismay of many outpatient providers who believe their patients need to be hospitalized, inpatient care is less likely to be a viable risk management option. Likewise, duration of inpatient care has decreased dramatically over the past few decades, such that the course of care is now typically less than

72 hours in length, meaning that highly distressed patients are very quickly returned to the outpatient system.

These facts exist despite the preferences or opinions of PCPs and BHCs, and present several obstacles and problems for any medical provider hoping to rely upon inpatient facilities as their primary strategy for managing suicidal patients. First, PCPs and BHCs must identify strategies for transporting at-risk patients to an appropriate facility, since it is not reasonable from a practice management or legal perspective to allow a patient who is suspected to be at imminent risk for suicide, and therefore inherently impaired in mental status and decision-making capacity, to drive themselves to the hospital. Above and beyond the fundamental issue that a person who has impaired judgment probably should not be allowed to operate a vehicle, such an approach does not provide for any clinical accountability during a crisis. PCPs and BHCs must therefore develop strategies for transporting at-risk patients, which could incur financial and social cost to the patient.

Second, because inpatient facilities increasingly admit only those patients who are the highest risk for suicide (i.e., imminent risk for suicide), most suicidal patients who present to the primary care clinic will not meet the threshold for hospitalization. In such cases, the decision to discharge patients from the emergency department without being admitted will almost never be communicated to the referring PCPs or BHCs by the evaluating facility, which results in no formal transfer of care or plan for clinical follow-up. The patient is typically released in such cases without any intervention and with the instruction to follow-up with an outpatient provider.

Third, even when a patient is admitted, more enduring factors contributing to suicide risk typically are not resolved during the course of the inpatient stay. Any resolution of the suicidal crisis that occurs during the inpatient stay is oftentimes due to a combination of two factors: the temporary removal of the patient from environmental stressors contributing to the crisis and natural attenuation that occurs by the very fact that suicidal episodes are time-limited in nature. Although removing the patient from environmental stressors can be an admirable and reasonable approach to care, the unfortunate fact is that patients will eventually (usually within only a few days) be returned to the very same stressful environment without learning any strategies for responding to these stressors in a new way. In light of this, it is no surprise that one of the highest risk periods for a suicidal patient is immediately following discharge from an inpatient facility. Patients with shorter hospital stays are at greatest risk, with longer stays reducing risk somewhat, though not appreciably (Qin & Nordentoft, 2005). Ironically, it appears that one of the final events to occur in these suicide victims' lives is to be evaluated by a mental health provider and judged to be at low risk for suicide, prompting the decision to discharge the patient. BHCs must therefore educate PCPs about the extreme risk associated with discharge from an inpatient facility and communicate the message that risk does not disappear once a patient is admitted. Likewise, the PCP and BHC must be prepared for the patient's eventual discharge and return to the primary care system. Given that medical visits increase dramatically during intensification of suicidal crises, it is likely that patients will follow-up in primary care very soon after discharge.

Detailing these limitations of hospitalization does not imply that there are never any instances in which inpatient care is appropriate and should be pursued. What is critical for the BHC is to understand when to make this recommendation to a PCP. Our recommendation is for BHCs and PCPs to consider hospitalization only for those patients meeting the operationalization for "high risk" of suicide. If the BHC believes these patients are imminently at risk for suicide, he or she should recommend inpatient evaluation to the PCP and facilitate the process of transporting the patient to a local emergency services facility for further evaluation. This strategy is consistent with recommended operationalizations of risk in specialty mental health settings (e.g., Bryan & Rudd, 2006; Wingate et al., 2004). BHCs should additionally keep in mind that the threshold for recommending hospitalization is always lower for multiple attempters than for nonmultiple attempters due to the relative difference in baseline suicide risk. In short, BHCs and PCPs must work together closely to determine when a patient's risk level has exceeded the capacity for the primary care team to safely manage.

With respect to hospitalization, one of the BHC's chief tasks is to help PCPs make consistent, evidence-based decisions about whether to refer a patient for further evaluation. In most cases, the suicidal patient will be best served on an outpatient basis from a mental health specialist, which can at times conflict with the PCP's preference or desire to refer the patient for hospitalization. Where clinically appropriate, an important role of the BHC is to engage the PCP in a conversation about the most appropriate level of care, although the fact remains that the ultimate decision to refer belongs to the PCP, who maintains full responsibility for the patient's care. Similarly, because the PCP is in charge of the patient's overall care, the PCP should ideally initiate the process of transferring care with the BHC's assistance and support.

CORE COMPETENCIES FOR BEHAVIORAL HEALTH CONSULTANTS

1. Describe how the BHC can indirectly impact the suicide risk of the entire patient population through consultation with PCPs.

2. Facilitate PCPs' understanding of their personal beliefs and attitudes about suicide and how these can impact interactions with suicidal patients.
3. Teach PCPs how to manage their emotional reactions to suicidal patients and establish effective therapeutic alliances.
4. Assist PCPs in improving screening of psychosocial and behavioral health issues in general and suicide risk in particular.
5. Be familiar with the content of the FDA's black box warning label for antidepressants.
6. Describe results of empirical studies investigating the association between suicidality and antidepressant use across the life span.
7. Educate PCPs about the research on suicidality and antidepressant use.
8. Assist PCPs in accurately educating patients about antidepressant use.
9. Provide short-term follow-up for patients initiating antidepressant treatment or dosing changes.
10. Assist PCPs in making decisions about when to refer suicidal patients for inpatient evaluation.

CHAPTER 9

Special Concerns With Suicidal Patients in Primary Care

Providing effective and appropriate care to suicidal patients is not always straightforward and simple in any clinical setting, and can at times be quite challenging. As compared with the specialty mental health setting, the tempo of primary care often serves to magnify the challenges inherent in working with suicidal patients. These challenges include patient ambivalence, or even outright refusal, to engage in specialty mental health care even when it is indicated; nonadherence to treatment recommendations, whether behavioral or pharmacological; and unrealistic expectations and beliefs about the treatment process. Each of these issues will be discussed in this chapter, along with suggestions and recommendations for responding to each. Finally, issues related to the management of multiple attempters within primary care—an issue that frequently raises considerable concern for providers—will also be addressed.

PATIENTS WHO ARE AMBIVALENT ABOUT SPECIALTY MENTAL HEALTH CARE

It is not uncommon for suicidal patients to have mixed feelings about accessing specialty mental health services. Although they desire an alleviation of their emotional distress, they also might report any number of barriers to accessing care such as negative beliefs or stigma about mental health, shame or embarrassment about treatment, difficulty in interpersonal settings, issues with trust, financial difficulties, and/or time limitations. Behavioral health consultants (BHCs) must recognize and accept this ambivalence and should engage the patient in motivational enhancement exercises to increase their willingness to seek out appropriate care.

When working with patients who are ambivalent about accessing specialty mental health services, BHCs (and primary care providers [PCPs]) will often be tempted to argue in favor of accessing specialty care, for instance, by listing off many reasons why the patient should go to care or offering counterarguments or potential solutions to the patient's presented barriers. As most providers can attest to, such approaches typically prompt the patient to simply argue back by providing reasons why the provider's points are not valid or practical. In other words, the suicidal patient begins to argue why he or she should not engage in specialty care. This creates an interpersonal dynamic that undermines the collaborative process critical for working with suicidal patients and can actually serve to decrease the likelihood of the patient following up with specialty care.

A mistake that many providers often make when working with ambivalent (also referred to as "resistant") patients is to focus too much attention initially on the barriers to accessing care, causing them to lose sight of the ultimate objective, to successfully connect the patient to a specialist. Providers can get caught up in "winning the argument" with the patient and fail to recognize the conflict as a manifestation of the discrepancy between the goals of the provider (to prevent death by suicide) and the goals of the patient (to retain the option of suicide as a method for reducing or eliminating psychological pain). It is also important for providers to consider that the patient's "resistance" is due to very real resource limitations: Perhaps, they really do not have a reliable source of transportation or cannot get enough time off from work to attend appointments. Whatever the source of the patient's ambivalence or reluctance to engage in specialty mental health care, providers should always be cautious about automatically assuming that patients are being "resistant" to treatment recommendations when perhaps the real problem is an inability to effectively problem-solve barriers to care.

The solution to working with ambivalent patients is to adopt a collaborative, problem-solving orientation. BHCs will find it useful to first identify a common goal that can then be pursued by both the patient and the BHC. The reason for first identifying a common goal to work on is because many suicidal patients, especially chronically suicidal patients, are often so caught up in their intense distress and problematic life that they have never taken the time to identify a goal to work toward or a direction to move in. The very notion of having something to work toward, or a metaphoric finish line to cross, can instill considerable hope and motivation. BHCs can elicit a patient's goals by asking questions such as, "What would you like to be different about your life? If you were no longer depressed [anxious, irritable, etc.], what would be different?" Questions such as these can provide an avenue for developing specific, measurable treatment goals. For a suicidal patient, the primary goal will almost always entail the alleviation of suffering and psychological pain of some kind. Once a reasonable and collaborative goal has been identified, the BHC can then frame specialty mental health treatment as a vehicle for accomplishing this goal. In this way, the BHC can circumvent many barriers or obstacles to accessing care by joining with the patient in a collaborative effort to achieve their personal goals.

Another strategy the BHC can employ is to negotiate smaller, more time-limited commitments regarding treatment from the patient in order to increase motivation and adherence. For example, instead of simply recommending that patients attend specialty mental health treatment in general, BHCs might ask patients to commit to attending a concrete number of mental health appointments. Patients generally prefer fewer psychotherapy sessions with the modal expectation of treatment length being only three sessions (Garfield, 1986; Gelso & Johnson, 1983). Not surprisingly, patient expectations for length of therapy are a key determinant for actual treatment duration (Pekarkik & Wierzbicki, 1986). Patients who are informed that treatment duration will be brief are significantly less likely to drop out of therapy prematurely than patients who are not given any defined time limit (Sledge, Moras, Hartley, & Levine, 1990). BHCs can therefore increase a patient's willingness to follow up with specialty mental health care by speaking directly to these preferences and expectations.

In the case of patients who report ambivalence about accessing specialty mental health services due to resource limitations (e.g., they have no vehicle, they work two jobs and cannot get time off, they work night shifts and sleep during the day, they cannot afford the copay), BHCs should assist the patient in problem-solving these barriers. Here again, the BHC should first identify the patient's primary goal (to reduce psychological suffering) and then ask the patient to list all of the perceived barriers to care. Once these barriers are identified, the BHC should reframe these as the parameters within which specialty mental health must be accessed.

For example, if the patient reports they do not own a vehicle and therefore cannot drive themselves to appointments, the BHC can ask the patient how they get around for other tasks such as grocery shopping, attending primary care appointments, visiting with others. This approach moves the patient away from focusing on which transportation options are unavailable to which transportations are available. The BHC can then take the patient's responses and propose them as the criteria a mental health specialist must meet in order to be a viable option for the patient. For example, the BHC might note that a mental health specialist must meet one or more of the following conditions: (1) has appointments on days and times when a family member can reliably transport the patient, (2) is located within walking distance of work and can meet with patients immediately before or after work, or (3) is located near a bus stop.

This same process can be used for other identified barriers to treatment such as financial limitations (e.g., identifying specialists with sliding fee scales, identifying specialists in training programs with reduced or waived fees, identifying relevant local clinical trials or research studies that offer free treatments) or work constraints (e.g., identifying specialists with weekend or after-hour appointments). A critical aspect of this problem-solving process is that it not only increases the likelihood of a suicidal patient accessing the appropriate level of mental health treatment, but it also teaches them the very problem-solving skills that are generally deficient in suicidal individuals.

We will return to the case of Mary to demonstrate how a BHC can work with an ambivalent patient. Based on the results of Mary's risk assessment (chronic high risk with acute overlay, severe risk), she would clearly benefit from outpatient specialty mental health care. However, Mary is reluctant to engage in this treatment option:

BHC [B]: Have you considered meeting with someone on a more regular basis to work on these problems?

MARY [M]: You mean like a therapist?

B: Yes.

M: I don't want to go to a therapist. That would be a waste of time.

B: Have you ever been in therapy before?

M: No.

B: Well, what would you like to be different about what's going on in your life right now?

M: I don't want to feel this way anymore.

B: And if you no longer felt this way, what would you be doing that you're not doing right now?

M: I wouldn't be crying all the time, and I'd have more energy. And I wouldn't be thinking about killing myself all the time.

B: What are you not doing right now because of the crying, low energy, and suicidal thoughts? What do these things get in the way of?

M: Well, I don't go out with friends anymore, and I just sit around all the time at home feeling horrible. I don't get anything done around the house because I can't get myself out of bed in the morning, and I don't walk my dog anymore because I just don't care.

B: So you would like to increase your activity level and resume walking your dog?

M: Well, yeah, but I can't right now because of how I feel.

B: Right. Well, those are reasonable goals that can definitely be accomplished. Based on what we've already talked about today, we can start working on these goals together, but I think you would also benefit from meeting with someone on a more regular basis in therapy. Getting you back into your social life, improving your mood, increasing your energy level, and helping you spend more time with your dog are the whole point of therapy. Would you be interested in meeting with someone to help you do these things?

M: I don't know.

B: Well, it's your choice. We know from a considerable amount of research that meeting with a mental health professional regularly can help you to improve your mood, energy, and social life. Once these things start to get better, you'll find that you think about suicide less often. If you're interested in making some of these changes in your life, I can provide you with a list of names and numbers of some local professionals you can call to start meeting with.

M: [sits quietly, considering options]

B: Well, how about this. What if you attended just three sessions of therapy, and after that third session you can decide if you think it would be helpful for you or not? If it's helpful, then great, but if it's not, then you haven't really lost much.

M: Okay. I'd be willing to do that.

B: Great. Let's get you a list of names.

In this scenario, the BHC recommends Mary start meeting with a specialty mental health care provider for psychotherapy and is immediately met with "resistance." Instead of engaging with her resistance, however, the BHC engages Mary in the identification of specific treatment goals. Once these goals are clearly articulated, the BHC defines psychotherapy in terms of Mary's stated goals in order to increase her motivation to access care. When Mary continues to express ambivalence, the BHC does not pressure her to access specialty care, which could inadvertently cause the patient to argue for why she should not follow up with a specialist. By respecting her autonomy to choose, the BHC further strengthens the collaborative relationship with her that increases Mary's likelihood of adhering to and following recommendations. Still confronted with ambivalence, the BHC proposes that the patient commit to a finite number of psychotherapy sessions as a "trial run," based on the assumption that it is more likely that Mary will commit to a more concrete and well-defined treatment duration than an unspecified, time-unlimited duration. This technique also lies on the fundamental motivational assumption that a behavior is easier to maintain once initiated than getting started in the first place. In other words, if the BHC can motivate Mary to just start attending therapy sessions in the first place, she is likely to continue attending. In this scenario, the BHC is able to move around Mary's primary barrier and has increased the likelihood that she will follow up with specialty care.

PATIENTS WHO REFUSE TO ACCESS SPECIALTY MENTAL HEALTH CARE

Some patients will outright refuse to access specialty mental health treatment. Reasons for this decision can include mental health stigma, negative experiences with past mental health treatment, or resource limitations and should therefore be investigated by the BHC. The clinical approach for working with patients who refuse specialty care does not differ substantially from those who are ambivalent in that BHCs should adopt a collaborative approach focused on motivation enhancement (described in the previous section). However, outright refusal of specialty care when it is clinically indicated presents a unique dilemma for the primary care team: What to do with a patient who needs a higher level of care but chooses not to access it? In such cases, the BHC should first and foremost assist in coordinating the care of all primary care team members likely to come into direct contact with the patient to ensure the patient receives a consistent message from everyone that accessing specialty care is the central component of the treatment plan. In coordinating the primary care team's efforts, BHCs should plan to teach team members how to use motivational enhancement techniques to increase the patient's likelihood of choosing specialty care.

A patient's refusal to access specialty care when indicated also raises considerable concern about risk management and liability. A widespread perspective within our society is that medical providers are completely responsible for a patient's health outcomes, which largely overlooks or minimizes the central role that a patient plays in their health care. This seems to be particularly true for mental health care and suicide. A general expectation exists that mental health providers should be able to predict when a suicide will occur and should be able to provide interventions that will completely prevent such an outcome in all cases. When a patient dies by suicide, it is often assumed that someone must have made an error; in many cases, the treating provider is the first person assumed to have made an error. Health care outcomes are not solely related to a provider's actions and decisions, however; patient actions and decisions are also a central contributor to health outcomes. In a collaborative, shared treatment approach, the provider maintains responsibility for making sound clinical decisions and providing the tools by which the patient can become healthy (e.g., medications, appropriate referrals to specialists, behavior change plans), and the patient maintains responsibility for following recommendations and implementing these tools as directed. If the recommendations or suggested interventions are not working as intended, the patient maintains responsibility for communicating this to the provider, and the provider maintains responsibility for determining why these approaches have failed and identifying alternatives. Providers therefore have the additional responsibility for creating an environment in which patients feel safe giving open and honest feedback to providers and listening to this feedback when given. Treatment is fundamentally a collaborative process between both patient and provider. This shared responsibility for health outcomes, including adverse events such as suicidal behaviors, is critical for both patients and providers to recognize, and should be conveyed directly and unambiguously to any patient who is refusing to access specialty mental health services. Simply put, medical care is only as good as the provider's interventions and the patient's willingness to follow these recommendations as directed.

When confronted with a patient who refuses to access specialty mental health services despite a recommendation to do so, the BHC should first engage the patient in a conversation about this shared responsibility for health outcomes to clarify expectations:

> *I definitely think we can find ways to reduce your pain and get you more socially engaged in life, but right now I feel like we're not working well as a team to make this happen. Maybe it would be helpful for us to take a moment to talk about our roles on this team. As I see it, my job on this team is to teach you what you can do to reduce your pain and get you more socially active and to give you tips and recommendations for achieving these goals, and your job is to tell me whether or not these strategies work so we can make adjustments if needed. Do you see us working as a team in a similar way, or do you have a different idea of how we could best work together?*

Once expectations about treatment responsibilities are established, the BHC can present the recommendation to access specialty mental health care as fitting within this framework of expectations:

> *So we agree that my job is to provide tips and strategies and then teach you how to actually use these strategies, and your job is to try them out and tell me what works, what does not work, and what needs to be changed. Along those same lines, I think one strategy that will help you reduce your pain and become more socially active is to start seeing a specialist who can work with*

you much more intensively than we can here. Are you willing to try out this strategy first, then let me know if it works or not?

In this sequence, the BHC reorients the patient to the shared responsibilities of both the BHC and patent and then obtains a commitment from the patient to meet these responsibilities. The BHC then presents a referral to specialty mental health as an example of how they are fulfilling their responsibilities as a provider and asks the patient to fulfill their responsibility as a patient. Here again, the BHC does not argue with the patient about seeing a mental health specialist but rather uses the patient's own priorities and commitments as a motivator for change.

Another strategy for working with patients who refuse specialty referrals is to educate them about the risks and benefits of engaging in treatment versus not engaging in treatment so they can make fully informed decisions about their health care options. Table 9.1 summarizes the standardized mortality ratios (SMRs) for death by suicide associated with previous suicide attempt history and several psychiatric diagnoses commonly seen in primary care. These ratios were calculated as part of a meta-analysis of 249 separate scientific studies in which mortality statistics were reported (Harris & Barraclough, 1997). The SMRs in Table 9.1 indicate the ratio of the actual number of suicides compared with the expected number of suicides associated with a given psychiatric condition. The SMR for suicide within the general population is always set to 1.00 for the sake of comparison. An SMR of 38.36 for previous suicide attempts therefore indicates that individuals who

TABLE 9.1

Risk for Suicide Among Individuals With Previous Suicide Attempts and Psychiatric Disorders Commonly Seen in Primary Care

Condition	*Standardized Mortality Ratio*
Previous suicide attempt	38.36
Major depressive disorder	20.35
Other mood disorder	16.10
Bipolar disorder	15.05
Adjustment disorder	13.79
Panic disorder	10.00
Personality disorder	7.08
Anxiety disorder	6.29
Substance use disorder	5.74
Somatization disorder	5.26

Note. Based on a meta-analysis conducted by Harris and Barraclough (1997).

have ever attempted suicide in the past are 38.36 times more likely to die by suicide than someone in the general population who has never attempted suicide, an SMR of 20.35 for major depressive disorder indicates that individuals with major depressive disorder are 20.35 times more likely to die by suicide than someone in the general population without this condition, and so on.

BHCs can alternatively talk to patients to about lifetime risk for suicide attempts as opposed to death by suicide. For example, although the lifetime risk for death by suicide associated with bipolar disorder is around 15%, the lifetime risk for suicide attempt associated with bipolar disorder is much higher (25%–50%; Goodwin & Jamison, 1990). What these numbers mean is that of those individuals diagnosed with bipolar disorder, anywhere from one-quarter to one-half will try to kill themselves, and 15% will die by suicide. Similarly, anywhere from 20% to 40% of individuals with schizophrenia will attempt suicide (Meltzer, 1995), with around 6% dying by suicide.

All of these numbers point to a rarely recognized fact: Psychiatric conditions can be fatal. It is arguable that for a percentage of patients, suicide attempts and death by suicide are secondary to the refractory nature of their mental illness. The notion that adverse events are an inherent and unavoidable consequence of certain health conditions is routinely accepted with certain medical specialties such as oncology or cardiology but has not yet received considerable attention within mental health disciplines. Cognitive-behavioral therapies are increasingly demonstrating efficacy as a treatment modality for reducing the risk of suicidality, with several trials finding a reduction in suicide attempts by half as compared with treatment as usual (e.g., Brown et al., 2005; Linehan et al., 2006). In terms of pharmacology, long-term maintenance treatment with lithium salts is associated with large reductions in the risk of both suicide attempts and deaths by suicide in bipolar disorder and moderate evidence for similar risk reductions among patients with recurrent major depressive disorder (Baldessarini, Tondo, & Hennen, 2003; Baldessarini et al., 2006). Clozapine treatment has likewise demonstrated considerable efficacy in reducing suicidality among psychotic patients (Meltzer, 1995).

In addition to findings of efficacy specific to suicidality, psychosocial and pharmacological treatments have clearly documented efficacy in reducing functional impairment and recurrence across the full range of psychiatric disorders, which are estimated to be present in approximately 90% of all deaths by suicide (Maris et al., 2000). It is critical to note, however, that of the approximately 31,000 individuals who die by suicide every year in the United States (Hoyert et al., 2006), up to one-half are in active treatment at the time of their death (Fawcett, 1999), demonstrating active treatment cannot prevent suicide completely. This is supported by the finding that in even the most rigorously designed clinical trials of the most efficacious treatments (e.g., Brown et al., 2005; Linehan et al., 2006), patients still attempt suicide and some still die. Based on these data, from a risk management and a clinical perspective, the expectation of risk associated with both treatment and non-treatment should be clearly established for all patients, especially those who refuse to access the most appropriate level of care (i.e., referral to a mental health specialist).

Consider the following example of a BHC explaining these issues to Mary, who in this iteration of our clinical vignette is completely refusing to access specialty care:

BHC [B]: Based on what we have talked about today, my recommendation would be for you to meet with a mental health specialist in our community to start working with you on a regular basis.

MARY [M]: I don't want to do that. I've done all that before and it doesn't work.

B: You've told me today that you have been struggling with these problems for many years. In fact, these problems have gotten so bad at times that you have tried to kill yourself on at least seven different occasions, right?

M: Yeah.

B: What is clear from our research is that individuals who try to kill themselves two or more times during their life—what we call "multiple attempters"—have a much higher risk for early death by suicide and other causes. In fact, we know that multiple attempters have around a 25% likelihood of dying by suicide at some point in their life. You've also told me that you have a chronic depression that has come and gone several times during your life, and that it is during these times that you attempt suicide. What we also know about recurrent depression is that once you have had two major depressive episodes, there is a 70%–80% likelihood of having additional episodes. In a nutshell, what you're describing to me today is a significant health condition that tends to be chronic over the entire life span. This condition can be fatal. As I already mentioned, this condition has around a 25% risk for death by suicide. Does all this make sense so far?

M: Yeah, but I don't really care. I'm not going to a therapist.

B: That's fine; it's your choice to make. I just want to make sure you have all the information so you can make the best treatment choice for you. I also want you to know that research has demonstrated that very specific types of mental health treatment, including a combination of medications and what we call cognitive-behavioral therapy, can reduce the likelihood of you attempting suicide again by up to 50%. These treatments can also reduce the likelihood of another depressive episode by 25%–50%.

P: Really? I didn't know that.

M: Yeah. A lot of people don't. I just want to make sure you understand what this means, though. What this means is that although good treatment doesn't necessarily eliminate completely the risk for further depressive episodes or suicide attempts, it can reduce their likelihood or probability. Does that make sense?

P: Yeah, it does. So what you're saying is that I'm stuck with this?

M: What I'm saying is that we know that your type of depression has a very high likelihood of coming back multiple times over the course of your life, but that treatment can reduce this risk considerably. Probably you will struggle with depression off and on over the course of your life, but the good news is that there are clear steps you can do to reduce the impact that this condition has on your life and well-being. I suppose the question to ask yourself is: Are you willing to try something that we know can improve your health?

P: I'm willing to do anything, but it hasn't worked before. I've been on medications and done therapy, and it hasn't worked. I'm still depressed.

M: Right. That's because of the type of depression you have. Like I said, treatment can reduce the likelihood of recurrence, and can often reduce the intensity or impact it has on your life, but not necessarily eliminate it. It's possible that the treatment you've already received prevented another depressive episode that you're not even aware of, or made one of your depressive episodes less severe. We'll never know for sure, but based on what we know about how recurrent depression works, and how treatment affects recurrent depression, it seems like that would be a safe bet to make. What we do know, however, is that you've tried to kill yourself several times when severely depressed, and right now you're severely depressed again and thinking about suicide on a daily basis. It just sounds like things aren't working very well right now for you, and I want to help you figure out some ways we can make things work better.

M: Yeah...I just don't know. I guess I did feel a little better when I was in treatment, even though I was still depressed. I just don't know.

B: What if you and I were to come up with a plan today to start working on some of these problems, and then you think about what you want to do about this depression and treatment. You certainly don't have to choose today. I'll talk with your PCP today, and I'll recommend we have you follow up with me later this week and see where you're at. How does that sound?

In this scenario, the BHC uses the same core motivational strategies used with ambivalent patients, including refusing to argue with Mary and respecting her autonomy. The BHC also engages Mary in identifying a common goal for treatment (i.e., reduction of depression), although, in this scenario, it is accomplished implicitly through the conversation about rates of recurrence in major depressive disorder. Important in this exchange is the BHC's communication of Mary's shared responsibility for health outcomes by explicitly endorsing the patient's right to choose treatment options and then explaining that the BHC wants to help Mary to make her own treatment decisions, as opposed to making the treatment decision for her. The BHC then educates Mary about her specific condition and the benefits of treatment but is careful to note that treatment does not have a 100% efficacy rate. This shapes Mary's expectations of the treatment process and even enables the BHC to reframe her perception of previous treatment not as a "failure" necessarily, but rather as a possible success or benefit that has gone unrecognized up to this point. Finally, as the BHC observes Mary's motivation to access care shifting in the desired direction, he chooses to "disengage" from the topic to reduce the likelihood of being perceived as pushy or controlling. This disengagement was possible in this scenario because although Mary was assessed to be at high risk for suicide, she is not so severely suicidal that suicide is imminent and outpatient safety cannot be maintained. The BHC then shifts to the behavioral planning stage in which specific interventions and recommendations are agreed upon and plans for a short-term follow-up are made.

Documentation of a patient's treatment refusal should include the BHC's recommendations to access specialty mental health care and any patient education regarding the risks of treatment versus nontreatment. BHCs should also note any motivational enhancement strategies used to increase the likelihood of patient follow-through and a clear notation of the patient's choice not to access care despite recommendations to so. Such documentation should occur at every patient contact by each member of the primary care team to demonstrate ongoing efforts of the entire team to provide the patient with the most appropriate level of care. Documentation of these points highlights the efforts of all health care providers to provide adequate and reasonable care, as well as the patient's responsibility to accept and implement appropriate medical recommendations and treatments.

PATIENTS WHO ARE NOT ADHERENT WITH TREATMENT RECOMMENDATIONS

A significant concern in any clinical setting when working with suicidal patients is nonadherence with treatment recommendations. It should not be surprising then that significantly reduced rates of suicide attempts have been found to be associated with treatments that target adherence to recommendations and early dropout. One treatment approach that prioritizes patient adherence is dialectical behavior therapy (DBT), which places "therapy-interfering behaviors" (i.e., adherence) as the second most important target for behavior (behind only suicidal behaviors). DBT's approach has been associated with a twofold to threefold reduction in patient dropout rates and a 50% reduction in suicidal behaviors (e.g., Linehan et al., 2006) as compared with control psychotherapies that do not emphasize these goals. Similarly, in Brown and colleagues' (2005) cognitive therapy protocol for suicide attempters, patient adherence was positioned as a central and primary target for treatment. Risk for repeat suicide attempt as compared with usual care in this study was reduced by half for up to 18 months posttreatment. Reductions in suicidality are not just limited to behavioral treatments, however, but also extend to pharmacotherapy. Early discontinuation of antidepressants (Valuck et al., 2004) and mood stabilizers (Yerevanian, Koek, & Mintz, 2007), for example, have been linked to significant increases in suicidal behaviors. The convergence of these and other studies indicates that adherence to treatment is a critical determinant for enhanced clinical outcomes and reduced risk for subsequent suicidal behavior.

The Importance of Patient Preference

A critical dimension of evidence-based medicine that is often overlooked or given too little consideration is patient preference. Some patients might prefer medication treatments to behavioral treatments, for example, or vice versa. Patient preferences can be influenced by past experience with treatment, beliefs about health care in general and mental health issues in particular, expectations about health care and treatment, and knowledge about health conditions. BHCs and PCPs must take these variables into consideration when developing treatment interventions and recommendations, since they will directly impact adherence. In a study by Conoley, Padula, Payton, and Daniels (1994), patients were more likely to adhere to homework assignments when the assignment was perceived to match their needs. These authors additionally found that providers who adopted a collaborative style to problem identification and homework assignments were more likely to obtain higher levels of matching between a patient's perceived problem and adherence to the assignment. Detweiler and Whisman (1999) have further proposed that a patient's perception of whether or not an intervention will be helpful will affect adherence. Simply put, patients who are prescribed a course of therapy that does not match their preferences and expectations are much less likely to follow the plan. From a practical standpoint, this demands that BHCs and PCPs be aware of a range of treatment options for mental health conditions, including suicidality, so that patients can be matched to an effective treatment with which they are most likely to adhere.

Medication Nonadherence

Medication nonadherence is a common problem in medical settings, with estimated costs associated with the consequences of nonadherence estimated to exceed $100 billion annually (Dunbar-Jacob & Mortimer-Stephens, 2001). Up to 60% of patients with chronic illnesses are poorly adherent to treatment recommendations—a fact that cuts across health condition, age, and treatment modalities (Dunbar-Jacob & Mortimer-Stephens, 2001). In comparison, psychotropic medication adherence for mood disorders ranges from 10% to 60%, with a median of 40%, with little change in this trend from 1976 to 2001 (Lingam & Scott, 2002). Among primary care patients, fewer than 10% receiving antidepressant therapy of any kind for depression (i.e., SSRI, tricyclic antidepressant) will complete an entire course of therapy—defined as 6 continuous months in duration—as recommended. When considering only the SSRIs, this rate increases to only 13.1% (Venturini, Sung, Nichol, & Sellner, 1999). Even when the definition of therapy completion is reduced to 4 months in duration, the completion rate still remains under 20%. Katon and colleagues (1992) found only a slightly better adherence rate of 34% when using a more flexible definition of adherence (i.e., filling at least four prescriptions in 6 months). When considering only severely depressed patients, SSRI adherence rates appear to be much better than the general population—up to 75% following the first 3 months of therapy (Goethe, Woolley, Cardoni, Woznicki, & Prez, 2007). Although this higher adherence rate is encouraging, the fact remains that around one-quarter of the more severely depressed patients are prematurely discontinuing antidepressant treatment for one reason or another, which is of concern given that this group is more likely to have greater morbidity, more functional impairment, and higher risk for suicide. In short, patient adherence to a full course of antidepressant therapy is low, with many discontinuing before an adequate therapeutic effect is likely to be experienced. This is disconcerting in light of evidence demonstrating markedly decreased risk for suicidality among adolescent patients continuing SSRI treatment for 6 months or longer as compared with those treated for 2 months or less (Valuck et al., 2004).

Several factors have been proposed as being likely contributors to antidepressant adherence including physician-patient alliance, demographics, symptom severity, patient knowledge, and side effect profile (Nemeroff, 2003). A major factor contributing to early discontinuation of pharmacotherapy that has received considerable attention is medication side effects (Bull et al., 2002; Goethe et al., 2007; Lin et al., 1995). Not surprisingly, the risk for early discontinuation increases with greater severity or intensity of medication side effects (Goethe et al., 2007; Lin et al., 1995). Early discontinuation is also associated with earlier onset (i.e., especially within the first 2 weeks) of side effects following antidepressant initiation (Goethe et al., 2007). Patient education can significantly improve adherence rates, however, when several important messages are communicated. Specifically, patients who are (1) educated that antidepressants must be taken consistently for 2 to 4 weeks for a noticeable effect and (2) given specific instructions for resolving questions about medication, and who are additionally directed (3) to take their medication daily, (4) to continue taking the medication even if feeling better, and (5) not to discontinue the medication without first talking with their prescriber are much less likely to discontinue antidepressant therapy within the first month of treatment (Lin et al., 1995). Bull and colleagues (2002) similarly found that patients who were instructed to continue taking their medication for a full 6 months despite side effects or subjective improvement were less likely to discontinue therapy prematurely when compared with patients who were not educated. BHCs can distribute to patients information handouts such as the one in Figure 9.1 to guide education efforts. Verbally reviewing the content of the handout with patients should be conducted by the BHC to ensure patients adequately understand relevant information.

As noted earlier, reductions in suicidality have been associated with adherence to a full 6-month course of antidepressant therapy (Valuck et al., 2004). BHCs who meet with patients to address barriers to medication continuation and educate them on antidepressant treatment can play a significant role in enhancing antidepressant adherence. Kolbasovsky, Reich, Romano, and Jaramillo (2005), for example, found that patients meeting with primary care behavioral health providers who emphasized medication adherence concurrent with cognitive-behavioral skills development had a 10% higher antidepressant adherence rate at 3 months postprescription when compared with patients who met with their PCP only (i.e., treatment as usual). Lin and colleagues (1995) similarly found that PCPs who spent time talking about a patient's previous experiences with antidepressant medications (i.e., focusing on motivations and beliefs about antidepressants) and scheduling pleasant behavioral activities increased early adherence. Given that antidepressant adherence is associated with decreased suicidality, BHCs who directly target adherence issues with patients and consult with PCPs to

What are antidepressants? Antidepressants are medications designed to alleviate the symptoms of clinical depression and other mood disorders.

How do antidepressants work? Antidepressants work by adjusting the levels of several types of chemicals in your brain called neurotransmitters. Possible side effects are the result of the same process.

Are antidepressants addictive? Antidepressants are not addictive.

Why has my PCP tried me on one antidepressant when I heard from a friend that they started taking another? Different antidepressants will affect different people in different ways. This is based upon sex, BMI, metabolism, and other family genetic factors. Your PCP may have to try several medications before they find one that works well for you.

When can I expect my antidepressants to work? It may up to 4 to 6 weeks before you notice any reduction in symptoms. This can depend on the specific medication prescribed.

What kind of symptoms will be improved if I start taking antidepressants? Most people notice improvement in the following areas:

a. Sleep
b. Appetite
c. Fatigue
d. Sex drive
e. Restlessness, agitation, or feeling physically slowed down
f. Feeling worse in the morning
g. Poor concentration

What kind of symptoms may not be improved if I start taking antidepressants? Many other symptoms like depressed mood and low self-esteem may respond only partially to medication. The medication you'll be taking is not a "happy pill"; it is unlikely to totally erase feelings of sadness or emptiness.

How long will it take before I begin to feel better? Length of treatment can vary widely from person to person. Typically, it may take 4–6 weeks for the major depressive symptoms to significantly decrease. It is important not to discontinue treatment at this point, since symptoms can return up to 80% of the time. In general, medication treatment goes at least 6 months beyond the point of symptom improvement. Then medication reduction under your provider's management can be started. If symptoms return during medication reduction, the dosage should be increased and continued for another 4–6 weeks before another trial on lower doses. Occasionally, a person may need to be on long-term medication management.

How will I know that my medication is working? The best signs that your medication is working include:

a. Improved sleep
b. Less daytime fatigue
c. Improved emotional control (fewer crying spells, better frustration tolerance)

FIGURE 9.1
Patient information handout on antidepressant medications.

Will I experience any side effects? There is the possibility of side effects and some people may experience one or two of the following. However, these side effects can most often be managed by dosage adjustment or by switching to another medication and, if present, usually go away in 7–10 days.

a. **Dry mouth**: drink plenty of water, chew sugarless gum, use sugarless candy
b. **Constipation**: eat more fiber-rich foods, take a stool softener
c. **Drowsiness**: go for walks, exercise more, take medication before bed
d. **Wakefulness**: take medications early in the day after waking up
e. **Blurred vision**: remind yourself this is temporary; talk with your provider if it continues
f. **Headache**: remind yourself this is temporary; take aspirin, acetaminophen, or other pain killers if needed
g. **Feeling speeded up**: remind yourself this is temporary; if not, call your provider
h. **Sexual problem**: talk with your provider because a change in medications may help
i. **Nausea or appetite loss**: take medication with food

Can I drink alcohol while taking antidepressants? Do not drink alcohol if you are taking antidepressant medication. Alcohol can block the effects of the medication. If you desire to drink occasionally or socially (never more than one drink per day), discuss this with your provider.

Don't antidepressants cause people to become suicidal? Some scientific studies have found that antidepressants are associated with a slight increase in suicidal thinking and behavior (from 2% to 4%) among children, adolescents, and young adults, but not increased risk for death by suicide. Other studies have found that antidepressants are associated with decreased risk for suicide among children and adolescents when they are taken as directed for at least 6 months. The Food and Drug Administration (FDA) has issued a warning about antidepressants that can be summarized as follows:

a. **Children, adolescents, and young adults up to 24 years old**: Antidepressants are associated with increased risk for suicidal thinking and behavior as compared with placebo ("sugar pill"). No deaths by suicide occurred in any of the child clinical trials.

b. **Adults 25 to 64 years old:** Antidepressants are associated with no change in risk for suicidal thinking and behavior as compared with placebo ("sugar pill"). Although a very small number of deaths by suicide occurred in the clinical trials, there were no differences between antidepressants and placebo.

c. **Adults 65 years and older:** Antidepressants are associated with decreased risk for suicidal thinking and behavior as compared with placebo ("sugar pill"). Although a very small number of deaths by suicide occurred in the clinical trials, there were no differences between antidepressants and placebo.

The FDA recommends that close monitoring of symptoms after you start or change antidepressant dosage is most important for obtaining the best results. **Make sure you keep all appointments with your health care providers.**

FIGURE 9.1
(continued)

CALL THE CLINIC RIGHT AWAY IF YOU OR A FAMILY MEMBER EXPERIENCE ANY OF THE FOLLOWING SYMPTOMS:		
Thoughts about suicide or dying Suicide attempts New or worse depression New or worse anxiety	Feeling agitated or restless Panic attacks Trouble sleeping New or worse irritability	Acting aggressive or violent Acting on dangerous impulses Extreme increase in activity or talking Other unusual changes in behavior/mood

FIGURE 9.1
(continued)

improve their ability to address adherence issues could therefore potentially impact patient suicidality.

Nonadherence With Behavioral Strategies

Treatment nonadherence is certainly not limited to pharmacological therapies and extends to behavioral therapies as well. Recent reviews of early withdrawal from psychotherapy estimate that up to 60% of patients will drop out prematurely (Barrett, Chua, Crits-Cristoph, Gibbons, & Thompson, 2008; Levensky, 2006) and approximately half will not complete homework assignments or other treatment recommendations (Detweiler & Whisman, 1999). Early drop out and homework nonadherence can limit the magnitude of clinical improvement, as evidenced by studies finding that implementation of behavioral recommendations and strategies has an additive contribution to clinical improvement (e.g., Addis & Jacobson, 2000; Burns & Nolen-Hoeksema, 1991; Persons, Burns, & Perloff, 1988). Of particular relevance to BHC work, adherence early in treatment (i.e., within the first two sessions) predicts early improvement, intermediate improvement, and long-term outcome (Addis & Jacobson, 2000).

Research on nonadherence is unfortunately quite limited, but some general guidelines for enhancing patients' adherence with behavioral recommendations have been identified, and are summarized in Table 9.2 (cf. Detweiler & Whisman, 1999). Interestingly, although provider empathy and patient adherence are both independently related to improved outcomes, provider empathy does not appear to enhance patient adherence to treatment recommendations (Burns & Nolen-Hoeksema, 1992).

In our experience, a prevalent reason for patients (especially highly distressed and/or suicidal patients) to refuse implementing behavioral strate-

TABLE 9.2
Empirically Supported Factors Associated With Increased Patient Adherence

Decreased task difficulty
Written reminders
Perception of choice when setting tasks and goals
Patient verbalizes arguments and reasons for why task should be completed
High perceived need for change
High level of motivation to engage in task
Matching recommendations and tasks to patient's strengths and preexisting abilities
Setting smaller, intermediate goals to enhance self-efficacy

Note. Adapted with permission from "The Role of Homework Assignments in Cognitive Therapy for Depression: Potential Methods for Enhancing Adherence," by J. B. Detweiler and M. A. Whisman, 1999, *Clinical Psychology: Research and Practice, 6,* 267–282.

gies is the assumption that the intervention(s) will not be effective. Such patients might express skepticism, question the validity of the technique, insist that it will not work for them, or outright denigrate the technique (or even the provider) as "stupid" or "ridiculous." Chronically suicidal patients tend to doubt the effectiveness of treatments and interventions more so than other patients, perhaps due to the increased frequency with which they have undergone a wide range of therapies (both pharmacological and behavioral) with multiple mental health providers with limited, if any, improvement. In many cases, poor adherence to treatment recommendations plays at least some part in the limited success of treatment, which is why such patients can be especially frustrating for the primary care team and BHC, especially when the patient dismisses an intervention before even attempting it.

When working with a nonadherent patient, BHCs should resist the temptation to argue with the patient or press too firmly for use of a particular technique or intervention, as this can undermine the therapeutic alliance and inadvertently decrease the patient's willingness to implement the strategy. One useful clinical approach for working with patient refusal is to elicit a commitment to using the technique for only a brief period (e.g., 2 weeks) and to further delay apprising the technique's utility until after the prescribed time period. Consider the following exchange between the BHC and Mary regarding the daily use of a relaxation technique targeting her anxiety:

BHC [B]: People who practice this breathing exercise at least three times every day for five minutes at a time find it very helpful for managing their anxiety.

MARY [M]: So you're telling me to just breathe, and that's supposed to help?

B: We know from our research that it's one of the most effective treatments, yes.

M: You're kidding me. You can't be serious. I didn't come in today to be told to just breathe. I'm not going to do this.

B: Tell me what you were expecting when you came in today.

M: I was expecting someone would actually take me seriously and help me.

B: Have you tried this breathing exercise in the past?

M: No. But I know how to breathe.

B: So even though you've never tried this before, you're certain it won't help.

M: Yeah.

B: Could you explain how you know it won't help if you've never tried before? What evidence or experience are you basing this on?

M: I just know.

B: Okay. Well, how about this: let's gather some data before we just toss it out, so that we can make sure we're making the best choice here. If you're willing to commit to doing this three times every day for five minutes at a time for the next two weeks, we can schedule a follow-up appointment at that time and you can come back in to tell me if it worked or not. If it doesn't work, then fine; we'll scrap this plan and we'll come up with a new plan that might work better. If it ends up working, then great; we'll talk about more things you can do to continue your improvement. How does that sound? Would you be willing to commit to using this breathing exercise three times every day for five minutes at a time for the next two weeks, and keep track of whether or not it works, and then come back in and we'll look at the data together?

M: Okay. I can do that.

B: All right. Then let's write that down on your behavioral prescription pad.

In this scenario, the BHC refuses to argue with Mary about using the relaxation technique since this approach would only strengthen the patient's resolve to oppose its implementation. Instead, the BHC identifies that Mary's reluctance is not based on any actual past experience or data and obtains buy-in for a more concrete and time-limited span of time. In essence, the BHC has effectively reduced the perceived difficulty of the task and established smaller, intermediate goals to enhance adherence. Furthermore, the BHC does not invalidate Mary's subjective experience by directly contradicting her; instead, the BHC implicitly acknowledges that Mary might very well be correct and invites her to engage in a collaborative process of confirming or disconfirming this possibility. By avoiding an argument with Mary and respecting her autonomy, the BHC has fostered a sense of ownership and choice regarding the recommendation. Finally, the BHC writes the recommendation on a behavioral prescription pad to increase the likelihood that she will remember to accomplish the task. Written assignments lead to superior recall and adherence as compared with verbal descriptions of homework (Cox, Tisdelle, & Culbert, 1988).

Patient nonadherence is likely to be identified at follow-up appointments when they report that they have not implemented or attempted the recommended behavioral strategies as prescribed. In such instances, BHCs should identify the barriers and obstacles for successful implementation (e.g., "What got in the way of you doing this?") and assist the patient in problem-solving these barriers (e.g., "What do we need to change in order to make this happen?"). Sometimes, unrealistic expectations about treatment interventions contribute to early abandonment of recommended strategies (e.g., "It didn't work the first time I tried it, so I stopped doing it" or "I still felt depressed even when I did it, so what's the point?"). Strategies for addressing unrealistic beliefs and expectations about interventions will be addressed in the next section.

PATIENTS WITH UNREALISTIC EXPECTATIONS ABOUT TREATMENT

"The Doctors Will Fix My Problems"

As mentioned earlier, a common assumption within our health care system is that the health care provider is the primary agent of change while the patient is simply the passive recipient of this change process. This perspective is at odds with what we know about actual health outcomes, however: Patient dynamics and variables play a very critical role, if for no other reason than via adherence to recommendations. Patients who verbalize low perceived responsibility for their health care are less likely to adhere fully to treatment recommendations and therefore are less likely to experience clinical recovery. BHCs should therefore directly engage patients who verbalize low perceived responsibility for outcomes in a conversation about the development of a collaborative approach:

"Let's talk a little bit about how we're going to work together to address the issue of suicide risk. Your PCP and I will do whatever we can to help target this intense pain that you're experiencing right now, but we can't do this alone. We need you to be a big part of this since it is your life that we're focusing on. Let me describe the approach to care that seems to get the best results. Your PCP and I will provide

you with the best treatments we can, which might include starting some medication, teaching you some strategies to help improve the way things are going for you right now, and helping you get connected with more intensive treatment than we can provide here at this clinic. We're going to ask you to try out new some ways of doing things that will target your problems and implement our recommendations as prescribed, even if doesn't seem like it's going to work at first. We also need for you to tell us what's working and what's not working so we can make sure we're making progress and make corrections if needed. If you're willing to try out some new strategies and work with us as a team, I'm confident that we'll start to see some improvements in your life and help you to start living a life that's worth living. Are you willing to work with us to start changing what's going on in your life?"

Without question, no intervention, whether behavioral or pharmacological, will be effective for reducing psychological distress or risk of suicide if it is not implemented as directed by the patient. Shared responsibility for health and well-being therefore must be communicated to suicidal patients, since the simple fact is that death by suicide hinges on the patient's choice to attempt or not to attempt suicide in the first place.

"Treatment Should Take Away All My Pain"

Another problematic expectation that some patients have regarding health care is the assumption that treatment should completely eliminate pain and suffering, whether physical or emotional, and that any continued experience of suffering is an indicator of treatment ineffectiveness or failure. Complete elimination or avoidance of emotional distress is not realistic for anyone, however, since stress is an inevitable life experience that arises naturally and automatically in response to aversive events and situations. Patients who express an expectation to never experience any pain are actually more likely to experience greater levels of emotional distress. For those with recurrent or chronic psychiatric conditions in particular, the expectation that treatment will completely eliminate emotional distress or further recurrence of the condition is simply unrealistic. Rather, treatment should be seen as reducing the probability of recurrence and the severity of functional impairment that accompanies recurrence.

The expectation that treatment should completely eliminate any and all psychological suffering and pain is a reflection of a common strategy for responding to psychological discomfort and uncomfortable thoughts: thought suppression. Thought suppression is the deliberate attempt to avoid or somehow distract oneself from those unwanted and intrusive thoughts that contribute directly to aversive emotional states. A rapidly growing body of research is demonstrating, however, that intentional thought suppression is remarkably counterproductive, in that it actually serves to increase the frequency and intensity of unwanted thoughts and the accompanying emotional distress (Abramowitz, Tolin, & Street, 2001; Wenzleff & Wegner, 2000). Indeed, individuals who utilize thought suppression as a coping strategy tend to have higher levels of cognitive reactivity and react more strongly to emotional thoughts as measured by elevated skin conductance levels when compared with those with lower levels of thought suppression (Wegner & Zanakos, 1994). The counterproductive effects of thought suppression have been observed across psychopathological conditions including intrusive obsessions (Wenzlaff & Wegner, 2000), posttraumatic stress disorder (PTSD; Amstadter & Vernon, 2006), and depression (Wenzlaff & Bates, 1998).

Higher levels of thought suppression are also associated with the presence and frequency of self-harm, suicidal ideation, and suicide attempts (Najmi, Wegner, & Nock, 2007), with thought suppression partially mediating the association between emotional reactivity and the frequency of self-harm and suicidal ideation (though not suicide attempts). Suicidal patients often find themselves in a vicious cycle: The harder they try not to think about suicide, the more frequent and intense these thoughts become, which leads to greater levels of emotional distress, which in turn fuels suicidal thinking as a strategy for reducing or avoiding this escalating emotional distress. BHCs should therefore intervene to reduce or modify those counterproductive treatment expectations that serve to maintain and heighten psychological distress and, in turn, suicidal risk. This is especially important when working with chronically suicidal patients, for whom complete elimination of emotional distress or suicidal urges is highly unlikely given that these individuals, by their very nature, have much greater vulnerabilities and predispositions to emotional dysregulation and suicidality.

BHCs can assist patients in developing more realistic expectations about emotional distress and health by identifying thought suppression and avoidance as the mechanisms by which the patient's suffering is maintained and by building more realistic expectations about the experience of distress in life. Unfortunately, the reality is that distress of some kind will assuredly be experienced at some point again in life; the point of treatment is to adequately prepare suicidal patients for responding to this distress in more adaptive ways. Related to this, as a part of helping suicidal patients to adopt more realistic treatment goals that do not necessarily entail the complete elimination of psychological distress, BHCs must offer patients options about how to develop greater capacities to respond to this distress effectively in order to function in everyday life. Treatment, then, should not be conceptualized as a suicide prevention program (or a suffering prevention program, for that matter) per se, but rather a program in which the patient develops a higher quality of life. In other words, through treatment, the patient learns to live a life worth living (cf. Linehan, 1993).

An example follows for how a BHC might explain this to Mary:

"It sounds like you have been struggling with depression off and on for many years. Several times during your life, when the depression and anxiety have gotten especially severe, you have attempted to kill yourself. Based on this pattern, you seem to have a chronic, recurrent depression. What we know from our research is that if you've had three or more major depressive episodes in your life—which it sounds like you have—there is a 70% to 80% chance that you'll have another one within three years. We also know that someone who has attempted suicide more than twice has a very high likelihood of attempting suicide again, and a very high risk for death by suicide.

"The best treatments we have right now appear to reduce the likelihood for another depressive episode by about half, and also reduce the likelihood for another suicide attempt by about half. What is clear is that our treatments cannot completely eliminate the possibility that you will ever be depressed again. What is possible, however, is that these treatments can reduce the impact that these problems have on your life so that you can live the life that you want to live. Similarly, it is very unlikely that you'll never think about suicide again because it's become such a habit for you. But just because you think about suicide doesn't mean you have to attempt suicide. This is something else that treatment can teach you: how to think about suicide without necessarily trying to kill yourself. In other words, treatment is about learning how to not let depression and suicidal thoughts get in the way of what's important to you, even when you are experiencing them."

Patients who unrealistically expect that mental health treatment should never be uncomfortable, or should completely eliminate their pain and suffering, generally struggle in treatments (especially psychotherapies) that focus on uncomfortable or distressing issues. BHCs can enhance adherence by addressing the patient's willingness to tolerate adverse effects and side effects of treatment in the short term in order to experience gains in the long term. This is especially important for suicidal patients, for whom the course of treatment almost always entails exposure to distressing thoughts and emotions that contribute to and maintain the suicidal crisis. For example, the BHC might employ a metaphor to target the patient's willingness to tolerate any distress associated with treatment:

- "Mental health treatment is kind of like surgery. You have to let the medical professional cut you open and do things in a controlled environment that would be harmful in any other setting. But in the end, it's what it takes to improve your health, and life. The question is whether or not you are willing to undergo the discomfort of this treatment in a controlled environment, under the care of a trained professional, in order to improve your life."

- "Suicidal thinking is kind of like a cancer of the mind, and mental health treatment is kind of like chemotherapy. Chemotherapy is very difficult and uncomfortable and results in a lot of side effects such as losing your hair, feeling nauseous, losing weight, and much more. With the treatment, the person stands a chance of living a longer, healthier, and higher quality of life. Without the treatment, the cancer will only get worse and the person's health and quality of life will be severely compromised. The question is, are you willing to have the uncomfortable side effects in order to live a longer, healthier life that's worth living?"

Central to targeting a patient's tolerance of treatment-associated distress is the recognition of their choice to willingly do so for the purpose of accomplishing their goals or improving their life. The BHC is uniquely positioned to significantly enhance patient adherence to treatment and should therefore address any factors or variables that impact the patient's commitment to the treatment process.

PATIENTS WITH PRIOR NEGATIVE EXPERIENCES WITH MENTAL HEALTH TREATMENT

Another common barrier for accessing specialty care is a history of negative experiences with mental health treatment, which can sour the patient's impressions of all mental health disciplines and professions. Inadequate clinical improvement seems to be a predominant factor affecting negative impressions of mental health providers, which could be due to poor therapeutic alliance with previous providers, lack of provider effectiveness (i.e., provider failure), or treatment failure. BHCs should attempt to identify the specific source of the patient's negative impressions and experiences with mental health treatment and gear interventions to specifically target those factors.

When discussing inadequate clinical improvements, the BHC should always take into consideration the patient's approach to, and engagement with, previous mental health treatment. For example, patients who state that mental health treatment is ineffective but also report inconsistent follow-up with their past treatment provider(s), whether in the form of frequent no-shows or cancellations or discontinuing medication treatments prematurely, are less likely to experience the full therapeutic benefits of treatment. In such cases, the BHC should address commitment to treatment issues and educate the patient on the superiority of receiving a full course of treatment, in contrast to the partial treatment course that results from inconsistent engagement in the treatment process.

For patients who report a high level of adherence to previous treatment but still experienced inadequate clinical improvement, one potential factor to consider is poor therapeutic alliance with previous mental health providers. Patients might comment that they did not like their provider or did not believe their provider fully understood the problem or issue. Likewise, patients might feel that previous providers were incompetent or "were not really listening to me." All of these issues speak to poor patient-provider relationship, which, as discussed in Chapter 3, is associated with treatment outcome. BHCs should respond to these concerns by educating the patient on the importance of a strong therapeutic alliance and normalizing the process of "shopping" for a provider with whom the patient feels comfortable (e.g., "It is not uncommon for people to meet with two, three, or sometimes even more mental health providers before they find someone with whom they feel comfortable and work well").

Alternatively, a mismatch between the patient's needs and the treatment approach could have contributed to inadequate gains. The patient may not have received the optimal treatment modality, for example. Perhaps they received medications alone when psychosocial treatments might have been better indicated, or vice versa. Alternatively, combined pharmacological and psychosocial interventions might have resulted in better outcomes, but the patient only received one treatment modality. Yet another possibility for consideration is the receipt of inadequate treatment due to misdiagnosis. For example, PTSD and major depressive disorder have a very high comorbidity rate (Institute of Medicine, 2007). Because depression has a generally higher prevalence rate in the general population, PTSD can often be "masked" by the depressive symptoms and therefore can easily be "missed" by providers, who consequently develop treatment plans that do not target the underlying trauma driving the symptomatic presentation and functional impairment. Another possibility is that the patient did not receive an empirically supported treatment—a situation that is shockingly common within the specialty mental health system, as outlined in a recent report by Baker, McFall, and Shoham (2008).

One final possibility is that patients did receive an appropriate, empirically supported treatment that was competently delivered by the provider, but the patient nonetheless did not improve as expected (i.e., treatment failure). Treatment failure can be expected in all realms of health care based on the simple fact that even very good treatments are not 100% effective in all cases. Understandably, patients who have adhered to treatments in the past without realizing considerable clinical improvements are less motivated to reinitiate care. Regardless of the reason suspected for less-than-ideal treatment outcomes in the past, the BHC should take a positive approach with the patient by reframing the "failure" as a critical step in identifying the optimal treatment regimen. Specifically, knowing which treatment modalities and approaches have not worked in the past can provide critical information about which treatments will work now, since we have effectively narrowed the field of options.

One final possibility for BHCs to consider is adverse or iatrogenic effects of previous treatment, such as medication side effects or emotional discomfort during psychotherapy. BHCs should address patients' concerns about emotional discomfort or pain in mental health treatment using the tips and strategies discussed in the previous section ("Treatment should take away all my pain").

MULTIPLE SUICIDE ATTEMPTERS IN PRIMARY CARE

Patients with histories of multiple suicide attempts present a unique challenge from BHCs and primary care teams, and as such, individuals have particularly high levels of psychopathology and greater interpersonal skills deficiencies (Forman et al., 2004; Rudd et al., 1996), a greater number of health conditions (Claassen et al., 2007), and an elevated mortality rate across all causes of death (including disease processes; Ostama & Lonnqvist, 2001). This increased risk for adverse health outcomes might be due, at least in part, to a propensity among multiple attempters to refuse to accept or access helping resources (Rudd, Joiner, & Rajab, 2005), which might be related to increased levels of hopelessness, pessimism, and cynicism regarding the efficacy of treatment or continued intervention. The combination of higher levels of psychosocial issues, more numerous health conditions (almost assuredly related to the psychosocial issues), and lowered propensity to access and adhere to treatment raises the likelihood for repeated visits to the primary care clinic.

In general, multiple attempters can be especially frustrating and challenging for health care providers to work with. They tend to visit the clinic frequently with multiple problems and concerns, are difficult to interact with, and tend not to follow recommendations. Recovery and clinical improvement for such patients therefore takes much longer and is easily derailed. For health care providers, working with multiple attempters can understandably be unrewarding at best and thoroughly punishing at worst. Furthermore, in light of significantly elevated rates for further suicide attempts and death by suicide among multiple attempters, it is not surprising that PCPs and BHCs are reluctant to provide treatments and interventions that could potentially be used in suicide attempts (e.g., medications).

When working with multiple attempters, primary care teams must work together as a team to support each other and monitor the ongoing, chronic nature of suicide risk for such patients. Although multiple attempters are, without a doubt, most appropriately treated in the specialty mental health care system, these patients will nonetheless return to the primary care clinic, whether for routine medical problems (e.g., common colds or infections) or for psychosocially driven issues (e.g., tension headaches, mood lability). It is during these contacts that the primary care team can assess the patient's engagement with and commitment to mental health treatment and reinforce adherence. For example, PCPs and BHCs can ask the patient to describe (and even demonstrate) skills they have recently learned in psychotherapy and how they have been implementing these skills in their life. BHCs, in particular, are well-positioned to support the mental health specialist's treatment plan by identifying and problem-solving any barriers or obstacles to successful skills implementation.

In short, primary care teams must recognize that simply connecting multiple attempters to a mental health specialist for treatment does not mean they will no longer be required to interact with or medically manage these patients. BHCs can therefore be pivotal in enhancing the care for multiple attempters through a variety of consultative strategies:

1. Educate PCPs about interpersonal dynamics and approaches for working with multiple attempters that reduce the likelihood of inadvertently reinforcing recurrent suicidal behaviors and treatment nonadherence.
   - Patients who report treatment nonadherence or refuse to access appropriate treatment should be approached with a more neutral interpersonal demeanor to avoid inadvertent reinforcement of nonadherence. Note that this is not the same as emotional detachment or indifference about the patient's problems or concerns.
   - Patients who report treatment adherence and engagement in recommended behaviors should be approached with a more interpersonally engaged and receptive demeanor marked by positive affect, which serves to reinforce adherence.
2. Develop clinic procedures for tracking chronically suicidal patients (see Chapter 3).
3. Influence PCP practice to use medications with lower risk profiles.

4. Organize the entire clinic team to adopt the common treatment goals of accessing specialty mental health care and adhering to the specialty mental health treatment plan (to include targeting early dropout potential).
5. Build the expectation among the primary care team that multiple attempters will be at chronically elevated risk for suicide and will therefore require longer-term, ongoing care that mirrors the approach of chronic disease management models.

CORE COMPETENCIES FOR THE BEHAVIORAL HEALTH CONSULTANT

1. Use motivational enhancement strategies to target barriers to treatment including ambivalence about accessing specialty mental health care, refusal to access care, and nonadherence to treatment recommendations.
2. Recognize and identify unrealistic expectations about treatment and target these beliefs to improve clinical outcomes.
3. Maintain a collaborative stance when working with nonadherent or ambivalent patients and work toward the common treatment goal to alleviate the patient's suffering.
4. Assist the primary care team in the long-term management of chronically suicidal patients (i.e., multiple attempters).
5. Support the specialty mental health provider's treatment plan by reinforcing treatment adherence and assisting the patient to problem solve barriers or obstacles to treatment implementation.

CHAPTER 10

Legal Issues in the Management of Suicide Risk in Primary Care

Concerns about being sued raise considerable angst among mental health clinicians, regardless of setting. Some of that concern is warranted, as malpractice claims against mental health practitioners have continued to grow from year to year, with suicide being one of the most frequent and costly claims (cf. Connor, 1994). Those in primary care settings have ventured into somewhat unknown territory, as we are just beginning to define clinical expectations and standards of care. Case law will continue to unfold in the coming years and will undoubtedly have considerable influence on the structure and function of behavioral health service delivery in primary care. There are two certainties, though: the nature of clinical practice in primary care settings is demonstrably different from traditional outpatient settings, and the standard of care is dependent on clinical context. The standard of care is dependent on clinical context. As discussed next, there are important differences between general outpatient mental health practice and that in primary care settings.

The volume of patients with mental health concerns in primary care is indisputably high. Accordingly, those evidencing some level of suicide risk will continue to grow, particularly as inpatient and residential treatment alternatives continue to dwindle (Luoma et al., 2002). It is to the benefit of behavioral health consultants (BHCs) in primary care to familiarize themselves with some very basic legal constructs. In particular, the concepts of the standard of care, negligence, foreseeability, and reasonable care all have importance and relevance to daily practice. An awareness of these concepts allows the practicing clinician to not only reduce the risk of liability, but more importantly, to improve the delivery of services.

An awareness of these concepts oftentimes compels clinicians to ask important questions and think in a more organized, efficient, and effective fashion about the clinical care they provide. What is the best approach to risk assessment in a brief timeframe? What level of risk can be appropriately managed in primary care? What type of management strategies work in primary care? What is the role of medications? All are important questions, and this text has been geared to answer them. As an adjunct, it is crucial for practitioners to recognize and understand the broader issues of liability in clinical practice, along with the unique constraints of primary care. It has been our experience that clinicians with a greater awareness of liability issues think in comprehensive fashion about clinical practice, communicate more effectively both with patients and in their clinical documentation, and provide empirically driven services that tend to be more targeted and effective.

THE STANDARD OF CARE AND NEGLIGENCE

Managing suicide risk in primary care raises many concerns among practicing clinicians, with legal ones often at the top of the list and fear of being sued fairly widespread (Baerger, 2001). Most prominent among the legal issues raised are the standard of care and negligence in clinical practice. The standard of care is a legal construct established in large part by the review and testimony of identified experts in a targeted case and defined as "that degree of care which a reasonably prudent person should exercise in same or similar circumstances" (Black, 1990, p. 1405). In terms of practicing clinicians, the standard of care depends greatly on context, that is, the idea of "same or similar circumstances." Primary care settings have a number of unique and defining characteristics, all of which drive the very nature of clinical practice and expectations that surround the standard of care. In particular, clinical practice in primary care is distinguished by a greater volume of patients seen in a typical day, brief appointments, considerably more breadth in the nature and severity of presenting problems (including medical comorbidity), dramatically less time available for suicide risk assessment and related intervention and management activities, greater frequency of collaborative decision-making, and limited follow-up (both in number and duration of sessions) (Bryan et al., 2009).

As decided in *Mathews v. Walker* (1973), the standard of care is violated when a professional fails to provide care consistent with the average practitioner in "same or similar circumstances." Expert reviewers are hired by the attorneys on both sides involved in a legal case. As a result, it is important for practicing clinicians to understand there will almost always be an expert identified in the case claiming that the care provided fell below the expected standard. When a practitioner fails to meet the standard of care, it is defined as negligence. There has been some debate about the standard of care in primary care settings, particularly areas like suicide risk assessment. One pivotal question has been whether the BHC "brings" a higher standard into the primary care setting. In answering this question, it is critical that clinicians understand the importance of context and the prevailing standard in "same or similar circumstances." Context undeniably matters. For example, there is great variability in the nature and expectation of care provided on an inpatient service relative to a general outpatient clinic, residential care facility, or emergency room. Lowering the risk of a malpractice action is relatively straightforward, particularly when keeping in mind the unique characteristics of suicide risk assessment in primary care. This text offers a specific, easily implemented, thorough, and effective approach, one that is well above the prevailing standard.

Negligence in clinical practice can take two primary forms, which are acts of commission (engaging in behavior that was inappropriate or not clinically indicated) and omission (failing to do something that was clinically indicated). In the area of suicidality, the more frequent problems are acts of omission, with clinicians facing claims that they failed to conduct an appropriate risk assessment and/or implement indicated management strategies. Ordinarily, complaints are that the clinician has misdiagnosed the patient or failed to recognize heightened suicide risk (VandeCreek, Knapp, & Herzog, 1987). As Simon (1988) noted, to be found negligent, it does not matter whether the act was accidental (unintentional) or the result of a lack of skill, knowledge, or training (unwitting).

Making a claim of negligence is one thing; actually proving negligence is another. For an act to be proven as negligent, it must be demonstrated that (a) there was a duty of care to the patient, (b) the duty of care was breached, (c) the patient suffered injury or harm, and (d) the injury or harm was directly caused by the clinician (Rachlin, 1984). As should be evident, establishing all four elements is not an easy task, particularly when a clinician has been consistent and thorough in day-to-day practice. In particular, proving a negligent act "caused" injury or harm to a patient can be a significant challenge for the plaintiff's attorney. Implementation of simple and standardized approaches to risk management in high-volume practices can therefore significantly reduce the likelihood of being found negligent by reducing the complexity of clinical practice and improving the overall consistency and quality of care provided.

FORESEEABILITY AND REASONABLE CARE

When it comes to suicide, all clinicians need to be aware of the constructs of foreseeability and reasonable care (Simon, 1988). When a claim or complaint is filed, two critical questions emerge. First, should the clinician have been able to reasonably anticipate a suicide attempt or death (based on a competent risk assessment), and second, did the clinician take the necessary steps to protect the patient and provide the appropriate care? As has been well documented, it is impossible to predict a suicide attempt or death in an individual case (Pokorny, 1983). Nonetheless, the standard of care clearly establishes that clinicians can conduct empirically driven risk assessments that will help identify salient risk factors, recognize when risk is elevated relative to normal functioning, and guide clinical interventions targeted to reduce risk (Rudd, Joiner, & Rajab, 2004). This text provides a clear and well-articulated guide on how to conduct such a risk assessment process, along with appropriate interventions geared toward reducing risk. It is reassuring for clinicians in primary care to understand that the expectations in case law are not unreasonable with respect to foreseeability and reasonable care. *Speer v. United States* (1981) recognized that, in outpatient settings, in particular, clinicians have limited control over patients' behavior. Even when provided with the best of care, patients will sometimes attempt suicide and potentially die as a result. Rudd et al. (2009) have discussed in some depth the risk of death inherent in psychiatric illness. It is a risk that case law has recognized. The court system understands that, in outpatient settings, there are only so many ways to protect patients and safeguard the environment. Despite these limitations, there are concrete and empirically supported steps that clinicians can take to offer patients protection both from impairing symptoms and their immediate environment (i.e. available methods). Taking the concrete steps discussed in previous chapters is critical to meeting the expectations of forseeability and reasonable care within primary care settings.

It is also important for clinicians to recognize that negligence is not necessarily about clinical judgment. Making an error in assigning level of risk is not a breach in the standard of care, as long as the clinician followed appropriate procedures and provided a clinical response consistent with the assessed level of risk. Sometimes, clinicians make an error in recognizing heightened levels of risk because a patient and/or family members were unwilling to share information openly and honestly. Sometimes, a patient's risk level changes shortly after risk assessment was conducted because of intervening variables and a new precipitant that could not have been anticipated.

As should be evident, keeping good clinical records is critical to demonstrating a clear and coherent link between the assessment process and clinical decision-making. A good entry, one related to high-quality clinical care and one that guards against liability, is one that communicates the elements of risk identified and how those influenced clinical decision-making. In short, a good entry identifies what the clinician saw and why he or she responded in the manner described. The easiest way to think about documentation is that a good chart entry explains the nature of the problem (in this case, suicide risk) and why the clinical response was appropriate. What were the elements of risk that drove the clinical response? Given the unique characteristics of a primary care setting, the key challenge is to be able to do this in an efficient and effective fashion. Use of a standardized format will certainly make it easier. At a minimum, it is recommended that the clinician use a checklist to guide both clinical activities as well as documentation. Some combination of a checklist format (such as the risk assessment template from chapter 4 or the outline of implicated clinical responses from chapter 5) with room for narrative expansion when needed is recommended.

As discussed in previous chapters, a systematic risk assessment can be conducted in a brief period. Similarly, documentation can be facilitated by a standardized form, one that provides for a quick indication of precipitant, current symptom picture, history of suicidal behavior, features of the current suicidal episode (e.g. ideation, plan, intent, access to method), and protective factors. Such a form can be put into checklist format, providing room for more detailed elaboration when needed. As with a standardized approach to assessment, being systematic in documentation is critical. Checklist formats demonstrate that the essential domains were addressed in the clinical exchange and can allow the practitioner the freedom to elaborate when and where needed. Most BHCs like to develop their own standardized chart entry formats, consistent with the unique characteristics of their setting and patient population.

THE INFLUENCE OF PRACTICE GUIDELINES

It is important for clinicians to recognize that clinical guidelines influence, but not determine, the standard of care. There are several clinical guidelines available in the literature on the assessment and management of suicidality (American Academy of Child and Adolescent Psychiatry, 2001; American Psychiatric Association, 2003; American Association of Suicidology, 2008; Suicide Prevention Resource Center, 2006). There is considerable overlap across the various guidelines, each articulating relevant content for risk assessment along with specific suggestions for clinical interventions to manage various levels of risk. The guidelines are exhaustive, covering the literature in specific detail.

It is also important to recognize that, to some degree, the guidelines define "expert" care within specialty mental health settings. There is a marked difference between reasonable care delivered in primary care and reasonable care delivered in specialty mental health. There is absolutely no expectation that the nature of care provided in a primary care setting be comparable to specialty mental health care. What is important for the BHC is to identify and refer patients requiring specialty care. One of the essential questions needing to be answered during a suicide risk assessment in primary care is whether the patient can be effectively managed in a primary care setting. As should be evident, a decision to provide care to a high-risk patient solely in primary care is by its very nature negligent since the primary care clinic is not equipped (in terms of frequency of visits needed and type of treatment) to provide the type of care indicated.

One of the contributions of this text is that it provides greater clarity for reasonable care in primary care settings, translating the existing guidelines in a format and fashion that is appropriate and manageable. In the primary care setting, risk assessment and management takes on distinctive features but nonetheless can be done in a manner consistent with published guidelines. From a liability perspective, it is important for the clinician to remember that, arguably, the most critical risk assessment decision is whether to refer the patient to a specialist, with clear recognition that those at chronic risk and high acute risk need to be referred directly to a mental health specialist for ongoing care and management. Those at lower levels of risk can be managed effectively in primary care if acute risk is monitored and the targeted management techniques discussed in this text are used.

COMMON FAILURE SCENARIOS

Bongar, Maris, Berman, and Litman (1988) provided 12 common failure scenarios related to outpatient suicide, with several of them relevant to our discussion of primary care settings:

- Failure to evaluate properly the need for pharmacotherapy
- Failure to implement hospitalization
- Failures in supervision and consultation
- Failure to evaluate suicide risk at intake and management transitions
- Failure to conduct a mental status examination and diagnose
- Failure to adequately document clinical judgments
- Failure to safeguard the environment.

For the most part, these scenarios are self-explanatory, but a few comments are warranted. Perhaps most obvious is the issue of routinely screening and conducting suicide risk assessments for suicidal patients. Suicide risk screening and assessment is a minimum practice expectation, and should include an assessment of mental status and notation of a diagnosis where warranted. Although mental status and diagnostic assessment are already fairly routine in BHC practice, suicide risk screening and assessment are not necessarily routinely conducted. The importance of routine risk assessment in BHC practice is critical because primary care settings are not generally equipped to manage the frequent, severe, and enduring needs of high risk and/or chronically suicidal patients. Without routine risk assessment, the BHC is unable to determine when a patient can be safely managed in the primary care system, and when a patient should be referred to the specialty mental health system.

If a suicidal patient is retained for short-term management in primary care, it is important to consider the role and function of pharmacotherapy as part of the broader management strategy, particularly with respect to targeted symptom reduction. This is particularly true for symptoms associated with higher levels of risk, including sleep disturbance, agitation, and anxiety. As noted earlier, hospitalization is identified as a common failure scenario. For those in primary care settings, the most important thing to consider is that when a patient is not hospitalized or referred for specialty care, it should be clear in the chart entry why this decision was made. In particular, it should be clear that the patient is at lower acute risk, does not evidence any chronic risk, symptoms are manageable, and that adequate protective factors are in place to facilitate their compliance with treatment.

The issue of supervision and consultation warrants elaboration. Supervision of interns, residents, postdoctoral students, and other trainees is common in primary care settings. Case law has established a clear expectation that the supervisor is responsible for the care provided by those under his or her supervision. This is particularly true if the supervising clinician endorses an assessment, treatment, or disposition decision without having seen the patient. In *Cohen v. State* (1976/1977), a psychiatrist discharged a patient from inpatient care solely on the resident's recommendation without personally evaluating the patient. The patient later died by suicide after discharge. In finding the psychiatrist liable for the decision of a supervisee, the court indicated the primary error was the supervising psychiatrist's decision not to personally evaluate the high-risk patient.

It is therefore recommended that in cases of suicidal risk that supervising clinicians personally see and evaluate the patient if hospitalization is not pursued. When a patient is hospitalized, we know that the appropriate steps to safeguard the patient and environment are in place. It is when a potentially high-risk patient is not hospitalized that careful scrutiny is needed. Related to this issue is concern about safeguarding the environment (e.g. restricting access to method, creating a safety plan, involving family in crisis management). This text provides some concrete steps to be taken in safeguarding the environment. However, it is important to recognize that the most effective step that can be taken by BHCs in primary care is to refer high-risk patients to specialty care in addition to immediately providing appropriate risk management strategies.

LIABILITY AND CLINICAL PRACTICE

All clinicians should readily recognize that the probability of a lawsuit is extremely low, despite the fact that 20% of psychologists and 50% of psychiatrists will lose a patient to suicide over the course of their careers (Chemtob, Hamada, Bauer, Kinney, & Torigoe, 1988). Rather than expend time, energy, and resources worrying about liability and lawsuits, it is best for clinicians to follow clear and empirically derived practices. The easiest and most straightforward method for reducing liability risk is to implement empirically-based practices and strategies that ensure the best care possible is provided to any patient at risk for suicide. This text allows clinicians in primary care to do just that, helping sculpt practice standards that are reasonable, efficient, and, most importantly, effective.

CORE COMPETENCIES FOR BEHAVIORAL HEALTH CONSULTANTS

1. Understand the legal constructs of the standard of care, negligence, foreseeability, and reasonable care.
2. Utilize a standardized risk assessment approach with suicidal patients.
3. Use concrete risk management strategies for patients at elevated risk for suicide.
4. Develop an approach to documentation that utilizes a blend of checklists and narrative entries.
5. Use empirically-supported assessment, risk management, intervention, and consultation strategies to reduce the likelihood of "failure scenarios" in primary care.

References

Abramowitz, J. S., Tolin, D. F., & Street, G. P. (2001). Paradoxical effects of thought suppression: A meta-analysis of controlled studies. *Clinical Psychology Review, 21*, 683–703.

Addis, M. E., & Jacobson, N. S. (2000). A closer look at the treatment rationale and homework compliance in cognitive-behavioral therapy for depression. *Cognitive Therapy and Research, 24,* 313–326.

Agargun, M. Y., Kara, H., & Solmaz, M. (1997). Sleep disturbances and suicidal behavior in patients with major depression. *Journal of Clinical Psychiatry, 58*, 249–251.

Akiskal, H. S., & Benazzi, F. (2005). Psychopathologic correlates of suicidal ideation in major depressive outpatients: Is it all due to unrecognized (bipolar) depressive mixed states? *Psychopathology, 38,* 273–280.

Ambady, N. Laplante, D., Nguyen, T., Rosenthal, R., Chaumeton, N., & Levinson, W. (2002). Surgeons' tone of voice: A clue to malpractice history. *Surgery, 132,* 5–9.

Ambady, N., Bernieri, F. J., & Richeson, J. A. (2000). Toward a histology of social behavior: Judgmental accuracy from thin slices of the behavioral stream. In M. P. Zanna (Ed.), *Advances in experimental social psychology.* San Diego, CA: Academic Press.

American Academy of Child and Adolescent Psychiatry. (2001). Practice parameter for the assessment and treatment of children and adolescents with suicidal behavior. *Journal of the American Academy of Child and Adolescent Psychiatry, 40*(7, Suppl.), 24S–51S.

American Academy of Pediatrics. (2000). Suicide and suicide attempts in adolescents. *Pediatrics, 105,* 871–874.

American Association of Suicidology. (2008). *Recognizing and responding to suicide risk.* Washington, DC: Author.

American Medical Association. (2003). *Guidelines for adolescent preventive services (GAPS): Recommendations monograph.* Retrieved November 26, 2008, from http://www.ama-assn.org/ama/upload/mm/39/gapsmono.pdf

American Psychiatric Association. (1994). *Diagnostic and statistical manual of mental disorders* (4th ed.). Washington, DC: Author.

American Psychiatric Association. (2000). Practice guideline for the treatment of patients with major depressive disorder [revision]. *American Journal of Psychiatry, 157*(4, Suppl.), 1–45.

American Psychiatric Association (2003). Practice guidelines for the assessment and treatment of patients with suicidal behaviors. *American Journal of Psychiatry*, *60*, 1–60.

Amstadter, A. B., & Vernon, L. L. (2006). Suppression of neutral and trauma targets: Implications for posttraumatic stress disorder. *Journal of Traumatic Stress, 19,* 517–526.

Appleby, L., Cooper, J., Amos, T., & Faragher. (1999). Psychological autopsy study of suicides by people aged under 35. *British Journal of Psychiatry, 175,* 148–174.

Appleby, L., Shaw, J., Amos, T., McConnell, R., Harris, C., McCann, K., et al. (1999). Suicide within 12 months of contact with mental health services: National clinical survey. *British Medical Journal, 318*, 1235–1239.

Arnow, B. A. (2004). Relationships between childhood maltreatment, adult health and psychiatric outcomes, and medical utilization. *Journal of Clinical Psychiatry, 65,* 10–15.

Asberg, M. (1997). Neurotransmitters and suicidal behavior: The evidence from cerebrospinal fluid studies. *Annals of the New York Academy of Sciences, 836,* 158–181.

Baerger, D. R. (2001). Risk management with the suicidal patient: Lessons from case law. *Professional Psychology: Research and Practice, 32,* 359–366.

Baker, T. B., McFall, R. M., & Shoham, V. (2008). Current status and future prospects of clinical psychology toward a scientifically principled approach to mental and behavioral health care. *Psychological Science in the Public Interest, 9,* 67–103.

Baldessarini, R. J., Tondo, L., & Hennen, J. (2003). Lithium treatment and suicide risk in major affective disorders: Update and new findings. *Journal of Clinical Psychiatry, 64*(Suppl. 5), 44–52.

Baldessarini, R. J., Tondo, L., David, P., Pompili, M., Goodwin, F. K., & Hennen, J. (2006). Decreased risk of suicides and attempts during long-term lithium treatment: A meta-analytic review. *Bipolar Disorders, 8*, 625–639.

Baldwin, S. A., Wampold, B. E., & Imel, Z. E. (2007). Untangling the alliance-outcome correlation: Exploring the relative importance of therapist and patient variability in the alliance. *Journal of Consulting and Clinical Psychology, 75,* 842–852.

Barrett, M. S., Chua, W., Crits-Cristoph, P., Gibbons, M. B., & Thompson, D. (2008). Early withdrawal from mental health treatment: Implications for psychotherapy practice. *Psychotherapy: Theory, Research, Practice, Training, 45,* 247–267.

Bastia, B. K., & Kar, N. (2009). A psychological autopsy study of suicidal hanging from Cuttack, India: Focus on stressful life situations. *Archives of Suicide Research, 13,* 100–104.

Beardsley, R. S., Gardocki, G. J., Larson, D. B., & Hidalgo, J. (1998). Prescribing of psychotropic medication by primary care physicians and psychiatrists. *Archives of General Psychiatry, 45,* 1117–1119.

Beck, A. T., Beck, R., & Kovacs, M. (1975). Classification of suicidal behaviors: I. Quantifying intent and medical lethality. *American Journal of Psychiatry, 132*, 285–287.

Beck, A. T., Brown, G., & Steer, R. A. (1989). Prediction of eventual suicide in psychiatric inpatients by clinical ratings of hopelessness. *Journal of Consulting and Clinical Psychology, 57*, 309–310.

Beck, A. T., Brown, G. K., & Steer, R. A. (1997). Psychometric characteristics of the scale for suicide ideation with psychiatric outpatients. *Behaviour Research and Therapy, 35*, 1039–1046.

Beck, A. T., Emery, G., & Greenberg, R. L. (1985). *Anxiety disorders and phobias*. New York: Basic Books.

Beck, A. T., Weissman, A., Lester, D., & Trexler, L. (1974). The measurement of pessimism: The Hopelessness Scale. *Journal of Consulting and Clinical Psychology, 42*, 861–865.

Beckham, E. E. (1992). Predicting patient dropout in psychotherapy. *Psychotherapy, 29*, 177–182.

Benazzi, F. (2005). Suicidal ideation and bipolar-II depression symptoms. *Human Psychopharmacology, 20*, 27–32.

Benazzi, F., & Akiskal, H. S. (2006). Psychometric delineation of the most discriminant symptoms of depressive mixed states. *Psychiatry Research, 141*, 81–88.

Benson, H. (1975). *The relaxation response*. New York: Morrow.

Berkanovic, E., Telesky, C., & Reeder, S. (1981). Structural and social psychological factors in the decision to seek medical care for symptoms. *Medical Care, 21*, 693–709.

Berman, A. L. (2006). Risk management with suicidal patients. *Journal of Clinical Psychology, 62*, 171–184.

Bernert, R. A., Joiner, T. E., Cukrowicz, K. C., Schmidt, N. B., & Krakow, B. (2005). Suicidality and sleep disturbances. *Sleep, 28*, 1135–1141.

Black, H. C. (1990). *Black's law dictionary*. St. Paul, MN: West.

Blount, A., Schoenbaum, M., Kathol, R., Rollman, B. L., Thomas, M., O'Donohue, W., & Peek, C. J. (2007). The economics of behavioral health services in medical settings: A summary of the evidence. *Professional Psychology: Research and Practice, 38*, 290–297.

Bongar, B., & Harmatz, M. (1991). Clinical psychology graduate education in the study of suicide: Availability, resources, and importance. *Suicide and Life-Threatening Behavior, 21*, 231–244.

Bongar, B., Maris, R. W., Berman, A. L., & Litman, R. E. (1998). Outpatient standards of care and the suicidal patient. In B. Bongar, A. L. Berman, R. W. Maris, M. M. Silverman, E. A. Harris, & W. L. Packman (Eds.), *Risk management with suicidal patients* (pp. 4–33). New York: Guilford Press.

Bostwick, J. B., & Pankratz, V. S. (2000). Affective disorders and suicide risk: A reexamination. *American Journal of Psychiatry, 157*, 1925–1932.

Bostwick, J. M. (2006). Do SSRIs cause suicide in children? The evidence is underwhelming. *Journal of Clinical Psychology*, *62*, 235–241.

Bray, J. H., Frank, R. G., McDaniel, S. H., & Heldring, M. H. (2004). Education, practice, and research opportunities for psychologists in primary care. In R. G. Frank, S. H. McDaniel, J. H. Bray, & M. Heldring (Eds.), *Primary care psychology*. Washington, DC: American Psychological Association.

Brown, G. K. (2006). *Suicide prevention in the community: Lessons learned.* Paper presented at the 2nd Suicide Interventions Strategic Planning Meeting, Seattle, WA.

Brown, G. K., Beck, A. T., Steer, R. A., & Grisham, J. R. (2000). Risk factors for suicide in psychiatric outpatients: A 20-year prospective study. *Journal of Consulting and Clinical Psychology, 68*, 371–337.

Brown, G. K., Henriques, G. R., Sosdjan, D., & Beck, A. T. (2004). Suicide intent and accurate expectations of lethality: Predictors of medical lethality of suicide attempts. *Journal of Consulting and Clinical Psychology, 72*, 1170–1174.

Brown, G. K., TenHave, T., Henriques, G. R., Xie, S. X., Hollander, J. E., & Beck, A. T. (2005). Cognitive therapy for the prevention of suicide attempts: A randomized controlled trial. *Journal of the American Medical Association, 294*, 563–570.

Brown, J. Cohen, P., Johnson, J. G., & Smailes, E. (1999). Childhood abuse and neglect: Specificity of effect on adolescent and young depression and suicidality. *Journal of the American Academy of Child and Adolescent Psychiatry, 38*, 1490–1496.

Brown, M. (1998). *The behavioral treatment of self-mutilation.* In Self-Mutilation Treatment and Research Symposium. Symposium conducted at the XVI Congress of the World Association for Social Psychiatry, Vancouver, BC, Canada.

Bryan, C. J., & Rudd, M. D. (2006). Advances in the assessment of suicide risk. *Journal of Clinical Psychology: In Session, 62*, 185–200.

Bryan, C. J., & Tomchesson, J. T. (2007, April). *Clinician definitions of common suicide-related terms*. Poster presented at the annual meeting of the American Association of Suicidology, New Orleans, LA.

Bryan, C. J., Corso, K. A., Neal-Walden, T. A., & Rudd, M. D. (2009). Managing suicide risk in primary care: Practice recommendations for behavioral health consultants. *Professional Psychology: Research and Practice, 40*, 148–155.

Bryan, C. J., Corso, K. A., Rudd, M. D., & Cordero, L. (2008). Improving identification of suicidal patients in primary care through routine screening. *Primary Care and Community Psychiatry, 13*, 143–147.

Bryan, C. J., Morrow, C. E., & Appolonio, K. A. K. (2009). Impact of behavioral health consultant interventions on patient symptoms and functioning in an integrated family medicine clinic. *Journal of Clinical Psychology, 65*, 281–293.

Bull, S. A., Hunkeler, E. M., Lee, J. Y., Rowland, C. R., Williamson, T. E., Schwab, J. R., & Hurt, S. W. (2002). Discontinuation of use and switching of antidepressants: Influence of patient-physician communication. *Journal of the American Medical Association, 288*, 1403–1409.

Burns, D. D., & Nolen-Hoeksema, S. (1991). Coping styles, homework compliance, and the effectiveness of cognitive-behavioral therapy. *Journal of Consulting and Clinical Psychology, 59*, 305–311.

Burns, D. D., & Nolen-Hoeksema, S. (1992). Therapeutic empathy and recovery from depression in cognitive-behavioral therapy: A structural equation model. *Journal of Consulting and Clinical Psychology, 60*, 441–449.

Burstein, A. G., Adams, R. L., & Giffen, M. B. (1973). Assessment of suicidal risk by psychology and psychiatry trainees. *Archives of General Psychiatry*, *29*, 792–793.

Caldwell, C. B., Gottesman, I. I. (1990). Schizophrenics kill themselves too: A review of risk factors for suicide. *Schizophrenia Bulletin*, *16*, 571–589.

Chemtob, C. M., Hamada, R. S., Bauer, G. B., Kinney, B., & Torigoe, R. Y. (1988). Patient suicide: Frequency and impact on psychiatrists. *American Journal of Psychiatry*, 145, 224–228.

Chiles, J. A., & Strosahl, K. D. (2005). *Clinical manual for assessment and treatment of suicidal patients*. Washington, DC: American Psychiatric Publishing.

Cigrang, J. A., Dobmeyer, A. C., Becknell, M. E., Roa-Navarrete, R. A., & Yerian, S. R. (2006). Evaluation of a collaborative mental health program in primary care: Effects on patient distress and health care utilization. *Primary Care and Community Psychiatry*, *11*, 121–127.

Claassen, C. A., Trivedi, M. H., Rush, A. J., Husain, M. M., Zisook, S., Young, E., et al. (2007). Clinical differences among depressed patients with and without a history of suicide attempts: Findings from the STAR*D trial. *Journal of Affective Disorders, 97*, *77*–84.

Clark, D. C., & Fawcett, J. (1994). The relation of parenthood to suicide. Archives of *General Psychiatry, 51*, 160.

Cohen v. State, 51 A.D. 2d 494, 382 N.Y.S. 2d 128 (App. Div. 1976), aff'd 364 N.E. 2d 1134 (N.Y. 1977).

Comtois, K. A., & Linehan, M. M. (2006). Psychosocial treatments of suicidal behaviors: A practice-friendly review. *Journal of Clinical Psychology: In Session, 62*, 161–170.

Conoley, C. W., Padula, M. A., Payton, D. S., & Daniels, J. A. (1994). Predictors of client implementation of counselor recommendations: match with problem, difficulty level, and building on client strengths. *Journal of Counseling Psychology*, *41*, 3–7.

Connor, M. A. (1994). *Clinicians and the law: A legal handbook for therapists and counselors*. Providence, RI: Manisses Communications Group.

Cooper-Patrick, L., Crum, R. M., & Ford, D. E. (1994). Identifying suicidal ideation in general medical patients. *JAMA*, *272*, 1757.

Cordero, L., Rudd, M. D., Bryan, C. J., & Korso, K. A. (2008). Accuracy of primary care medical providers understanding of the FDA black box warning label for antidepressants. *Primary Care and Community Psychiatry, 13*, 109–114.

Corson, K., Gerrity, M. S., & Dobscha, S. K. (2004). Screening for depression and suicidality in a VA primary care setting: 2 items are better than 1 item. *The American Journal of Managed Care, 10*, 839–845.

Coryell, W., & Schessler, M. (2001). The dexamethasone suppression test and suicide prediction. *American Journal of Psychiatry, 158,* 748–753.

Cox, D. J., Tisdelle, D. A., & Culbert, J. P. (1988). Increasing adherence to behavioral homework assignments. *Journal of Behavioral Medicine, 11,* 519–522.

Cummings, N. A., & O'Donahue, W. T. (2008). *Eleven blunders that cripple psychotherapy in America: A remedial unblundering.* New York: Routledge.

Das, S., & O'Keefe, J. H. (2006). Behavioral cardiology: Recognizing and addressing the profound impact of psychosocial stress on cardiovascular health. *Current Atherosclerosis Reports, 8,* 111–118.

Debski, J., Spadafore, C. D., Jacob, S., Poole, D. A., & Hixson, M. D. (2007). Suicide intervention: Training, roles, and knowledge of school psychologists. *Psychology in the Schools, 44,* 157–170.

DeLeon, P. H., Giesting, B., & Kenkel, M. B. (2003). Community health centers: Exciting opportunities for the 21st century. *Professional Psychology: Research and Practice, 34,* 579.

DeRubeis, R. J., & Feeley, M. (1990). Determinants of change in cognitive therapy for depression. *Cognitive Therapy and Research, 14,* 469–482.

DeRubeis, R. J., Hollon, S. D., Amsterdam, J. D., Shelton, R. C., Young, P. R., Salomon, R. M., O'Reardon, J. P., Lovett, M. L., Gladis, M. M., Brown, L. L., & Gallop, R. (2005). Cognitive therapy vs medications in the treatment of moderate to severe depression. *Archives of General Psychiatry, 62,* 409–416.

Dervic, K., Brent, D. A., & Oquendo, M. A. (2008). Completed suicide in childhood. *Psychiatric Clinics of North America, 31,* 271–291.

Detweiler, J. B., & Whisman, M. A. (1999). The role of homework assignments in cognitive therapy for depression: Potential methods for enhancing adherence. *Clinical Psychology: Research and Practice, 6,* 267–282.

Deykin, E. Y., Keane, T. M., Kaloupek, D., Fincke, G., Rothendler, J., Siegfried, M., & Creamer, K. (2001). Posttraumatic stress disorder and the use of health services. *Psychosomatic Medicine, 63,* 835–841.

Dimidjian, S., Hollon, S. D., Dobson, K. S., Schmaling, K. B., Kohlenberg, R. J., Addis, M. E., et al. (2006). Randomized trial of behavioral activation, cognitive therapy, and antidepressant medication in the acute treatment of adults with major depression. *Journal of Consulting and Clinical Psychology, 74,* 658–670.

Drew, B. L. (2001). Self-harm behavior and no-suicide contracting in psychiatric inpatient settings. *Archives of Psychiatric Nursing, 15,* 99–106.

Druss, B., & Pincus, H. (2000). Suicidal ideation and suicide attempts in general medical illnesses. *Archives of Internal Medicine, 160,* 1522–1526.

Dunbar-Jacob, J., & Mortimer-Stephens, M. K. (2001). Treatment adherence in chronic disease. *Journal of Clinical Epidemiology, 54,* S57–S60.

Duval, F., Mokrani, M., Correa, H., Bailey, P., Valdebenito, M., Monreal, J., et al. (2001). Lack of effect of HPA axis hyperactivity on hormonal responses to D-fenfluramine in major depressed patients: Implications for pathogenesis of suicidal behavior. *Psychoneuroendocrinology, 26,* 521–537.

Eddleston, M. E., Buckley, N. A., Gunnell, D., Dawson, A. H., & Konradsen, F. (2006). Identification of strategies to prevent death after pesticide self-poisoning using a Haddon matrix. *Injury Prevention, 12*, 333–337.

Edwards, R. R., Smith, M. T., Kudel, I., & Haythornthwaite, J. (2006). Pain-related catastrophizing as a risk factor for suicidal ideation in chronic pain. *Pain, 126*, 272–279.

Egeland, J. A., & Sussex, J. N. (1985). Suicide and family loading for affective disorders. *Journal of the American Medical Association, 254*, 915–918.

Elliott, R. L. (2007). Depression in primary care. *Ethnicity and Disease, 17*(Suppl. 2), 28–33.

Erlangsen, A., Candudas-Romo, V., & Conwell, Y. (2008). Increased use of antidepressants and decreasing suicide rates: A population-based study using Danish register data. *Journal of Epidemiology and Community Health*, *62*, 448–454.

Fawcett, J. (1999). Profiles of completed suicides. In D. Jacobs (Ed.), *The Harvard Medical School guide to suicide assessment and intervention* (pp. 115–124). San Francisco, CA: Jossey-Bass.

Fawzy, F. I., Fawzy, N. W., Hyun, C. S., Elashoff, R., Guthrie, D., Fahey, J. L., et al. (1993). Malignant melanoma: Effects of an early structured psychiatric intervention, coping, and affective state on recurrence and survival 6 years later. *Archives of General Psychiatry, 50*, 681–689.

Feldman, B. N., & Freedenthal, S. (2006). Social work education in suicide intervention and prevention: An unmet need? *Suicide and Life-Threatening Behavior, 36*, 467–480.

Food & Drug Administration. Center for Drug Evaluation and Research. (2007). Retrieved September 30, 2010, from http://www.fda.gov/cder/drug/antidepressants/default.htm

Forman, E. M., Berk, M. S., Henriques, G. R., Brown, G. K., & Beck, A. T. (2004). History of multiple suicide attempts as a behavioral marker of severe psychopathology. *American Journal of Psychiatry, 161*, 437–443.

Fountoulakis, K. N., Iacovides, A., Foeiou, F., Nimatoudis, J., Bascialla, F., Ioannidou, C. et al. (2004). Neurobiological and psychological correlates of suicidal attempts and thoughts of death in patients with major depression. *Neuropsychobiology, 29*, 42–52.

Frankenfield, D. L., Keyl, P. M., Gielen, A., Wissow, L. S., Werthamer, L., & Baker, S. P. (2000). Adolescent patients—healthy or hurting?: Missed opportunities to screen for suicide risk in the primary care setting. *Archives of Pediatrics & Adolescent Medicine*, *154*, 162–168.

Frasure-Smith, N. (1991). In-hospital symptoms of psychological stress as predictors of long-term outcome after acute myocardial infarction in men. *American Journal of Cardiology, 68*, 121–127.

Garcia-Shelton, L. (2006). Meeting U.S. health care needs: A challenge to psychology. *Professional Psychology: Research and Practice, 37*, 676–682.

Garfield, S. L. (1986). Research on client variables in psychotherapy. In S. L. Garfield & A. E. Bergin (Eds.), *Handbook of psychotherapy and behavior change* (3rd ed., pp. 213–256). New York: Wiley.

Gatchel, R. J., & Oordt, M. S. (2003). *Clinical health psychology and primary care.* Washington, DC: American Psychological Association.

Gelso, C. J., & Johnson, D. H. (1983). *Explorations in time-limited counseling and psychotherapy.* New York: Teachers College Press.

Gibbons, R. D., Brown, C. H., Hur, K., Marcus, S. M., Bhaumik, D. K., Erkens, J. A., Herings, R. M. C., & Mann, J. J. (2007). Early evidence on the effects of regulators' suicidality warnings on SSRI prescriptions and suicide in children and adolescents. *American Journal of Psychiatry, 164*, 1356–1363.

Gortner, E. T., Gollan, J. K., Dobson, K. S., & Jacobson, N. S. (1998). Cognitive-behavioral treatment for depression: Relapse prevention. *Journal of Consulting and Clinical Psychology, 66*, 377–384.

Goethe, J. W., Woolley, S. B., Cardoni, A. A., Woznicki, B. A., & Piez, D. A. (2007). Selective serotonin reuptake inhibitor discontinuation: Side effects and other factors that influence medication adherence. *Journal of Clinical Psychopharmacology, 27*, 451–458.

Goldney, R. D., Fisher, L. J., Wilson, D. H., & Cheok, F. (2001). Suicidal ideation and health-related quality of life in the community. *Medical Journal of Australia, 175*, 546–549.

Goldstein, T. R., Bridge, J. A., & Brent, D. A. (2008). Sleep disturbance preceding completed suicide in adolescents. *Journal of Consulting Clinical Psychology, 76*, 84–91.

Goodwin, F. K., & Jamison, K. R. (1990). *Manic-depressive illness.* New York: Oxford University Press.

Goodwin, R., Gould, M. S., Blanco, C., & Olfson, M. (2001). Prescription of psychotropic medications to youths in office-based practice. *Psychiatric Services, 52*, 1081–1087.

Gray, G. V., Brody, D. S., & Johnson, D. (2005). The evolution of behavioral primary care. *Professional Psychology: Research and Practice, 36*, 123–129.

Grossman, J., Dontes, A., Kruesi, M. J. P., Pennington, J., & Fendrich, M. (2003). Emergency nurses' responses to a survey about means restriction: An adolescent suicide prevention strategy. *Journal of the American Psychiatric Nurses Association, 9*, 77–85.

Grove, W. M., & Meehl, P. E. (1996). Comparative efficiency of informal (subjective, impressionistic) and formal (mechanical, algorithmic) prediction procedures: The clinical-statistical controversy. *Psychology, Public Policy, and Law, 2*, 293–323.

Gunnell, D., Saperia, J., & Ashby, D. (2005). SSRIs and suicide in adults: Meta-analysis of drug company data from placebo controlled, randomized controlled trials submitted to MHRA's safety review. *British Medical Journal, 330*, 385–390.

Guy, J., Brown, C., & Poelstra, P. (1990). Who gets attacked: A national survey of patient violence directed at psychologists in clinical practice. *Professional Psychology: Research and Practice, 21*, 493–495.

Hamilton, B. E., Minino, A. M., Martin, J. A., Kochanek, K. D., Strobino, D. M., & Guyer, B. (2005). Annual summary of vital statistics. *Pediatrics, 119*, 345–360.

Harris, E. C., & Barraclough, B. (1997). Suicide as an outcome for mental disorders: A meta-analysis. *British Journal of Psychiatry, 170,* 205–228.

Harriss, L., & Hawton, K. (2005). Suicidal intent in deliberate self-harm and the risk of suicide: The predictive power of the Suicide Intent Scale. *Journal of Affective Disorders, 86,* 225–233.

Harvard Injury Control Research Center. (n.d.). *Means matter.* Retrieved February 17, 2010, from www.meansmatter.org

Hawton, K., & Harriss, L. (2006). Deliberate self-harm in people aged 60 years and over: Characteristics and outcome of a 20-year cohort. *International Journal of Geriatric Psychiatry, 21,* 572–581.

Hayes, S. C., & Smith, S. (2005). *Get out of your mind and into your life: The new acceptance and commitment therapy.* Oakland, CA: New Harbinger.

Hayes, S. C., Wilson, K. G., Gifford, E. V., Follete, V. M., & Strosahl, K. (1996). Experiential avoidance and behavioral disorders: A functional dimensional approach to diagnosis and treatment. *Journal of Consulting and Clinical Psychology, 64,* 1152–1168.

Henriques, G., Wenzel, A., Brown, G. K., & Beck, A. T. (2005). Suicide attempters' reaction to survival as a risk factor for eventual suicide. *American Journal of Psychiatry, 162,* 2180–2182.

Howard, K. I., Kopta, M. S., Krause, M. S., & Orlinsky, D. E. (1984). The dose-effect relationship in psychotherapy. *American Psychologist, 41,* 159–164.

Hoyert, D. L., Heron, M. P., Murphy, S. L., & Kung, H. (2006). Deaths: Final data for 2003. *National Vital Statistics Reports, 54.* Retrieved November 27, 2008, from http://www.cdc.gov/nchs/data/nvsr/nvsr54/ nvsr54_13.pdf

Hunt, S. A., Baker, D. W., Chin, M. H., Cinquegrani, M. P., Feldman, A. M., Francis, G. S., et al. (2001). *ACC/AHA guidelines for the evaluation and management of chronic heart failure in the adult: A report of the American College of Cardiology/ American Heart Association Task Force on Practice Guidelines (Committee to Revise the 1995 Guidelines for the Evaluation and Management of Heart Failure).* Retrieved April 3, 2010, from http://www.acc.org/clinical/guidelines/failure/hf_index.htm

Ingram, R. E., Miranda, J. & Segal, Z. V. (1998). *Cognitive vulnerability to depression.* New York: Guilford Press.

Institute of Medicine. (2002). *Reducing suicide: A national imperative.* Washington, DC: National Academies Press.

Institute of Medicine. (2007). *Treatment of posttraumatic stress disorder: An assessment of the evidence.* Washington, DC: National Academies Press.

Jacobson, N. S., Dobson, K. S., Truax, P. A., Addis, M. E., & Koerner, K. (1996). A component analysis of cognitive-behavioral treatment for depression. *Journal of Consulting and Clinical Psychology, 64,* 294–305.

Jacobson, N. S., Martell, C. R., & Dimidjian, S. (2001). Behavioral activation treatment for depression: Returning to contextual roots. *Clinical Psychology: Science and Practice, 8,* 255–270.

Jain, S., Shapiro, S. L., Swanick, S., Roesch, S. C., Mills, P. J., Bell, I., & Schwartz, G. E. R. (2007). A randomized controlled trial of mindfulness meditation versus relaxation training: Effects on distress, positive states of mind, rumination, and distraction. *Annals of Behavioral Medicine*, *33*, 11–21.

Jarrett, R. B., Kraft, D., Doyle, J., Foster, B. M., Eaves, G. G., & Silver, P. C. (2001). Preventing recurrent depression using cognitive therapy with and without a continuation phase: A randomized clinical trial. *Archives of General Psychiatry, 58*, 381–388.

Jobes, D. A. (2006). *Managing suicidal risk: A collaborative approach*. New York: Guilford Press.

Jobes, D. A., Eyman, J. R., & Yufit, R. I. (1995). How clinicians assess suicide risk in adolescents and adults. *Crisis Intervention & Time-Limited Treatment*, 2, 1–12.

Jobes, D. A., & Mann, R. E. (1999). Reasons for living versus reasons for dying: Examining the internal debate of suicide. *Suicide and Life-Threatening Behavior, 29*, 97–104.

Jobes, D. A., Wong, S. A., Conrad, A. K., Drozd, J. F., & Neal-Walden, T. (2005). The collaborative assessment and management of suicidality versus treatment as usual: A retrospective study with suicidal outpatients. *Suicide and Life-Threatening Behavior, 35*, 483–497.

Joiner, T. E. (2005). *Why people die by suicide*. Cambridge: Harvard University Press.

Joiner, T. E., Conwell, Y., Fitzpatrick, K. K., Witte, T. K., Schmidt, N. B., Berlim, M. T., Fleck, M. P. A., & Rudd, M. D. (2005). Four studies on how past and current suicidality relate even when "Everything but the kitchen sink" is covaried. *Journal of Abnormal Psychology, 114*, 291–303.

Joiner, T. E., Johnson, F., & Soderstrom, K. (2002). Association between serotonin transporter gene polymorphism and family history of attempted and completed suicide. *Suicide and Life-Threatening Behavior, 32*, 329–332.

Joiner, T. E., Rudd, M. D., & Rajab, M. H. (1997). The modified scale for suicidal ideation: Factors of suicidality and their relation to clinical and diagnostic variables. *Journal of Abnormal Psychology, 106*, 260–265.

Joiner, T. E., Sachs-Ericsson, N. J., Wingate, L. R., Brown, J. S., Anestis, M. D., & Selby, E. A. (2007). Childhood physical and sexual abuse and lifetime number of suicide attempts: A persistent and theoretically important relationship. *Behaviour Research and Therapy, 45*, 539–547.

Joiner, T. E. Jr., Steer, R. A., Brown, G., Beck, A. T., Pettit, J. W., & Rudd, M. D. (2003). Worst-point suicidal plans: A dimension of suicidality predictive of past suicide attempts and eventual death by suicide. *Behaviour Research and Therapy, 41*, 1469–1480.

Judd, L. J. (1997). The clinical course of unipolar major depressive disorders. *Archives of General Psychiatry, 54*, 989–991.

Juurlink, D. N., Herrmann, N., Szalai, J. P., Kopp, A., & Redelmeier, D. A. (2004). Medical illness and the risk of suicide in the elderly. *Archives of Internal Medicine, 164*, 1179–1184.

Kabat-Zinn, J. (1990). *Full catastrophe living. Using the wisdom of your body and mind to face stress, pain, and illness*. New York, Delacorte.

Kabat-Zinn, J., Massion, A. O., Kristeller, J., Peterson, L. G., Fletcher, K. E., Pbert, L., Lenderking, W. R., & Santorelli, S. F. (1992). Effectiveness of a mediation-based stress reduction program in the treatment of anxiety disorders. *American Journal of Psychiatry*, *149*, 936–943.

Kahn, A., Kahn, S., Kolts, R., & Brown, W. A. (2003). Suicide rates in clinical trials of SSRIs, other antidepressants, and placebo: Analysis of FDA reports. *American Journal of Psychiatry*, *160*, 790–792.

Kaplan, S. H., Gandek, B., Greenfield, S., Rogers, W., & Ware, J. E. (1995). Patient and visit characteristics related to physicians' participatory decision-making style: Results from the Medical Outcomes Study. *Medical Care*, *33*, 1176–1187.

Katon, W., Von Korff, M., & Lin, E., Bush, T., Lipscomb, P., & Russo, J. (1992). A randomized trial of psychiatric consultation with distressed high utilizers. *General Hospital Psychiatry, 14*, 86–98.

Katon, W., Von Korff, M., Lin, E., Bush, T., & Ormel, J. (1992). Adequacy and duration of antidepressant treatment in primary care. *Medical Care, 30*, 67–76.

Katz, L. Y., Cox, B. J., Gunasekara, S., & Miller, A. L. (2004). Feasibility of dialectical behavior therapy for suicidal adolescent inpatients. *Journal of the American Academy of Child and Adolescent Psychiatry*, *43*, 276–282.

Katz, L. Y., Kozyrskyj, A. L., Prior, H. J., Enns, M. W., Cox, B. J., & Sareen, J. S. (2008). Effect of regulatory warnings on antidepressant prescription rates, use of health services and outcomes among children, adolescents and young adults. *Canadian Medical Association Journal*, *178*, 1005–1011.

Katz, S. J, Kessler, R. C., Frank, R. G., Leaf, P., & Lin, E. (1997). Mental health care use, morbidity, and socioeconomic status in the United States and Ontario. *Inquiry-Blue Cross and Blue Shield Association*, *34*, 38–50.

Kerr, D. C. R., Owen, L. D., Pears, K. C., & Capaldi, D. M. (2008). Prevalence of suicidal ideation among boys and men assessed annually from ages 9 to 29 years. *Suicide and Life-Threatening Behavior*, *38*, 390–402.

Kessler, R. C., Berglund, P., Borges, G., Nock, M., & Wang, P. S. (2005). Trends in suicide ideation, plans, gestures, and attempts in the United States, 1990–1992 to 2001–2003. *Journal of the American Medical Association*, *293*, 2487–2495.

Kessler, R. C., Berglund, P. A., Bruce, M. L., Koch, J. R., Laska, E. M., Leaf, P. J., et al. (2001). The prevalence and correlates of untreated serious mental illness. *HSR: Health Sciences Research, 36*, 987–1007.

Kessler, R. C., Berglund, P. A., Demler, O, Jin, R., & Walters, E. E. (2005). Lifetime prevalence and age-of-onset distributions of DSM-IV disorders in the National Comorbidity Survey Replication. *Archives of General Psychiatry, 62*, 593–602.

Kessler, R. C., Chiu, W. T., Demler, O., & Walters, E. E. (2005). Prevalence, severity, and comorbidity of 12-month DSM-IV disorders in the National Comorbidity Survey replication. *Archives in General Psychiatry*, *62*, 617–628.

Kessler, R. C., Demler, O., Frank, R. G., Olfson, M., Pincus, H. A., Walters, E. E., et al. (2005). Prevalence and treatment of mental disorders, 1990 to 2003. *The New England Journal of Medicine, 352*, 2515–2523.

Kessler, R. C., McGonagle, K. A., Zhao, S., Nelson, C. B., Hughes, M., Eshleman, S., et al. (1994). Lifetime and 12-month prevalence of DSM-III-R psychiatric disorders in the United States: Results from the National Comorbidity Survey. *Archives of General Psychiatry, 51,* 8–19.

Kessler, R. C., Ormel, J., Demler, O., & Stang, P. E. (2003). Comorbid mental disorders account for the role impairment of commonly occurring chronic physical conditions: Results from the National Comorbidity Survey. *Journal of Occupational and Environmental Medicine, 45,* 1257–1266.

Khan, A., Khan, S., Kolts, R., & Brown, W. A. (2003). Suicide rates in clinical trials of SSRIs, other antidepressants, and placebo: Analysis of FDA reports. *American Journal of Psychiatry, 160,* 790–792.

Kirsch, I., Deacon, B. J., Huedo-Medina, T. B., Scoboria, A., Moore, T. J., & Johnson, B. T. (2008). Initial severity and antidepressant benefits: A meta-analysis of data submitted to the Food and Drug Administration. *PLoS Medicine, 5,* e45.

Kisely, S., Linden, M., Bellantuono, C., Simon, G., & Jones, J. (2000). Why are patients prescribed psychotropic drugs by general practitioners? Results of an international survey. *Psychological Medicine, 30,* 1217–1225.

Kleespies, P. M., Penk, W. E., & Forsyth, J. P. (1993). The stress of patient suicidal behavior during clinical training: incidence, impact, and recovery. *Professional Psychology: Research and Practice, 24,* 293–303.

Kolbasovsky, A., Reich, L., Romano, I., & Jaramillo, B. (2005). Integrating behavioral health into primary care settings: A pilot project. *Professional Psychology: Research and Practice, 36,* 130–135.

Kovacs, M., & Beck, A. T. (1977). The wish to die and the wish to live in attempted suicides. *Journal of Clinical Psychology, 33,* 361–365.

Kroenke, K. (2006). Patients presenting with somatic complaints: Epidemiology, psychiatric comorbidity and management. *International Journal of Methods in Psychiatric Research, 12,* 34–43.

Kroenke, K., & Mangelsdorf, A. D. (1989). Common symptoms in ambulatory care: Incidence, evaluation, therapy, and outcome. *American Journal of Medicine, 86,* 262–266.

Kroenke, K., Spitzer, R. L., & Williams, J. B. W. (2001). The PHQ-9 validity of a brief depression severity measure. *Journal of General Internal Medicine, 16,* 606–613.

Kung, H. S., Hoyert, J., Xu, J., & Murphy, S. L. (2008). Deaths: Final data for 2005. *National Vital Statistics Report, 56*(10). Retrieved November 27, 2008, from http://www.cdc.gov/nchs/data/nvsr/ nvsr56/nvsr56_10.pdf

Kurian, B. T., Ray, W. A., Arbogast, P. G., Fuchs, C., Dudley, J. A., & Cooper, W. O. (2007). Effect of regulatory warnings on antidepressant prescribing for children and adolescents. *Archives of Pediatrics & Adolescent Medicine, 161,* 690–696.

Lasser, K. E., Allen, P. D., Woolhandler, S. J., Himmelstein, D. U., Wolfe, S. M., & Bor, D. H. (2002). Timing of new black box warnings and withdrawals for prescription medications. *Journal of the American Medical Association, 287,* 2215–2220.

Lepine, J., & Briley, M. (2004). The epidemiology of pain in depression. *Human Psychopharmacology: Clinical and Experimental, 19,* S3–S7.

Lester, D. (2005). Predicting suicide in nations. *Archives of Suicide Research, 9,* 219–223.

Lester, D., Beck, A. T., & Mitchell, B. (1979). Extrapolations from attempted suicides to completed suicides: A test. *Journal of Abnormal Psychology, 88*, 78–80.

Leubbert, K., Dahme, B., & Hasenbring, M. (2001). The effectiveness of relaxation training in reducing treatment-related symptoms and improving emotional adjustment in acute non-surgical cancer treatment: A meta-analytical review. *Psycho-Oncology*, *10*, 490–502.

Levensky, E. R. (2006). Nonadherence to treatment. In J. E. Fisher & W. T. O'Donohue (Eds.), *Practitioner's guide to evidence-based psychotherapy* (pp. 442–452). New York: Springer.

Levinson, W., Roter, D. L., Mullooly, J. P., Dull, V. T., & Frankel, R. M. (1997). Physician-patient communication: The relationship with malpractice claims among primary care physicians and surgeons. *Journal of the American Medical Association, 277,* 553–559.

Libby, A. M., Brent, D. A., Morrato, E. H., Orton, H. D., Allen, R., & Valuck, R. J. (2007). Decline in treatment of pediatric depression after FDA advisory on risk of suicidality with SSRIs. *American Journal of Psychiatry*, *164*, 884–891.

Lieb, K., Zanarinin, M. C., Schmahl, C., Linehan, M. M. & Bohus, M. (2004). Borderline personality disorder. *The Lancet, 364*, 453–461.

Lin, E. H. B., Von Korff, M., Katon, W., Bush, T., Simon, G. E., Walker, E., & Robinson, P. (1995). The role of the primary care physician in patients' adherence to antidepressant therapy. *Medical Care, 33*, 67–74.

Lineberry, T. W., Bostwick, J. M., Beebe, T. J., & Decker, P. A. (2007). Impact of the FDA black box warning label on physician antidepressant prescribing and practice patterns: Opening Pandora's suicide box. *Mayo Clinical Proceedings,* 82, 518–520.

Linehan, M. M. (1993). *Cognitive-behavioral treatment of borderline personality disorder.* New York: Guilford Press.

Linehan, M. M. (1997). Behavioral treatments of suicidal behaviors. Definitional obfuscation and treatment outcomes. *Annals of the New York Academy of Sciences, 836*, 302–328.

Linehan, M. M., Comtois, K. A., & Korslund, K. E. (2004). *Dialectical behavior therapy versus nonbehavioral treatment-by-experts in the community: Clinical outcomes.* In J. R. Kuom & N. Lindenboim (Chairs), Symposium conducted at the 112th Convention of the American Psychological Association, Honolulu.

Linehan, M. M., Comtois, K. A., Murray, A. M., Brown, M. Z., Gallop, R. J., Heard, H. L., et al. (2006). Two-year randomized controlled trial and follow-up of dialectical behavior therapy vs. therapy by experts for suicidal behaviors and borderline personality disorder. *Archives of General Psychiatry, 63,* 757–766.

Linehan, M. M., Goodstein, J. L., Nielsen, S. L., & Chiles, J. A. (1983). Reasons for staying alive when you are thinking of killing yourself: The reasons for living inventory. *Journal of Consulting and Clinical Psychology, 51*, 276–286.

Lingam, R., Scott, J. (2002). Treatment non-adherence in affective disorders. *Acta Psychiatrica Scandinavica, 105,* 164–172.

Liu, X., Gentzler, A. L., Tepper, P., Kiss, E., Kothencne, V. O., Tamas, Z., Vetro, A., & Kovacs, M. (2006). Clinical features of depressed children and adolescents with various forms of suicidality. *Journal of Clinical Psychiatry, 67,* 1442–1450.

Loo, R. (1986). Suicide among police in federal force. *Suicide and Life-Threatening Behavior, 16,* 379–388.

Luoma, J. B., Martin, C. E., & Pearson, J. L. (2002). Contact with mental health and primary care providers before suicide: A review of the evidence. *American Journal of Psychiatry, 159,* 909–916.

Lynch, T. R., Chapman, A. L., Rosenthal, M. Z., Kuo, J. R., & Linehan, M. M. (2006). Mechanisms of change in dialectical behavior therapy: Theoretical and empirical observations. *Journal of Clinical Psychology, 62,* 459–480.

MacLeod, A. K., & Tarbuck, A. F. (1994). Explaining why negative events will happen to oneself: Parasuicides are pessimistic because they can't see any reason not to be. *British Journal of Clinical Psychology, 33,* 317–326.

MacLeod, A. K., Rose, G. S., & Williams, M. G. (1993). Components of hopelessness about the future in parasuicide. *Cognitive Therapy and Research, 17,* 441–455.

Malone, K. M., Oquendo, M. A., Haas, G. L., Ellis, S. P., Li, S., & Mann, J. (2000). Protective factors against suicidal acts in major depression: Reasons for living. *American Journal of Psychiatry, 157,* 1084–1088.

Maltsberger, J. T., & Buie, D. H. (1974). Countertransference hate in the treatment of suicidal patients. *Archives of General Psychiatry, 30,* 625–633.

Maltsberger, J. T. (1986). *Suicide risk: The formulation of clinical judgment.* New York: New York University Press.

Mann, J. J., & Currier, D. (2007). A review of prospective studies of biological predictors of suicidal behavior in mood disorders. *Archives of Suicide Research, 11,* 3–16.

Maris, R. W., Berman, A. L., & Silverman, M. M. (2000). *Comprehensive textbook of suicidology.* New York: Guilford Press.

Martin, D. J., Garske, J. P., & Davis, M. K. (2000). Relation of the therapeutic alliance with outcome and other variables: A meta-analytic review. *Journal of Consulting and Clinical Psychology, 68,* 438–450.

Martinez, C., Rietbrock, S., Wise, L., Ashby, D., Chick, J., Moseley, J., Evans, S., & Gunnell, D. (2005). Antidepressant treatment and the risk of fatal and non-fatal self harm in first episode depression: Nested case-control study. *British Medical Journal, 330,* 2–7.

Mathews v. Walker, 34 Ohio App. 2nd 128, 296 N.E. 2nd 569 (1973).

McManus, B. L., Kruesi, M. J. P., Dontes, A. E., Defazio, C. R., Piotrowski, J. T., & Woodward, P. J. (1997). Child and adolescent suicide attempts: An opportunity for emergency departments to provide injury prevention education. *The American Journal of Emergency Medicine, 15,* 357–360.

McNamee, J. E., & Offord, D. R. (1990). Prevention of suicide. *Canadian Medical Association Journal, 142,* 1223–1230.

Meltzer, H. Y. (1995). Multiple outcome criteria in schizophrenia: An overview of outcome with Clozapine. *European Psychiatry, 10*(Suppl. 1), 19S–25S.

Mieczkowski, T. A., Sweeney, J. A., Haas, G. L., Junker, B. W., Brown, R. P., & Mann, J. J. (1993). Factor composition of the Suicide Intent Scale. *Suicide and Life-Threatening Behavior, 23,* 37–45.

Miklowitz, D. J., Alatiq, Y., Goodwin, G. M., Geddes, J. R., Fennell, M. J. V., Dimidjian, S., Hauser, M., & Williams, M. G. (2009). A pilot study of mindfulness-based cognitive therapy for bipolar disorder. *International Journal of Cognitive Therapy,* 2, 373–382.

Milin, R., Walker, S., & Chow, J. (2003). Major depressive disorder in adolescence: A brief review of the recent treatment literature. *Canadian Journal of Psychiatry, 48,* 600–606.

Miller, M. C. (1999). Suicide-prevention contracts. In D. G. Jacobs (Ed.), *The Harvard Medical School guide to suicide assessment and intervention.* San Francisco: Jossey-Bass.

Miller, W. R., & Rollnick, S. (2002). *Motivational interviewing: Preparing people for change.* New York: Guilford Press.

Minnix, J. A., Romero, C., Joiner, T. E., & Weinberg, E. F. (2007). Change in "resolved plans" and "suicidal ideation" factors of suicidality after participation in an intensive outpatient treatment program. *Journal of Affective Disorders, 103,* 63–68.

Mohr, D. C., Ho, J., Duffecy, J., Baron, K. G., Lehman, K. A., Jin, L., & Reifler, D. (2010). Perceived barriers to psychological treatments and their relationship to depression. *Journal of Clinical Psychology, 66,* 394–409.

Mokdad, A. H., Marks, J. S., Stroup, D. F., & Gerberding, J. L. (2004). Actual causes of death in the United States, 2000. *JAMA, 291,* 1238–1245.

Motto, J. A. (1979). The psychopathology of suicide: A clinical model approach. *American Journal of Psychiatry, 136,* 516–520.

Nademin, E., Jobes, D. A., Downing, V., & Mann R. (2005). *Reasons for living among college students: A comparison between suicide and non-suicidal samples.* Unpublished manuscript.

Najmi, S., Wegner, D. M., & Nock, M. K. (2007). Thought suppression and self-injurious thoughts and behaviors. *Behaviour Research and Therapy, 45,* 1957–1965.

Narrow, W. E., Regier, D. A., Rae, D. S., Manderscheid, R. W., & Locke, B. Z. (1993). Use of services by persons with mental and addictive disorders: Findings from the National Institute of Mental Health Epidemiologic Catchment Area Program. *Archives of General Psychiatry, 50,* 95–107.

Nemeroff, C. B. (2003). Improving antidepressant adherence. *Journal of Clinical Psychiatry, 64*(Suppl. 18), 25–30.

Newport, D. (2004). Pituitary-adrenal responses to standard and low-dose dexamethasone suppression tests in adult survivors of child abuse. *Biological Psychiatry,* 55, 10–20.

Newport, J. D., Heim, C., Bonsall, R., Miller, A. H., & Nemeroff, C. B. (2004). Pituitary-adrenal responses to standard and low-dose dexamethasone suppression tests in adult survivors of child abuse. *Biological Psychiatry, 55*, 10–20.

Nock, M. K., & Kessler, R. C. (2006). Prevalence of and risk factors for suicide attempts versus suicide gestures: Analysis of the National Comorbidity Survey. *Journal of Abnormal Psychology*, *115*, 616–623.

Nock, M. K., & Prinstein, M. J. (2004). A functional approach to the assessment of self-mutilative behavior. *Journal of Consulting and Clinical Psychology, 72*, 885–890.

Nutting, P. A., Dickinson, L. M., Rubenstein, L. V., Keeley, R. D., Smith, J. L., & Elliott, C. E. (2005). Improving detection of suicidal ideation among depressed patients in primary care. *Annals of Family Medicine*, *3*, 529–536.

O'Carroll, P. W., Berman, A. L., Maris, R. W., Moscicki, E. K., Tanney, B. L., & Silverman, M. M. (1996). Beyond the Tower of Babel. *Suicide and Life-Threatening Behavior, 26*, 237–252.

Olfson, M., Marcus, S. C., Druss, B., Elinson, L., Tanielian, T., & Pincus, H. A. (2002). National trends in outpatient treatment of depression. *Journal of the American Medical Association*, *287*, 203–209.

Olfson, M., Shea, S., Feder, A., Fuentes, M., Nomura, Y., Gameroff, M., et al. (2000). Prevalence of anxiety, depression, and substance use disorders in an urban general medicine practice. *Archives of Family Medicine, 9*, 876–883.

Oquendo, M. A., Placidi, G. P. A., Malone, K. M., Campbell, C., Keilp, J., Brodsky, B., et al. (2003). Positron emission tomography of regional brain metabolic responses to a serotonergic challenge and lethality of suicide attempts in major depression. *Archives of General Psychiatry, 60*, 14–22.

Ostama, A., & Lonnqvist, J. (2001). Excess mortality of suicide attempters. *Social Psychiatry and Psychiatric Epidemiology, 36*, 29–35.

Owens, D., Horrocks, J., & House, A. (2002). Fatal and nonfatal repetition of self-harm: Systematic review. *British Journal of Psychiatry, 181*, 193–199.

Palmer, B. A., Pankratz, V. S., & Bostwick, J. M. (2005). The lifetime risk of suicide in schizophrenia: A reexamination. *Archives of General Psychiatry*, 62, 247–253.

Patterson, J., Peek, C. J., Heinrich, R. L., Bischoff, R. J., & Scherger, J. (2002). *Mental health professionals in medical settings: A primer*. New York: W.W. Norton.

Pekarkik, G., & Wierzbicki, M. (1986). The relationship between clients' expected and actual treatment duration. *Psychotherapy, 23*, 532–534.

Persons, J. B., Burns, D. D., & Perloff, J. M. (1998). Predictors of dropout and outcome in private practice patients treated with cognitive therapy for depression. *Cognitive Therapy and Research*, *12*, 557–575.

Peterson, L. G., Peterson, M., O'Shanick, G. J., & Swann, A. (1985). Self-inflicted gunshot wounds: Lethality of method versus intent. *American Journal of Psychiatry, 142*, 228–231.

Pfaff, J. J., & Almeida, O. P. (2005). Detecting suicidal ideation in older patients: Identifying risk factors within the general practice setting. *The British Journal of General Practice*, 55, 269–273.

Pfeffer, C. R. (2007). The FDA pediatric advisories and changes in diagnosis and treatment of pediatric depression. *American Journal of Psychiatry*, *164*, 843–846.

Pirkis, J., & Burgess, P. (1998). Suicide and recency of health care contacts: A systematic review. *British Journal of Psychiatry, 36*, 29–35.

Plutchik, R., van Praag, H. M., & Conte, H. R. (1989). Correlates of suicide and violence risk: III. A two-stage model of countervailing forces. *Psychiatry Research, 28*, 215–225.

Pokorny, A. D. (1983). Prediction of suicide in psychiatric patients. *Archives of General Psychiatry*, 40, 249–257.

Pope, K., & Tabachnick, B. (1993). Therapists' anger, hate, fear, and sexual feelings: National survey of therapist responses, client characteristics, critical events, formal complaints, and training. *Professional Psychology: Research and Practice, 24*, 142–152.

Price, J. H., Kinnison, A., Dake, J. A., Thompson, A. J., & Price, J. A. (2007). Psychiatrists' practices and perceptions regarding anticipatory guidance on firearms. *American Journal of Preventive Medicine*, *33*, 370–373.

Qin, P., & Nordentoft, M. (2005). Suicide risk in relation to psychiatric hospitalization: Evidence based on longitudinal registers. *Archives of General Psychiatry, 62*, 427–432.

Rachlin, S. (1984). Double jeopardy: Suicide and malpractice. *General Hospital Psychiatry*, 6, 302–307.

Reeves, A., Wheeler, S., & Bowl, R. (2004). Assessing risk: confrontation or avoidance—what is taught on counsellor training courses? *British Journal of Guidance and Counselling*, *32*, 235–247.

Regier, D. A., Narrow, W. E., Rae, D. S., Manderscheid, R. W., Locke, B. Z., Goodwin, F. K. (1993). The de facto U.S. mental and addictive disorders service system: Epidemiologic Catchment Area prospective 1-year prevalence rates of disorders and services. *Archives of General Psychiatry, 50*, 85–94.

Renberg, E. S. (2001). Self-reported life-weariness, death-wishes, suicidal ideation, suicidal plans and suicide attempts in general population surveys in the north of Sweden 1986 and 1996. *Social Psychiatry and Psychiatric Epidemiology, 36*, 429–436.

Reynolds, C. F., Frank, E., Perel, J. M., Imber, S. D., Cornes, C., Miller, M. D., et al. (1999). Nortriptyline and interpersonal psychotherapy as maintenance therapies for recurrent major depression: A randomized controlled trial in patients older than 59 years. *Journal of the American Medical Association, 281*, 39–45.

Reynolds, P., & Eaton, P. (1986). Multiple attempters of suicide presenting at an emergency department. *Canadian Journal of Psychiatry*, *31*, 328–330.

Rihmer, Z., & Akiskal, H. S. (2006). Do antidepressants t(h)reat(en) depressives? Toward a clinically judicious formulation of the antidepressant-suicidality FDA advisory in light of declining national suicide statistics from many countries. *Journal of Affective Disorders, 94*, 3–13.

Rihmer, Z., & Kiss, K. (2002). Bipolar disorders and suicidal behaviour. *Bipolar Disorders, 4*, 21–25.

Rihmer, Z., & Pestality, P. (1999). Bipolar II disorder and suicidal behavior. *Psychiatric Clinics of North America, 22*, 667–673.

Rinne, T., de Kloet, E. R., Wouters, L., Goekoop, J. G., DeRijk, R. H., & van den Brink, W. (2002). Hyperresponsiveness of hypothalamic-pituitary-adrenal axis to combined dexamethasone/corticotrophin-releasing hormone challenge in female borderline personality disorder subjects with a history of sustained childhood abuse. *Biological Psychiatry, 52*, 1102–1112.

Robinson, P., Wischman, C., & Del Vento, A. (1996). *Treating depression in primary care: A manual for primary care and mental health providers*. Reno, NV: Context Press.

Robinson, P. J. (2004). Adapting empirically supported treatments to the primary care setting: A template for success. In W. T. O'Donohoe, M. R. Byrd, N. A. Cummings, & D. A. Henderson (Eds.), *Behavioral integrative care: Treatments that work in the primary care setting* (pp. 53–72). New York: Routledge.

Robinson, P. J., & Reiter, J. T. (2007). *Behavioral consultation and primary care: A guide to integrating services*. New York: Springer.

Roy, A. (1992). Genetic and biologic risk factors for suicide in depressive disorders. *Psychiatric Quarterly, 64*, 345–358.

Roy, A., Gorodetsky, E., Yuan, Q., Goldman, D., & Enoch, M. (2010). Interaction of FKBP5, a stress-related gene, with childhood trauma increases the risk for attempting suicide. *Neuropsychopharmacology, 35*(8), 1674–1683.

Rudd, M. D. (2006a). Fluid vulnerability theory: A cognitive approach to understanding the process of acute and chronic risk. In T. E. Ellis (Ed.), *Cognition and suicide: Theory, research, and therapy* (pp. 355–367). Washington, DC: American Psychological Association.

Rudd, M. D. (2006b). *The assessment and management of suicidality*. Sarasota, FL: Professional Resource Press.

Rudd, M. D. (2009). Psychological treatments for suicidal behavior: What are the common elements of treatments that work? In D. Wasserman (Ed.), *Oxford textbook of suicidology* (pp. 427–438). Oxford: Oxford University Press.

Rudd, M. D., Berman, A. L., Joiner, T., E., Nock, M. K., Silverman, M. M., Mandrusiak, M., Van Ordern, K., & Witte, T. (2006). Warning signs for suicide: Theory, research, and clinical applications. *Suicide and Life-Threatening Behavior, 26*, 255–262.

Rudd, M. D., Cordero, L., & Bryan, C. J. (2009). What every psychologist should know about the Food and Drug Administration's black box warning label for antidepressants. *Professional Psychology: Research and Practice, 40*, 321–326.

Rudd, M. D., Cukrowicz, K. C., & Bryan, C. J. (2008). Core competencies in suicide risk assessment and management: Implications for supervision. *Training and Education in Professional Psychology, 2*, 219–228.

Rudd, M. D., Joiner, T., & Hasan, R. M. (1996). Relationships among suicide ideators, attempters, and multiple attempters in a young-adult sample. *Journal of Abnormal Psychology, 105*, 541–551.

Rudd, M. D., Joiner, T. E., & Rajab, M. H. (2001). *Treating suicidal behavior: An effective, time-limited approach*. New York: Guilford.

Rudd, M. D., Joiner, T. E., & Rajab, M. H. (1995). Help negation after acute suicidal crisis. *Journal of Consulting and Clinical Psychology, 63*, 499–503.

Rudd, M. D., Joiner, T. E., & Rajab, M. H. (2004). *Treating suicidal behavior: An effective, time-limited approach*. New York: Guilford Press.

Rudd, M. D., Joiner, T. E., Brown, G. K., Cukrowicz, K., Jobes, D. A., & Cordero, L. (2009). Informed consent with suicidal patients: Rethinking risks in (and out of) treatment. *Psychotherapy, 46*, 459–468.

Rudd, M. D., Mandrusiak, M., & Joiner, T. E. (2006). The case against no-suicide contracts: The commitment to treatment statement as a practice alternative. *Journal of Clinical Psychology, 62*, 243–251.

Rudd, M. D., Rajab, M. H., Orman, D. T., Stulman, D. A., Joiner, T. E., & Dixon, W. (1996). Effectiveness of an outpatient intervention targeting suicidal young adults: Preliminary results. *Journal of Consulting and Clinical Psychology, 64*, 179–190.

Ryan, N. (2005). Treatment of depression in children and adolescents. *Lancet, 366*, 933–940.

Schulberg, H. C., Hyg, M. S., Bruce, M. L., Lee, P. W., Williams, J. W., & Dietrich, A. J. (2004). Preventing suicide in primary care patients: The primary care physician's role. *Psychiatry and Primary Care, 26*, 337–345.

Schulberg, H. C., Lee, P. W., Bruce, M. L., Raue, P. J., Lefever, J. J., Williams, J. W., et al. (2005). Suicidal ideation and risk levels among primary care patients with uncomplicated depression. *Annals of Family Medicine, 3*, 523–528.

Scocco, P., & De Leo, D. (2002). One-year prevalence of death thoughts, suicide ideation and behaviours in an elderly population. *International Journal of Geriatric Psychiatry, 17*, 842–846.

Segal, Z. V., Pearson, J. L., & Thase, M. E. (2003). Challenges in preventing relapse in major depression: Report of a National Institute of Mental Health Workshop on state of the science relapse prevention in major depression. *Journal of Affective Disorders, 77*, 97–108.

Segal, Z. V., Williams, J. M. G., & Teasdale, J. D. (2002). *Mindfulness-based cognitive therapy for depression—A new approach to preventing relapse*. New York: Guilford Press.

Shea, S. (2002). *The practical art of suicide assessment: A guide for mental health professionals and substance abuse counsellors*. Hoboken, NJ: John Wiley & Sons.

Shneidman, E. (1981). Suicide thoughts and reflections, 1960–1980. *Suicide and Life-Threatening Behavior, 11*, 195–364.

Shneidman, E. (1984). Aphorisms of suicide and some implications for psychotherapy. *American Journal of Psychotherapy, 38*, 319–328.

Silverman, M. M., Berman, A. L., Snddal, N. D., O'Carroll, P. W., & Joiner, T. E. (2007). Rebuilding the Tower of Babel: a revised nomenclature for the study of suicide and suicidal behaviors part 2: suicide-related ideations, communications, and behaviors. *Suicide and Life-Threatening Behavior*, *37*, 264–277.

Simon, G. E. (1992). Psychiatric disorder and functional somatic symptoms as predictors of health care use. *Psychiatric Medicine, 10*, 49–60.

Simon, G. E., & Savarino, J. (2007). Suicide attempts among patients starting depression treatment with medications or psychotherapy. *American Journal of Psychiatry, 164*, 1029–1034.

Simon, G. E., Savarino, J., Operskalski, B., & Wang, P. S. (2006). Suicide risk during antidepressant treatment. *American Journal of Psychiatry*, *163*, 41–47.

Simon, R. J. (1988). *Concise guide to clinical psychiatry and the law.* Washington, DC: American Psychiatric Press.

Simon, T. R., Swann, A. C., Powell, K. E., Potter, L. B., Kresnow, M., & O'Carroll, P. W. (2001). Characteristics of impulsive suicide attempts and attempters. *Suicide and Life-Threatening Behavior, 32*, 49–59.

Sledge, W. H., Moras, K., Hartley, D., & Levine, M. (1990). Effect of time-limited psychotherapy on patient dropout rates. *American Journal of Psychiatry, 147*, 1341–1347.

Smith, G. R., Monson, R. A., & Ray, D. C. (1986). Patients with multiple unexplained symptoms: Their characteristics, functional health, and health care utilization. *Archives of Internal Medicine, 146*, 69–72.

Smith, G. W., & Bloom, I. (1985). A study of the personal meaning of suicide in the context of Baechler's typology. *Suicide and Life-Threatening Behavior, 15*, 3–13.

Smith, M. T., Perlis, M. L., & Haythornthwaite, J. A. (2004). Suicidal ideation in outpatients with chronic musculoskeletal pain: An exploratory study of the role of sleep onset insomnia and pain intensity. *Clinical Journal of Pain, 20*, 111–118.

Speca, M., Carlson, L. F., Goodey, E., & Angen, M. (2000). A randomized, wait-list controlled clinical trial: The effect of mindfulness meditation-based stress reduction program on mood and symptoms of stress in cancer outpatients. *Psychosomatic Medicine*, *62*, 613–622.

Steenbarger, B. N. (1994). Duration and outcome in psychotherapy: An integrative review. *Professional Psychology: Research and Practice, 25*, 111–119.

Stein, D., Apter, A., Ratzoni, G., Har-Even, D., & Avidan, G. (1998). Association between multiple suicide attempts and negative affects in adolescents. *Journal of the American Academy of Child and Adolescent Psychiatry*, *37*, 488–494.

Stenager, E. N., & Jensen, K. (1994). Attempted suicide and contact with primary health authorities. *Acta Psychiatrica Scandinavica, 90*, 109–113.

Stetter, F., & Kupper, S. (2002). Autogenic training: A meta-analysis of clinical outcome studies. *Applied Psychophysiology and Biofeedback*, *27*, 45–98.

Stravynski, A., Boyer, R. (2001). Loneliness in relation to suicide ideation and parasuicide: A population-wide study. *Suicide and Life-Threatening Behavior*, *31*, 32–40.

Strosahl, K., Chiles, J. A., & Linehan, M. (1992). Prediction of suicide intent in hospitalized parasuicides: Reasons for living, hopelessness, and depression. *Comprehensive Psychiatry*, *33*, 366–373.

Strosahl, K. D., & Sobel, D. (1996). Behavioral health and the medical cost offset effect: Current status, key concepts and future applications. *HMO Practice, 10*, 156–162.

Strosahl, K. D. (1996). Primary mental health care: A new paradigm for achieving health and behavioral health integration. *Behavioral Healthcare Tomorrow, 5*, 93–96.

Strosahl, K. D. (1998). Integrating behavioral health and primary care services: The primary mental health model. In A. Blount (Ed.), *Integrated primary care: The future of medical and mental health collaboration* (pp. 139–166). New York: W. W. Norton.

Strosahl, K. D. (2001). The integration of primary care and behavioral health: Type II change in the era of managed care. In N. Cummings, W. O'Donohoe, S. Hayes, & V. Follette (Eds.), *Integrated behavioral healthcare: Positioning mental health practice with medical/surgical practice* (pp. 45–70). New York: Academic Press.

Strupp, H. H. (1980). Success and failure in time-limited psychotherapy: A systematic comparison of two cases. Comparison IV. *Archives of General Psychiatry, 37*, 947–954.

Suicide Prevention Resource Center. (2006). *Core competencies in the assessment and management of suicidality*. Newton, MA: Author.

Suicide Prevention Resource Center. (2006). *Assessment and management of suicide risk*. Boston: Author.

Swahn, M. H., & Potter, L. B. (2001). Factors associated with the medical severity of suicide attempts in youths and young adults. *Suicide and Life-Threatening Behavior, 32*, 21–29.

Tarrier, N., Taylor, K., & Gooding, P. (2008). Cognitive-behavioral interventions to reduce suicidal behavior. *Behavior Modification, 32*, 77–108.

Tiefenbacher, S., Novak, M. A., Marinus, L. M., Chase, W. K., Miller, J. A., & Meyer, J. S. (2004). Altered hypothalamic-pituitary-adrenocortical function in rhesus monkeys (*Macaca mulatta*) with self-injurious behaviors. *Psychoneuroendocrinology, 29*, 501–515.

Turvey, C. L., Conwell, Y., Jones, M., Phillips, C., Simonsick, E., Pearson, J. L., & Wallace, R. (2002). Risk factors for late-life suicide: A prospective, community-based study. *American Journal of Geriatric Psychiatry, 10*, 398–406.

U.S. Preventive Services Task Force. (2004). Screening for suicide risk: Recommendation and rationale. *Annals of Internal Medicine, 140*, 820–821.

U.S. Public Health Service. (1999). *The Surgeon General's call to action to prevent suicide*. Washington, DC: Author.

Unutzer, J. Schoenbaum, M., Druss, B. G., & Katon, W. J. (2006). Transforming mental health care at the interface with general medicine: Report for the President's Commission. *Psychiatric Services, 57*, 37–47.

Unutzer, J., Katon, W., Callahan, C. M., Williams, J. D., Hunkeler, E., Harpole, L., et al. (2002). Collaborative care management of late-life depression in the primary care setting: A randomized controlled trial. *Journal of the American Medical Association, 288,* 2836–2845.

Valuck, R. J., Libby, A. M., Orton, H. D., Morrato, E. H., Allen, R., & Baldessarini, R. J. (2007). Spillover effects on treatment of adult depression in primary care after FDA advisory on risk of pediatric suicidality with SSRIs. *American Journal of Psychiatry, 164,* 1198–1205.

Valuck, R. J., Libby, A. M., Sills, M. R., Giese, A. A., & Allen, R. R. (2004). Antidepressant treatment and risk of suicide attempt by adolescents with major depressive disorder: A propensity-adjusted retrospective cohort study. *CNS Drugs, 18,* 1119–1132.

Van Orden, K. A., Witte, T. K., Cukrowicz, K. C., Braithwaite, S. R., Selby, E. A., & Joiner, T. E. (2010). The interpersonal theory of suicide. *Psychological Review, 117,* 575–600.

Van Orden, K. A., Witte, T. K., Gordon, K. H., Bender, T. W., & Joiner, T. E. (2008). Suicidal desire and the capability for suicide: Tests of the interpersonal-psychological theory of suicidal behavior among adults. *Journal of Consulting and Clinical Psychology, 76,* 72–83.

VandeCreek, L., & Knap, S., & Herzog, C. (1987). *Tarasoff and beyond: Legal and clinical considerations in the treatment of life-endangering patients.* Sarasota, FL: Professional Resource Press.

Venturini, F., Sung, J. C. Y., Nichol, M. B., & Sellner, J. C. (1999). Utilization patterns of antidepressant medications in a patient population served by a primary care medical group. *Journal of Managed Care Pharmacy, 5,* 243–249.

Verger, P., Brabis, P., Kovess, V., Lovell, A., Sebbah, R., Villani, P., et al. (2007). Determinants of early identification of suicidal ideation in patients treated with antidepressants or anxiolytics in general practice: A multilevel analysis. *Journal of Affective Disorders, 99,* 253–257.

Vyrostek, S. B., Annest, J. L., & Ryan, G. W. (2004). Surveillance for fatal and nonfatal injuries—United States, 2001. *Morbidity and Mortality Weekly Reports, 53*(7), 1–57.

Walsh, B. W. (2006). *Treating self-injury: A practical guide.* New York: Guilford Press.

Wang, P. S., Berglund, P., Olfson, M., Pincus, H. A., Wells, K. B., & Kessler, R. C. (2005). Failure and delay in initial treatment contact after first onset of mental disorders in the National Comorbidity Survey Replication. *Archives of General Psychiatry, 62,* 603–613.

Wang, P. S., Demler, O., & Kessler, R. C. (2002). Adequacy of treatment for serious mental illness in the United States. *American Journal of Public Health, 92,* 92–98.

Wang, P. S., Demler, O., Olfson, M., Pincus, H. A., Wells, K. B., & Kessler, R. C. (2006). Changing profiles of service sectors used for mental health care in the U.S. *American Journal of Psychiatry, 163,* 1187–1198.

Wang, P. S., Lane, M. Olfson, M., Pincus, H. A., Wells, K. B., & Kessler, R. C. (2005). Twelve-month use of mental health services in the United States: Results from the national Comorbidity Survey replication. *Archives of General Psychiatry, 62*, 629–640.

Wegner, D. M., & Zanakos, S. (1994). Chronic thought suppression. *Journal of Personality, 62*, 610–640.

Wells, K. B., Hays, R. D., Burnam, M. A., Rogers, W., Greenfield, S., & Ware, J. E. (1989). Detection of depressive disorder for patients receiving prepaid or fee-for-service care: results from the Medical Outcomes Study. *JAMA, 262*, 3298–3302.

Wells, K. B., Stewart, A., Hays, R. D., Burnam, M. A., Rogers, W., Daniels, M., et al. (1989). The functioning and well-being of depressed patients: Results from the Medical Outcomes Study. *Journal of the American Medical Association, 262*, 914–919.

Wenzel, A., Brown, G. K., & Beck, A. T. (2009). Evidence-based treatments for the prevention of suicidal acts. In A. Wenzel, G. K. Brown, & A. T. Beck (Eds.), *Cognitive therapy for suicidal patients: Scientific and clinical applications* (pp. 79–100). Washington, D.C.: US: American Psychological Association.

Wenzlaff, R. M., & Bates, D. E. (1998). Unmasking a cognitive vulnerability to depression: How lapses in mental control reveal depressive thinking. *Journal of Personality and Social Psychology, 75*, 1559–1571.

Wenzlaff, R. M., & Bates, D. E. (1998). Unmasking a cognitive vulnerability to depression: How lapses in mental control reveal depressive thinking. *Journal of Personality and Social Psychology, 75*, 1559–1571.

Wenzlaff, R. M., & Wegner, D. M. (2000). Thought suppression. In S. T. Fiske (Ed.), *Annual review of psychology* (Vol. 51, pp. 59–91). Palo Alto, CA: Annual Reviews.

Williams, J. M. G., Barnhofer, T., Crane, C., & Beck, A. T. (2005). Problem solving deteriorates following mood challenge in formerly depressed patients with a history of suicidal ideation. *Journal of Abnormal Psychology, 114*, 421–431.

Williams, J. M. G., Barnhofer, T., Crane, C., & Duggan, D. S. (2006). The role of overgeneral memory in suicidality. In T. E. Ellis (Ed.), *Cognition and suicide: Theory, practice, and therapy* (pp. 173–192). Washington, DC: American Psychological Association.

Williams, J. W., Rost, K., Dietrich, A. J., Ciotti, M. C., Zyzanski, S. J., & Cornell, J. (1999). Primary care physicians' approach to depressive disorders. *Archives of Family Medicine, 8*, 58–67.

Wingate, L. R., Joiner, T. E., Walker, R. L., Rudd, M. D., & Jobes, D. A. (2004). Empirically informed approaches to topics in suicide risk assessment. *Behavioral Sciences and the Law, 22*, 651–665.

Wintemute, G. J., Parham, C. A., Beaumont, J. J., Wright, M., & Drake, C. (1999). Mortality among recent purchasers of handguns. *The New England Journal of Medicine, 341*, 1583–1589.

Wintersteen, M. B. (2006, December). *Engaging primary care providers in suicide prevention.* Invited address at the State/Tribal/Adolescents at Risk Suicide Prevention Meeting sponsored by the Substance Abuse and Mental Health Services Administration, Bethesda, MD.

Wyder, M., Ward, P., & De Leo, D. (2009). Separation as a suicide risk factor. *Journal of Affective Disorders, 116*, 208–213.

Yerevanian, B. I., Koek, R. J., & Mintz, J. (2007). Bipolar pharmacotherapy and suicidal behavior. Part 1: Lithium, divalproex, and carbamazepine. *Journal of Affective Disorders, 103*, 5–11.

Zimmerman, M., Lish, J. D., Lush, D. T., Farber, N. J., Plescia, G., & Kuzma, M. A. (1995). Suicidal ideation among urban medical outpatients. *Journal of General Internal Medicine, 10*, 573–576.

Index